THE SOIL

FERTILISERS AND MANURES

Crown 8vo. With Illustrations. Price 5s. net

CONTENTS

FERTILISERS CONTAINING NITROGEN—THE FUNCTION AND COM-
PARATIVE VALUE OF NITROGENOUS MANURES—PHOSPHATIC MANURES
—THE FUNCTION AND USE OF PHOSPHATIC FERTILISERS—THE
POTASSIC FERTILISERS—FARMYARD MANURE—PERUVIAN GUANO
AND OTHER MIXED FERTILISERS—MATERIALS OF INDIRECT FER-
TILISING VALUE—THEORIES OF FERTILISER ACTION—SYSTEMS OF
MANURING CROPS—THE VALUATION AND PURCHASE OF FERTILISERS
—THE CONDUCT OF EXPERIMENTS WITH FERTILISERS.

THIS book, which is a companion volume to the same author's
book on "The Soil," deals not only with the history, origin, and
nature of the various fertilisers and manures in use in this country,
but also with their effect upon the yield and quality of crops in
practice. Much unpublished material has been drawn from the
Rothamsted experiments, but other series of field experiments
have also been utilised to furnish examples elucidating the
principles upon which manuring should be based. As befits a
book intended for the practical man as well as the student of
agricultural science, a good deal of attention is given to the
making, value, and utilisation of farmyard manure, while another
important chapter deals with the manuring of each of the staple
crops of the farm according to the character of the rotation in
which it finds a place.

Photograph showing transition from Rock into Subsoil and Soil by Weathering
(Hythe Beds, Great Chart, Kent).

THE SOIL

AN INTRODUCTION TO THE SCIENTIFIC STUDY OF THE GROWTH OF CROPS

BY A. D. HALL, M.A. (Oxon.)

DIRECTOR OF THE ROTHAMSTED STATION
(LAWES AGRICULTURAL TRUST)

FOREIGN MEMBER OF THE ROYAL ACADEMY OF AGRICULTURE
OF SWEDEN

SECOND EDITION, REVISED AND ENLARGED

LONDON

JOHN MURRAY, ALBEMARLE STREET, W.

1912

DEDICATED TO

THE WORSHIPFUL COMPANY OF GOLDSMITHS

THE FIRST PUBLIC BODY IN THIS COUNTRY TO
CREATE AN ENDOWMENT FOR THE
INVESTIGATION OF THE SOIL

FIRST EDITION	. .	*March* 1903
Reprinted	. .	*September* 1904
SECOND EDITION	.	*September* 1908
Reprinted	. .	*April* 1910
Reprinted	. .	*May* 1912

INTRODUCTION

THE study of the soil, which is fundamental in any application of science to that part of agriculture which deals with the growth of crops, has received greatly increased attention during the past few years. The crude chemical point of view, which in the main regarded the soil as a nutritive medium for the plant, has been altogether extended, by a consideration of the soil as the seat of a number of physical processes affecting the supply of heat and of air and water to the plant, and again as a complex laboratory, peopled by many types of lower organisms, whose function is in some cases indispensable, in others noxious, to the higher plants with which the farmer is concerned. These three kinds of reaction—chemical, physical, and biological—interact upon one another and upon the crop in many ways; they are affected by, and serve to explain, the various tillage operations which have been learnt by the accumulated experience of the farming community, and the hope for future progress lies in the further adaptation for practical ends of these processes at work in the soil. But it must not be supposed that science is yet in a position to reform the procedure of farming, or even to effect an immediate increase in the productivity of the land : agriculture is the oldest and most widespread art the world has known, the application of scientific method to it is very much an affair of the day before yesterday. Nor can we see our way to any radical acceleration of the turnover of agricultural operations that shall be economical; the seasons and the vital processes of the living organism are stubborn facts, unshapable as yet by man with all his novel powers. But even if the best farming practice is still a step beyond its complete explanation by science, yet the most practical man will find his perception stimulated and his power of dealing with an emergency quickened by an appreciation of the reasons underlying the tradition in which he has been trained ; and such an introduction to the knowledge of the soil it is the aim of this little book to supply. The book is primarily intended for the students of our agricultural colleges and schools, and for the farmer who wishes to know something about the materials he is handling day by day. While a certain knowledge of chemistry is assumed, it is hoped that the subject is so treated as to be intelligible to the non-technical reader who is without this preliminary grounding. Though the book is in no sense an exhaustive treatise, it has been my desire to give the reader an outline of all the recent investigations which have opened up so many soil problems and thrown new light on difficulties that are experienced in practice. The scope of the book precludes the giving of references and authorities for all the statements which are made ; but, for the sake of the more advanced student, a bibliography has been appended, which will take him to the original sources and give him the means of learning both sides of the more controversial questions.

The same reason—want of space—has prevented me

from giving an adequate justification of some of the points of view indicated. Any worker in so novel and unsurveyed a field as the study of the soil still presents, must arrive at certain personal conclusions, and I have tried to steer a middle course between an over insistence on these points on the one hand, and the colourlessness that would come from their entire exclusion on the other. No great part of a text-book can pretend to be original, but in the sections dealing with the chemical analysis and the physics of the soil, I have incorporated a good many unpublished measurements and observations; for the mass of the results on which the book is based, I am chiefly indebted to the work of Lawes and Gilbert, as set out in the *Rothamsted Memoirs*, and to the writings of Warington in this country, of King, Hilgard, and Whitney in America, of Wollny in Munich.

I have to thank Professor J. Percival, of the South-Eastern Agricultural College, for notes respecting the association of plants with specific soils, and many suggestions on biological questions; Major Hanbury Brown, C.M.G., head of the Egyptian Irrigation Department, for information concerning "salted" lands in Egypt; Mr F. J. Plymen, who has been associated with me in carrying out a soil survey of the counties of Kent and Surrey, and has executed many of the observations recorded here; Mr W. H. Aston, one of my pupils, to whom I owe the observations on p. 135; and finally, Dr J. A. Voelcker, to whom I am greatly indebted for reading the proof-sheets, and making many valuable suggestions thereon.

A. D. HALL.

HARPENDEN, *December* 1902.

PREFACE TO THE SECOND EDITION

A CONSIDERABLE number of additions and alterations have been incorporated in the present edition. These include a revision of the method recommended for the mechanical analysis of soils, the method now given being that adopted by the members of the Agricultural Education Association in this country. Owing to researches which have appeared since the publication of the first edition, I have greatly modified the views I then expressed on the nature of clay, and on the part played by zeolitic silicates in the retention of ammonium and other salts by the soil. During the last six years, however, the greatest additions to our knowledge of the soil are those dealing with bacteria; in consequence, the chapter on the living organisms of the soil has been largely rewritten and added to. A number of minor corrections have been made in the text, some of which represent the removal of errors, and others modifications due to more recent research. For the mistakes which must still remain, and which will become evident in the course of time, I must ask my readers' pardon beforehand; in dealing with so complex a subject as the soil we are still far from final conclusions, many of our most trusted conclusions are only rough approximations to the truth, and by the progress of research they may at any time require remodelling until they are hardly recognisable.

A. D. HALL.

THE ROTHAMSTED EXPERIMENTAL STATION,
May 1908.

CONTENTS

INTRODUCTORY

CHAPTER I

THE ORIGIN OF SOILS

CHAPTER II

THE MECHANICAL ANALYSIS OF SOILS

CHAPTER III

THE TEXTURE OF THE SOIL

xi

CHAPTER IV

TILLAGE AND THE MOVEMENTS OF SOIL WATER

CHAPTER V

THE TEMPERATURE OF THE SOIL

CHAPTER VI

THE CHEMICAL ANALYSIS OF SOILS

CHAPTER VII

THE LIVING ORGANISMS OF THE SOIL

CHAPTER VIII

THE POWER OF THE SOIL TO ABSORB SALTS

CHAPTER IX

CAUSES OF FERTILITY AND STERILITY OF SOILS

CHAPTER X

SOIL TYPES

APPENDICES

LIST OF ILLUSTRATIONS

THE SOIL

INTRODUCTORY

In the Scientific Study of Soils, Chemical, Physical, and Biological Considerations are involved.

THE whole business of agriculture is founded upon the soil; for the soil the farmer pays rent, and upon his skill in making use of its inherent capacities depends the return he gets for his crops. Taking rent as a rough measure of the productive value of land, it is clear that enormous differences must exist in the nature of the soil, for in the same district some land may be rented at £2, and other land at as little as 5s. per acre. Of course rent is not wholly determined by the nature of the soil, but depends also on the proximity of a market, and the adaptability of the land to special purposes; a light sandy or gravelly soil, almost worthless for general agricultural purposes, may be valuable in the neighbourhood of a large town, because its earliness and responsiveness to manure make it specially suitable for market gardening.

In some cases the difference between soils is seen in the quality of the crop produced rather than in the productiveness; for example, the "red lands" of Dunbar are famous for the high quality of the potatoes grown upon them: such potatoes will sell at 80s. to 90s.

1

per ton, when potatoes grown upon the Lincoln warp soils are at 60s., and those from the black soils of the fen country are only fetching 45s. to 50s. This extra price for the red land potatoes is due to the fact that they can be cooked a second time, after cooling, without changing colour, whereas the ordinary potato is apt to blacken a little when once cooked and allowed to grow cold.

The scientific study of soils is concerned with the differences indicated above ; its endeavour is to obtain such a knowledge of the constitution of the soil and the part it plays in the nutrition of the plant, as will make clear the cause of the inferiority of any given piece of land, and ultimately enable the farmer to correct it. The problems involved are far more complex than they appear; at first sight nothing would seem easier than to make a chemical analysis of the soil and find out in what respects it differs from another soil of known value ; then the deficiencies or the excesses, as compared with the good soil, could be corrected by suit- able manuring. The matter is not, however, quite so simple, for if on the one hand the soil can be considered as a great reservoir of plant food which can be recovered in crops, on the other hand it is equally correct to regard the soil as a manufactory, a medium for trans- forming raw material in the shape of manure into the finished article—the crop. In new countries where virgin soil is being exploited, and in districts where the systems of agriculture are primitive, the former point of view is the correct one ; nothing is given to the soil beyond that amount of labour which will enable some of its inherent value to be realised in a crop. Little by little the capital, which may be practically boundless, as in the great wheat lands of Manitoba, or initially little enough, as on a Connemara heath, is being drawn

PRINTED IN GREAT BRITAIN BY
OLIVER AND BOYD LTD.
EDINBURGH

upon and not replaced. But in a Kentish hop-garden or other land where an intensive system of cultivation is practised, the crop does not remove as much as it receives; often the land is intrinsically poor, and owes its value to the manner in which it will elaborate the raw material supplied as manure. And not only are these very special soils gaining, rather than losing fertility with each crop, but, from a general point of view, all countries that are being highly farmed, like parts of Great Britain, are steadily increasing in fertility at the expense of other countries which are growing crops on virgin soil; in the linseed, the maize, the cotton seed, that are fed to our stock, there travels to our soil some of the wealth of the lands upon which these crops were grown. Hence the study of the inherent resources of the soil is perhaps less important than an examination of the manner in which the soil deals with such materials supplied under cultivation.

The complete knowledge of the soil and the part it plays in the nutrition of the plant requires investigation along three lines, which may be roughly classed as —chemical, physical or mechanical, and biological; naturally these points of view are not independent of one another, but are only so separated for convenience of study.

In the first place, we know that the plant derives certain substances necessary to its development from the soil: nitrogen and all the ash constituents reach the plant in this manner. We have, therefore, to investigate the proportions in which these constituents are present in the soil, the state of combination in which they may respectively exist, and the variations in these factors normally exhibited by typical soils, all of which questions may be described under the head of chemical analysis. Further investigations of a chemical nature deal with the power of various soils to retain manure, the causes of sterility or fertility, and the measures that can be adopted for the amelioration of soils.

The soil is, however, not merely a storehouse of food for the plant, since water is equally indispensable to its existence, and is immediately derived from the soil; hence it is of prime importance to study the causes which underlie the movement of water in the land, and its supply to the growing crop. In the relation between soil and water the cultivation to which the land is subjected plays a prime part, hence it will be necessary to trace the effect of each of the main operations of tillage upon the structure of the soil. Again, the texture of the soil and the proportions of water and air it retains, affect its temperature and that responsiveness to change of season which we roughly indicate by the terms "early" and "late" soils. The general consideration of these questions may be termed soil physics.

Finally, the soil is not a dead mass, receiving on the one hand manure, which it yields again to the crop by purely mechanical or chemical processes; it is rather a busy and complex laboratory where a multitude of minute organisms are always at work. By the action of some of these organisms, vegetable residues and manures are reduced, we might almost say digested, to a condition in which they will serve as food for plants; others are capable of bringing into combination, or "fixing," the free nitrogen gas of the atmosphere, and therefore add directly to the capital of the soil; others again are noxious or destructive to the food stores in the soil.

The work of these organisms is much affected by cultivation; in fact, it would not be too much to say that most of the operations upon the farm have received a new light from the knowledge that has been acquired in the last few years of the living processes taking place in the soil. In this direction also new developments of agriculture seem to be possible, and though the progress is only small as yet, we see indications that the productive capacity of the land may be permanently increased by the introduction of certain organisms capable of assisting the work of the higher plants.

On the biological side we have also to study the association of certain plants with particular soils; an examination of the natural flora of any district will show that some species are almost confined to sandy soils, others to soils containing chalk, rarely wandering on to different types of soil; again, particular weeds are characteristic of clay land, others of sand; and some even of our cultivated crops show a marked intolerance for particular soils.

The full story of the soil cannot yet be told; small wonder that in the course of the many centuries man has been cultivating the face of the earth, he has found out much which science can barely explain, still less improve upon. Nor are the problems simple—the food, the water, the temperature, the living organisms in the soil are all variables, affected by cultivation and climate, themselves also variable; they all act and react upon one another and upon the crops; hence we can easily understand that the smallest farm may present problems beyond the furthest stretch of our knowledge.

CHAPTER I

THE ORIGIN OF SOILS

Sedentary Soils, and Soils of Transport—Weathering—The Composition of Rock-forming Minerals and their Weathered Products—Distinction between Soil and Subsoil—General Classification of Soils.

THE study of soils must begin with some knowledge of their origin and their relationship to the rocks that underlie them, out of which, in most cases, they have been formed.

Perhaps the best way of arriving at an idea of the natural processes which result in soil, is to visit a river valley and examine, first a quarry on the flanks of the hills, and then one of the cuttings for gravel or brick earth, which often lie a little above the river level.

The face of the quarry shows at a depth of 10 feet or so from the surface the massive rock, unaltered as yet by any action of the weather. Closer examination, however, shows that even at this depth the rock is not quite solid; if it be a stratified rock the planes of bedding are apparent, along which the rock can be split. Joints again traverse the rock at right angles to the bedding planes, and along both joints and bedding planes it is evident that water makes its way, for the edges of the cracks are slightly altered and discoloured. Nearer the surface, the cracks and lines of

weakness in the rock become more palpable; in some
cases the joints have been forced open by the intrusion
of the roots of trees; minor cracks have started from
the main ones, and the disintegration of the rock at
the edges of the cracks has proceeded further, till at a
distance of 3 or 4 feet from the surface the whole
material is loose and shattery, though still preserving
the appearance of solid rock. Still nearer the surface,
the rock structure seems to have disappeared; rock
may be there in lumps and fragments, but it is embedded in small material that may fairly be termed soil
or earth. Still nearer the surface the rock fragments
become smaller, and the proportion of fine earth larger,
till in the top 9 inches or so a new change begins.
Here the stones are generally small, and the material
is dark from the admixture of decaying vegetable
matter, residues of the crops that have covered the
surface for long ages. This is the *soil* proper, generally
shading gradually into the *subsoil* below, which in its
turn passes insensibly into the underlying rock. It is
obvious that a soil such as we have been describing has
been directly formed from the rock—it is, in fact, the
rock disintegrated and reduced by frost and snow, air
and rain; all those agencies we group together under
the name of "weathering." We are dealing with a
soil formed *in situ*, or, as it is sometimes termed, a
sedentary soil.

The frontispiece shows a photograph of such a case
of weathering of rock into subsoil and soil, as seen in a
section of the Hythe Beds, near Great Chart, Kent.

But when we examine the section of the gravel pit
or the brick earth workings lower down in the valley,
the sequence is not the same; we still have the soil
proper passing into the subsoil, but this is fairly uniform
throughout instead of showing a progressive change

as we descend; if it be gravel, the stones continue of
the same size; if brick earth, neither stones nor hard
stratified clay make their appearance. Should the
exposed section be deep enough, we find at last the
subsoil suddenly giving place to entirely different
material—solid chalk, or massive clay, or sandstone, as
the case may be—perhaps incapable, when disintegrated,
of furnishing the stuff of which the upper stratum of
gravel or brick earth is composed. In this upper
stratum we see the clearest evidence of the action of
water; the brick earth is free from stones and is of even
texture, the gravel contains hardly any fine material,
and its constituent stones are worn and partly rounded;
only running water can thus sift the heterogeneous
results of the weathering of rocks, and grade them into
different deposits. From what can be seen of the
present work of the river, it is clear that the brick earth
was deposited where the water was moving very slowly,
in quiet bays and in cut-offs, which only from time to
time get filled up with muddy flood water; the gravel
must have been laid down in the strongest wash of the
currents.

Soils and subsoils of this type, which bear no
particular relation to the underlying rocks, but have
travelled from a distance by means of running water
or some kindred agency, are known as *soils of transport*,
or, to use the terminology of the Geological Survey,
as *drift* soils.

Weathering.

The study of geology teaches us that nearly all the
rocks termed stratified or sedimentary, which cover
the greater part of the surface of the British Islands,
have been formed from the waste of previous rocks by
weathering, and by the subsequent redeposit and con-

solidation of the weathered material. A grain of sand,
for example, is practically indestructible; it may have
become cemented to the other grains on the sea beach
where it was lying, and give rise to the rock we term
sandstone; the rock thus formed may have been elevated
into dry land, broken up into loose grains, and washed
down to the sea to form a new beach, over and over again
in the world's history; so long a time has elapsed since
water first began to work on the earliest rocks. For this
reason, if we want to trace out the origin of a soil in
detail, we must in most cases go beyond the sedimentary rock from which it immediately derives, back to the
so-called primitive or crystalline rocks, which represent
in a sense the original materials of the earth's crust.

Here we shall find certain fundamental minerals,
which in a weathered state, altered both mechanically
and chemically, go to form both the sedimentary rocks
and the soil which is our immediate study. Though
the number of distinct minerals is immense, practically
the mass of the earth's crust is made up of a few only;
silica, various complex silicates of alumina, iron, lime,
magnesia, potash, and soda, together with carbonate of
lime, which is generally of organic origin, are all that
need be considered in relation to soils.

The various agencies which reduce rocks to soil,
grouped under the general term of weathering, may be
distinguished as mechanical—including the work of alternations of temperature, frost, wind, rain, and glacial ice—
and chemical, the complex effects of solution and oxidation that are brought about by water, especially when
charged with carbonic acid.

In dry climates the alternations of temperature
between day and night set up sufficient strain to fracture
even large rocks, and eventually reduce them to dust.
The dust and sand of the deserts of Central Asia, the

barren lands of the United States, and many parts of
both North and South Africa, are formed in this way;
because of the dryness of the atmosphere, radiation is
extreme, and the temperature of the rock surface will
rise to 60° C. in the day and fall below zero at night.
Crystalline rocks soon disintegrate under such alternations of temperature, and the fine angular dust thus
formed is transported by wind into the plains and valleys,
giving rise to soils largely wind-borne. Richthoven has
supposed that the immense *loess* deposits of China are in
the main dust that has been blown from the Central
Asian deserts. Even in a humid country like our own the
wind plays a considerable part in forming soil, material
being constantly removed from any bare surface and
deposited elsewhere as dust. When all the country
was in its natural state and clothed with vegetation,
the amount of transport as dust must have been considerably smaller than at present, but even then worm
casts brought up in the spring would crumble in dry
weather, and be moved to lower levels by the wind.
The thickness of the dust deposit may be gauged
by the rapidity with which shingle beds newly won
from the sea become covered with vegetation; in
the neighbourhood of Dungeness shingle beds known
to be less than fifty years old are already clothed
with a scanty flora. On scraping away a few inches
of the shingle the interstices between the stones are
found to be filled with a fine black sand, which
can only have been wind-borne; this rapidly increases
as the first vegetation checks the velocity of the
wind above the stones and arrests the dust, till at last
it reaches the surface and the grass begins to spread
over the stones. Exact dates are difficult to obtain,
but probably considerably less than a century is sufficient to form a thin turf over a bare shingle bed.

But the great weathering agency in temperate climates is undoubtedly frost acting upon water contained within the rocks and stones; the water expands as it changes into ice, and exerts an enormous pressure—indeed about 100 atmospheres would be required to keep water in a liquid condition at — 1° C. All rocks when freshly exposed, hold, by capillary attraction, a certain amount of water known as the "quarry water," which amounts in the white chalk to as much as 19 per cent. A piece of such chalk will be shattered into fragments by a single night's frost. Even after the quarry water has been dried out the most close-grained rocks will absorb a small quantity of water. The face of polished granite rapidly deteriorates in severe climates, owing to the freezing of the water that finds its way into the minute divisions between the crystals: Cleopatra's Needle, which had retained its smooth face for centuries in Egypt, soon became affected after its removal to London, and has to be protected by a waterproof varnish, as have all the granite monuments in Canada.

In nature also, all rocks are traversed by joints and bedding planes; these cracks are filled with water and opened and extended by its conversion into ice in the winter, till finally a block is wedged off and a fresh surface exposed to the action. Where flagstones are quarried, the workmen are in the habit of saturating the surface of the rock with water before the winter sets in: thus the rock is split along its bedding planes more effectively than by any artificial means. The fragments that have been broken off the main rock will be continually reduced in size by successive frosts, until they reach the ultimate fragments which are no longer penetrated by water; even in a soil the disintegration is still proceeding.

The weathering agencies just described would gradu-

ally cover any exposed rock with a layer of débris,
which would protect the lower layers from further action
were it not that the rain is always washing the finer
particles into the valleys and so leaving the rock open to
fresh attack.   Even on grass land the fine mould brought
to the surface by worms, moles, ants, etc., is constantly
travelling downhill by the agency of rain.   On arable
land containing stones it is a common expression to say
that the stones "grow" : however thoroughly the surface
may be picked clean of stones, in a year or two they will
seem as numerous as ever; the fine soil gets washed
away to lower levels, leaving the stones standing upon
the surface.   Even the stones themselves gradually creep
downhill, the rain undermines them till they fall over,
they must fall a little lower down the slope, until they
eventually reach the valley and are subject to further
transport by running water.   At the bottom of many of
the smaller dry valleys on the chalk rests an enormous
accumulation of flints of all sizes ; in one case in a small
upland valley the deposit was 6 or 7 feet thick, and the
unworn flints were so close as to be practically in
contact, only the interstices being occupied by soil ; yet
the surface carried good crops.

The material which thus creeps down the sides of
the valleys is further sorted out by the streams and
rivers and deposited as beds of gravel, sand, or clay,
the "alluvium" which underlies the level river meadows.
The coarser the material the more readily will it
settle, the finer particles are only deposited when the
velocity of the stream has been almost entirely checked.
The gravel and sand are deposited in and about the
stream course itself, the finer material falls on the meadows
in flood time, so that their level is gradually raised from
year to year.   Wherever the meadows get water-logged
the surface vegetation will begin to accumulate as

peat; the stream also wanders about from side to
side of the valley, hence borings through any extensive deposit of alluvium will disclose alternating beds
of gravel, sand, brick earth, and peat, of variable
extent and thickness. The great alluvial flats or
marshes at the mouths of many of our rivers are
formed in this manner; the deposit takes place in the
sea or in the estuary, until the tides and currents work
the material up to high-water mark, after which only
fresh-water beds are laid down.

Although most of the materials of which rocks are
composed are in the ordinary sense insoluble in water,
few of them, except the pure sand grains, can resist the
attack of water charged with carbonic acid. The rain
water when it reaches the ground has little carbonic acid
in solution, but the gases in the soil contain a considerable quantity derived from the decay of vegetable matter
in the surface layer, and the water in contact with these
gases will dissolve a proportionate amount. The proportion of carbonic acid in the soil gases varies very
much both with the permeability of the soil and the
proportion of humus, but at a depth of 1·5 metres
Wollny found it vary from 3·84 per cent. to 14·6 per
cent. at various periods of the year. At greater depths
the amount is still higher, so that the percolating water
becomes a weak solution of carbonic acid, and attains a
considerable solvent power. Not only are the alkaline
silicates attacked by the weak acid thus formed, but as
lime, magnesia, and iron protoxide also form soluble
bicarbonates, all minerals containing these bases are
liable to attack. Probably some of the organic acids
produced by the decay of vegetable matter in the surface soil aid in the solvent power of soil water; yet,
undoubtedly, water containing carbonic acid is the great
natural solvent, and some of the more striking cases of

its action in breaking down rocks will be discussed later under the heads of felspar, augite, and calcium carbonate.

The attack of frost and water upon rocks is much assisted by the roots of plants and trees; if we examine a fresh section of the soil over a quarry or brick pit, the roots of ordinary field plants can be traced downwards for 4 feet or more, while the roots of a tree may be seen working far into tiny fissures of the almost unaltered rock. The roots follow the water in the fissures: at first they can enter very minute cracks; as they grow, the pressure they exert widens the cracks; finally, the roots decay and leave a channel down which water can percolate freely. The fine roots themselves have a certain solvent action; after plants had been grown in a pot filled with powdered granite rock, which had been freed from all fine particles by washing, an appreciable quantity of mud and clay was found to have been formed.

The opening up of the subsoil to weathering by the action of roots is also carried out by worms, which have been observed making their burrows to the depth of 5 feet, thus introducing both air and water into the lower strata. But the great work of worms in regard to soil lies rather in the production of the fine surface layer of mould rich in vegetable matter: Darwin calculated that on an ordinary chalky pasture the whole of the fine surface soil to a depth of 10 inches was passed through worms and cast up on the surface in the course of fifty years. During their passage through the gizzard of the worms the stony particles will receive a certain amount of rubbing and be reduced in size, so that some of the finer particles in the soil owe their origin to worms. The deposit of the fine soil on the surface in the shape of worm casts, which are afterwards spread by the action of rain and wind, explains why chalk, ashes, or even stones placed on pasture land gradually sink below the surface. Darwin found in one case that a layer of burnt marl spread on the surface had sunk 3 inches in fifteen years, in another case a layer of chalk was buried 7 inches after an interval of twenty-nine years; in neither case, however, can we estimate the part played by the accretion of dust in forming this deposit. When we consider for how long a period worms must have been working in our cultivated soils, it is clear that the whole must have been through them over and over again, and that much of the fineness of the surface soil must be due to their action, both in actually grinding the fragments and in constantly bringing the finest portions back to the top.

In addition to the alluvial deposits proper, which are still in process of formation, beds of gravel, sand, and brick earth occur in many river valleys, as terraces on the flanks of the hills, often much cut and denuded by the modern river. These high level formations prob- ably represent alluvial deposits of a former epoch where the general slope of the land was greater and the rivers, fed by a higher rainfall in the hills, ran in greater volume. That the material of which these deposits con- sist has been sorted by running water is evident from the uniformity of size it possesses in each bed : while the coarseness of the gravel, and the fact that in some cases the stones are not made from the immediately underlying rock, all point to a great lapse of time and a river of higher transporting power than the present one. The wide deposits of brick earth in the neighbourhood of London and in East Kent were probably laid down either by floods on the river meadows or in quiet bays and lagoons of an estuary.

Over a great part of Britain north of the Thames, especially in the midlands and the eastern counties, the surface of the land is covered with beds of clay and sand which owe their origin to glacial ice. In

Scotland, the north of England, and Wales, these beds
are full of ice-scratched stones, and clearly represent
material that has been ground down by a moving
glacier: but the origin of the glacial drift of the eastern
counties is more obscure, for water seems to have played
some part in its formation. The beds are mostly stiff
and clayey in character, and by their included fragments
show from what formation, as a rule not very remote,
they have been derived.

Rock-forming Minerals.

In the solid crust of the earth D'Orbigny has
estimated that the chief minerals are present in the
following proportions—felspars, 48 per cent.; quartz,
35 per cent.; micas, 8 per cent.; talc, 5 per cent.;
carbonates of lime and magnesia, 1 per cent.;
hornblende, augite, etc., 1 per cent.; other minerals
and weathered products, 2 per cent.

The following table shows the composition of these
chief minerals, with a few others that play some part in
the formation of soil:—

	Silica.	Potash.	Soda.	Magnesia.	Lime.	Alumina.	Ferrous Oxide.	Ferric Oxide.	Water.
Quartz	100	...	...	...	...	...	...	...	...
Felspar Orthoclase	64·2	17	...	...	...	18·4	...	...	...
Felspar Albite	68·6	...	11·8	...	...	19·6	...	...	...
Felspar Anorthite	43·1	...	...	...	20	36·9	...	...	...
Mica	45 to 50	6 to 10	0 to 1·5	...	...	26 to 36	...	...	1 to 4·7
Hornblende / Augite	39 to 49	...	...	10 to 27	10 to 15	3 to 15	3 to 20	...	...
Olivine	41	...	...	49·2	...	...	9·8	...	...
Talc	63·5	...	...	31·7	...	...	...	...	4·8

Quartz, the crystalline form of silica, is found massive and in veins in the primitive rocks, and in fragments of all sizes in the granites, gneisses, and similar rocks. From the waste of these crystalline rocks are derived the sandstones of all geological ages and directly or indirectly the sands now existing. In a sandstone rock the grains of quartz are bound together by a cement, which may be oxide or carbonate of iron, as in the Lower Greensand of Surrey and Beds, and in some of the Wealden sandstones, or carbonate of lime, as in the Kentish Rag, or even silica itself, as in the hard blocks of tertiary sandstone, which are left as "grey wethers" on the surface of the chalk. In some of the older sandstones the rock is practically homogeneous; heat, pressure, and solution having thoroughly felted the grains together. Many sandstones weather rapidly, through the solution of the cement binding the grains together; the resulting sand has the same texture as it possessed before it was cemented into a rock.

The grains of sand that are first weathered from a crystalline rock possess an angular shape, but are soon rubbed down in running water into rounded grains with a surface like fine ground glass. Hence the degree of angularity which the sand grains show gives some indication of the amount of wear and tear they have suffered since their origin as sand. Below a certain size, however, quartz grains seem no longer capable of rubbing against one another, but remain angular even after long travel in running water. Daubrée has shown that angular fragments of sand of less than 0·1 mm. in diameter will travel in water without becoming rounded, hence any rounding of smaller grains of sand must have been due to solution.

Silica in the crystalline state is very slightly soluble

in water, a certain amount of solution taking place even at ordinary temperatures: most natural waters show a little silica in solution, though this more probably arises from the decomposition of natural silicates by water containing carbonic acid, rather than from the direct solution of quartz.

Amorphous silica in the form of "flint" plays a conspicuous part in the constitution of many soils in the south and east of England; owing to their durability and the former greater extension of the chalk, they are found in many districts remote from the chalk, even in the drift beds of the Channel Islands. When first won from the chalk, flints possess a clear black translucent structure, and are easily fractured and crushed; when weathered, either in flint gravels or on the surface of the soil, they become yellow or brown in colour, more opaque, and much harder, so that weathered flints are always preferred for road-making. The surface also becomes covered with a white incrustation, extending to a depth of $\frac{1}{16}$ of an inch or more; this is, however, only incipient weathering, probably due to the freezing of the small amount of water that soaks in at the surface.

The Felspars constitute the most important group of minerals found in the crystalline rocks: they are double silicates of alumina and some other base, potash, soda, or lime, of the general formula R_2O, Al_2O_3, $6SiO_2$, where R_2O may be either K_2O, Na_2O, or CaO. In granites and gneisses the common felspar is orthoclase or potash felspar; in the volcanic rocks plagioclase felspars predominate, in which the base is lime, generally with some admixture of soda and potash.

The felspars are all distinguished by the ease with which they are attacked by water containing carbonic acid, those containing lime more readily so than the potash felspar. The lime or the alkali is removed in solution, some of the silica is also removed; the alumina remains as a hydrated silicate, $Al_2O_3, 2SiO_2, 2H_2O$, called kaolinite. Owing to this disintegration of felspar, the crystalline rocks in which felspar is present weather rapidly, the other materials, quartz, mica, hornblende, become loosened from the matrix, and the whole rock becomes rotten. The granite of Cornwall and Devon is generally covered to a considerable depth, as much as 100 feet in some cases, with a layer of kaolinite, in which the unchanged quartz and mica are embedded; the kaolinite, freed by washing from the quartz, mica, etc., forms the "china clay" or kaolin of commerce. In the same way the basalts and other kindred rocks give rise to a red clay, consisting of kaolinite and the red iron oxides resulting from the oxidation of the magnetite and the hornblende, augite, etc., which contain ferrous silicates. From the decomposition of the felspars, augite, hornblende, etc., all our clays arise; as these minerals also generally contain potash, they are the source of the potash required by crops, which is always more abundant as clay predominates in the soil.

Daubrée caused 3 kilos of fragments of felspar to revolve in an iron cylinder with 3 litres of water, so that they practically performed a journey of 460 kilometres, with the result that 2·72 kilos of mud were formed, of which 36 grams were clay, and in the water there were 12·6 grams of potash in solution as silicate.

Senft examined the action of water charged with carbonic acid upon two granites, one (A) composed of orthoclase, quartz, and potash mica, the other of (B) plagioclase, quartz, and magnesia mica, and obtained in solution—

	A.	B.
Potash as Bicarbonate .	15 to 25 per cent.	5 to 8 per cent.
Soda as Bicarbonate . .	2 „ 6 „	8 „ 10 „
Lime as Bicarbonate . .	1 „ 2 „	4 „ 5 „
Magnesia as Bicarbonate .	a trace	10 „ 15 „
Silica	a little	a little
Iron as Bicarbonate . .	a trace	a trace

The undissolved residue of **A** was a white, of **B** a yellow, clay containing fragments of quartz and flakes of mica.

The following analyses show the change that takes place in passing from orthoclase felspar to kaolin; in the third column the analysis of kaolin is recalculated to show what arises from 100 parts of felspar, on the assumption that none of the alumina is removed by solution :—

	Orthoclase Felspar.	Kaolin.	Kaolin from 100 Felspar.
Silica . .	64·2	46·8	23·1
Alumina . .	18·4	37·3	18·4
Potash . .	17	2·5	1·1
Water . .	...	13	6·4
	99·6	99·6	49

Mica is essentially a double silicate of alumina and potash, with some oxide of iron : the potash being replaced by magnesia in black mica or biotite. Mica splits up into minute flakes as the rock weathers, but these flakes are fairly resistent to chemical change, and may be detected in most sands and sandstones. Ultimately, however, they pass into hydrated silicates of alumina, and are rarely to be detected in the soils resting upon sedimentary rocks.

Hornblende and Augite, though differing in crystalline shape, are chemically identical, and consist of silicates of varying proportions of lime, magnesia, alumina, ferrous and ferric oxides; manganese and the alkali metals are generally also present. They constitute, with plagioclase felspar and magnetic oxide of iron, the chief part of the rocks that are sometimes roughly termed "greenstone"— basalts, diorites, etc., of both volcanic and plutonic origin. They decompose under the action of carbonic acid charged water, especially those containing much lime, while those with much magnesia are the most resistent; the products of the action are kaolinite, oxides of iron, and carbonates of lime and magnesia. The following analysis (Ebelmar) show the chemical change in the weathered layers of a basalt from Bohemia and a greenstone or dolerite from Cornwall :—

	BASALT.		GREENSTONE.	
	Unaltered.	Weathered.	Unaltered.	Weathered.
Silica . . .	44·4	42·5	51·4	44·5
Potash . . .	4·8	2·0	1·6	1·2
Soda . . .	2·7		3·9	1·7
Lime . . .	11·3	2·5	5·7	1·4
Magnesia . .	9·1	3·3	2·8	2·7
Alumina . .	12·2	17·9	15·8	22·1
Iron Protoxide .	12·1	...	12·9	...
Iron Peroxide .	3·5	11·5	3·0	17·6
Titanium Oxide .	trace	1·2	0·7	1·0
Water . . .	4·4	20·4	1·7	8·6

The loss amounts to about 44 per cent. in the case of the basalt, and 34 per cent. in that of the greenstone.

Another example may be given of the analysis

(Hanamann) of a basalt from Bohemia, with that of
the weathered crust and of the resulting soil :—

	Rock.	Weathered Crust.	Soil.
Silica . . .	41·84	39·7	39·17
Potash . . .	0·82	0·83	0·94
Soda . . .	3·45	2·51	1·03
Lime . . .	11·16	8·02	4·72
Magnesia . .	3·63	3·20	2·92
Alumina . .	17·51	16·94	16·58
Iron Protoxide .	3·71	...	...
Iron Peroxide . .	12·77	15·05	14·22
Phosphoric Acid .	0·5	0·48	0·48
Carbonic Acid . .	0·88	2·67	0·61
Water . . .	3·56	10·5	19·28

Olivine is essentially a silicate of magnesia and
protoxide of iron, not uncommon in some basalts,
which easily weathers and becomes a soft hydrated
silicate, called serpentine, to which *talc* is very similar
in composition. These magnesian silicates are not
of great importance in the British Islands; only in the
Lizard district of Cornwall are they extensively
developed and give rise to poor, barren soils.

Calcium Carbonate, though present in many of the
older rocks in its crystalline form of Calcite or Iceland
Spar, is there to be regarded rather as a secondary product
brought by infiltering water than an original mineral.
It is soluble in water charged with carbonic acid;
hence when the complex silicates containing lime
are weathered, the lime is removed in this form. The
calcium carbonate is redeposited when the water loses
the carbonic acid either by evaporation or by diffusion
on contact with air. In a massive form calcium carbonate forms many of the sedimentary formations—the
older ones hardened to limestones, and the more recent
ones soft like the chalk ; in these cases it has been secreted

from natural waters by living organisms, foraminifera, corals, etc., and only gets a crystalline structure by later change. Calcium carbonate from organic sources is present to some extent in nearly all sedimentary rocks; the vast majority of the fossils there found are constituted of calcite.

In the limestone and chalk rocks the calcium carbonate is never quite pure; in the white chalk, which is the purest, the proportion of calcium carbonate, after excluding the flints, is only about 98 per cent.; in others the proportion of clay and mud which were simultaneously deposited gradually increases, so that we can find rocks of every gradation between chalk and clay or sandstone.

Owing to its solubility, the weathering of limestone takes the form of the removal of calcium carbonate more or less completely, leaving a fine-grained residue of the insoluble clay or sand. In the case of chalk and of the purer limestones, the insoluble residue consists mainly of a fine red or yellow clay; the chalk downs, when not obscured by drift formations, are covered with a sticky, reddish soil, only as a rule a few inches in thickness, and though the actual chalk is so close, in many cases this soil is almost deprived of all its calcium carbonate. Almost exactly similar material may be obtained in the laboratory by dissolving a few pounds of chalk or limestone in dilute hydrochloric acid. Whenever a section is exposed in chalk or limestone rocks, it will be noticed that the dividing line between soil and rock is very irregular; thin as the soil may be as a whole, in places it descends into cavities and "pipes" in the rock, sometimes 20 or 30 feet deep. In these depressions the soil is the same reddish clay as occurs on the surface, mixed with flints in the case of the upper chalk; they are essentially the results of solution, and represent the lines along which the drainage of the rain water has been more active, owing to a joint or fissure in the rock below.

Other minerals which do not constitute any large proportion of the earth's crust, but still play some part in the soil, are apatite, glauconite, selenite, limonite, and iron pyrites.

Apatite, or crystallised phosphate of lime,— $Ca_5(PO_4)_3F$,—is present in small quantities in many of the fundamental rocks, and is probably the ultimate source of the phosphoric acid of soils. Apatite also occurs massive in some of the older strata, and has been worked as a raw material, for the manufacture of phosphatic manures, in Norway and Canada.

Selenite, hydrated sulphate of lime, $CaSO_4, 2H_2O$, termed gypsum when massive, is not a fundamental mineral, but occurs in most clay rocks in well developed crystals. Diffused through the soil and dissolved in soil water, selenite doubtless provides most of the sulphur required by plants.

Limonite, hydrated oxide of iron, occurs in lumps and bands in many of the sedimentary rocks; in a diffused state it is the main colouring matter of soils; in heavy, undrained soils it often forms a layer or "pan" some inches below the surface. It is deposited from water containing bicarbonate of iron on exposure to the air; the rusty deposits and stains from chalybeate springs and wells consist of limonite. The action appears to be as follows—the hydrated peroxides of iron in the soil when in contact with humus (decayed vegetable matter) and water charged with carbonic acid become first reduced to the ferrous state by the organic matter, and then dissolved as bicarbonate. On exposure to the air, the excess of carbonic acid escapes by diffusion, the ferrous carbonate, as it is precipitated, is also oxidised by the oxygen of the air, and deposited as limonite. It will be noticed that stones taken from peaty land are always bleached white, through the removal of iron, and the surface sand of heathy land is always similarly bleached. On examining a section of any purely sandy formation, the surface soil will be found to be bleached below the layer of vegetable matter to the depth of a foot or more. Then comes a layer an inch or two thick nearly black in colour, where the sand is more or less cemented together by limonite, and below this the normal brown or yellow sand begins. The black band is formed at the depth to which the air usually penetrates the soil; it consists of limonite deposited at the evaporating surface of the soil water, which contains the iron dissolved from the bleached surface sand. In a similar manner arises the hard layer of limonite, the "iron pan" or "moor-band pan," found just below the cultivated soil on many undrained lands, and again the deposit of "bog iron ore" which is generally to be seen beneath the black peaty accumulation in any swampy place. The solution of iron as bicarbonate, and its precipitation as limonite, do not occur in soils containing any calcium carbonate, being essentially a sign of an acid condition of the soil and its need for lime or chalk.

Glauconite is a hydrated silicate of iron, alumina, and potash with a little lime and magnesia, which occurs as dark green grains in many sedimentary rocks, especially of the Cretaceous age. It is to the presence of this material that the Greensand formations owe their name; it is sometimes also to be seen in chalk and in the tertiary sandstones. It readily weathers to brown oxides of iron.

Zeolites. Akin to glauconite are certain hydrated double silicates of aluminium and the alkalis or alkaline

earths, called generically zeolites, which play a very
important part in the soil, though they may not be
present in large amounts. These bodies, which result
from the weathering of the felspars, contain a considerable proportion of water, loosely combined and readily
displaced, but their distinguishing feature is the ease
with which the secondary bases they contain, the calcium,
magnesium, sodium or potassium, are replaced by other
metals, whenever their salts are brought into contact
with the zeolites. Little is known of the actual nature of
the zeolitic bodies in the soil, but certain zeolites occur
from time to time in a pure state. The best known of
them is natrolite, which crystallises in fine needles
possessing the composition—$Na_2O, Al_2O_3, 3SiO_2, 2H_2O$,
a little calcium being generally present also.

Iron Pyrites, FeS_2, occurs in small brass yellow
cubic crystals in many of the older rocks, especially
those of a clay character; another form, in fibrous
masses of a lighter colour, is called marcasite, and is
common in the more modern clays, especially the
London clay, and again in round balls in the chalk.
Marcasite readily oxidises in moist air to ferrous sulphate and sulphuric acid: and many clay soils contain
basic sulphates, soluble in dilute acids but not in water,
that have arisen in this way. Selenite and the soluble
sulphates present in well waters, especially in clay soils,
are probably secondary products arising from the oxidation of marcasite. In a finely divided condition iron
pyrites forms the colouring matter of many dark green
or olive rocks and clays.

Soil and Subsoil.

Although the transition from soil to subsoil is
gradual, the distinction between the two is, as a rule,
easy to be made; the change begins an inch or so

below the usual limit of cultivation on arable soils, on pastures at the depth to which the mass of the roots penetrate. The most obvious difference between the two lies in the comparative richness of the staple in decaying vegetable matter or humus, which indeed would be entirely confined to the surface layers were it not for the decay of the deeper roots and the work of worms. To the humus is also due the difference in colour; not only does the colour deepen towards black as the proportion of humus increases, but by it the sands and clay are to a greater or less extent bleached through the removal of the iron oxides which colour them, hence the inorganic material is lighter and duller in colour in the soil than in the subsoil. In stiff clays the subsoil often shows signs of imperfect oxidation at comparatively slight depths. On an old pasture on the Gault Clay a trench was dug, the top 3 inches were black or nearly so and gradually changed to a stiff brown loam which extended to a depth of 9 or 10 inches, becoming lighter and more distinctively yellow as the admixture of humus diminished; below this depth the clay became mottled, grey, and yellow mixed, till at a depth of 4 feet practically the whole was a dark blue unweathered clay, owing its colour to iron pyrites and glauconite or kindred silicates of iron protoxide. One of the greatest distinctions between soil and subsoil lies in their respective texture; in humid climates like our own the soil is almost invariably composed of coarser grains than the subsoil, though in arid climates soil and subsoil appear to be almost uniform. This is due to the rain constantly percolating through even the stiffest soils and washing down the finest particles; in heavy rains also, water runs off the surface into the ditches, carrying with it the finest particles of the soil and leaving behind the coarser grains on the surface.

Naturally, this loss of the finer particles is greater as the soil is more worked and made open to percolation and washing; to some extent it is counterbalanced by the work of worms bringing the fine mould to the surface from below, so that the difference is least in an old pasture. *Per contra*, it is greatest in an old garden soil, where the constant working and further opening of the soil by the introduction of bulky manure often results in so complete a washing down of all the finer particles that the soil proper loses its power of cohering, falls into dust when dry, and is popularly said to be "worn out."

In addition to its humus the soil is nearly always richer than the subsoil in all the essential elements of plant food, despite the fact that crops have been raised on it for generations; the crops, in fact, have been the cause of the difference, for the deeper roots draw food from the subsoil and leave it behind on the surface as the plants decay. Potash is perhaps an exception in this connection; being essentially a product of the weathering of felspar, and removable from the soil by water containing carbonic acid, it is often more abundant in the comparatively unweathered subsoil. The richness of the humus, its greater warmth and the freer access of air also cause it to be more abundantly supplied with those organisms which play such an important part in preparing the food of the higher plants: as will be seen later, subsoils become almost without living organisms at a very slight depth.

For all these reasons,—the absence of humus, and of the organisms associated with it, the comparative poverty in inorganic plant food, the presence sometimes of unoxidised material, and on stiff soils the great change of texture,—the subsoil is often comparatively unfertile and may be almost barren. Desirable as it is to work

the subsoil and open it to the access of air and the free
penetration of roots, all methods of cultivation should
be avoided that would bury the surface soil and bring
the subsoil to the top. A plough which inverts the
soil should not go below the former limit of cultivation,
and if it is desired to deepen this limit, it should be
done by degrees, half an inch or so each year. Immense
damage has been done to the fertility of many of the
heavier soils by rash ploughing with steam, especially
where the old "lands" were thrown down, burying the
fertile soil in the furrows and baring the raw clay on
the tops of the ridges.

General Classification of Soils.

Although a distinction has been drawn between
sedentary soils and soils of transport, there are few
sedentary soils that do not contain material which has
been carried from some other formation at a distance;
only on great stretches of flat country belonging to a
single geological formation may be expected a soil
purely derived from the rock below. Especially in
Britain, where the outcrops of the different formations
are generally narrow, and where the surface is always
undulating, we find that the continual creeping of soil
particles to lower levels has resulted in an admixture
of foreign material in most soils. "La couche très-
mince de la terre végétale est un monument d'une
haute antiquité" (Elie de Beaumont), so that in many
places the soil contains the débris of formations now
removed by denudation. In the south-east of England
the soils that rest on the chalk, which may be only
from a few inches to a few feet below, contain
abundance of quartz sand, even up to 75 per cent.
No such sand exists in the chalk itself, so that it has
come from the lower tertiary beds which once over-

spread the chalk. On the wide flats of Weald Clay
in the same district, the soil contains sand that has crept
from the central hills of the Weald or from the Lower
Greensand escarpment, often several miles away. The
following analysis of a soil resting on a brick earth
bed in the valley of the Kentish Stour, shows that the
brick earth, which itself contains little or no chalk, has
become covered with chalky rain-wash from the hills
flanking the valley:—

Depth—Inches . .	0 to 6	6 to 12	12 to 18	18 to 24
Calcium Carbonate %	9·20	7·16	2·6	0·96

In the main, however, the bed below gives its character, both chemical and physical, to the soil; and the
ordinary rough classification of soils into sands, clays,
marls, and loams, follows closely the nature of the
underlying geological stratum. A coarse-grained
sandstone gives rise to a typically sandy soil, such as
the soils derived from the Bagshot beds, which form
the New Forest and the heathy land in the Aldershot
district; on the Lower Greensand lie the sandy heaths
in west Surrey, Hampshire, and in Beds; again, on
the Bunter beds of the New Red Sandstone lie many
of the uncultivated commons and parks of the Midlands,
such as Sutton Park, Cannock Chase, and Delamere
Forest. These coarse sandy soils, which have so often
remained unenclosed as forests and commons, are generally deficient in chalk, and accumulate peat wherever a
parting of clay gives rise to stagnant water.

Clay soils are common in nearly every part of
Britain; they arise from the great clay strata of all
ages, like the London Clay, the Weald Clay, and the
Oxford Clay, or from metamorphic rocks like slate, or
from the crystalline rocks like granite and basalt, or
even from the limestones by solution.

Between the sands and the clays come mixtures of all grades, better working than the clays and more fertile than the pure sands; sometimes the clay formation itself contains sand, as in the upper beds of the London Clay, or we may have a fine-grained sandstone mixed with clay, as in some of the carboniferous rocks. In all these cases, when chalk is absent, and drainage incomplete, there will be an accumulation of humus, resulting in a peaty formation.

Some argillaceous limestones give rise to typical "marls," mixtures of chalk and clay; *e.g.*, some of the beds of the Lias and of the Keuper.

Other limestones with a sandy basis, and fine-grained sandstones cemented by carbonate of lime, give rise to "loams," which are free-working soils, mainly composed of fine sand with some clay and a little calcium carbonate. The alluvial soils in the valleys are loams, passing in places into gravels; these are generally the richest soils; as a rule they are mixtures derived from many formations, and so are well supplied with humus and the mineral elements of plant food; they are deep, and not over consolidated, thus admitting of the percolation of water and the descent of roots; yet they are fine-grained enough to prevent them drying out too rapidly. But though these terms, sands, clays, marls, loams, and peaty soils, serve for rough descriptive purposes, a more exact determination of the constituent particles is necessary to properly characterise a soil, and for this we must resort to what is termed the "mechanical analysis" of a soil.

CHAPTER II

THE MECHANICAL ANALYSIS OF SOILS

Nature of Soil Constituents: Sand, Clay, Chalk, and Humus—
Methods of Sampling Soils—Methods for the Mechanical
Analysis of a Soil—Interpretation of Results.

IT has already been indicated that as soils are derived
from the waste of rocks, they consist of a mass of
particles of various minerals and of all sizes, together
with a certain amount of humus of vegetable origin,
and that they may be roughly classified according to
the predominance of the coarse-grained particles called
" *sand*," or the very fine material known as " *clay*."

The mechanical analysis of a soil consists in pushing
this rough " eye and hand " classification a stage further
into the region of exact measurement, and in determining the minute physical structure of the soil by
estimating the proportions in which particles of various
sizes are mixed together in the soil. Upon the physical
structure of the soil so determined, or as we should
practically term it, the *texture*, depend some of its
most important features, particularly its behaviour with
regard to the supply of water to crops and its amenability to cultivation.

In the first place, it will be necessary to discuss a
little more thoroughly the nature of the four substances

to which the texture of the soil has been referred—the sand, clay, chalk, and humus—of which the first two are of most importance, since soils which are mainly characterised by chalk or humus are less commonly in cultivation.

Sand.—On the seashore, in beds of an alluvial nature, and in formations of all geological ages, we are familiar with sand ; in the main it consists of grains of quartz, rounded by continual rubbing, and more or less coloured by oxide of iron. It represents the quartz contained in the fundamental rocks, weathered and worn by water : in some cases of comparatively recent origin, in others it is material that has repeatedly been formed into a sedimentary rock, disintegrated afresh and sorted by the action of running water. The coarser the grains of which a sand is made up, the more rapid must have been the current from which it was deposited. The following table shows the rate of flow which is necessary to carry sand grains of various sizes :—

Diameter of Grains, mm.	Velocity of Current, mm. per sec.
0·5	64
0·3	32
0·16	16
0·12	8
0·072	4
0·047	2
0·036	1
0·025	0·5

A closer examination of most sands will show that they do not consist wholly of quartz grains, but also contain rounded fragments of many of the minerals present in the fundamental rocks which have any resistance to weathering. Flakes of mica are common,

C

fragments of more or less altered felspar, of oxide of iron, and even of tinstone, rutile, and zircon, may be identified. In fine-grained sands the fragments of minerals other than quartz become as a rule more abundant, till they begin to predominate over the quartz grains in the finest silts and muds that are deposited from very gently moving water. Under the microscope the quartz grains show a crystalline structure, and a surface more or less dulled and rounded according to the travel the grains have suffered. In mass the chief characteristic of sand is its want of coherence when dry.

Clay.—The material we call clay is characterised by certain properties that are shown when the clay has been " puddled," *i.e.*, kneaded when in a moist condition. The clay is *plastic*, it can be moulded and worked into various shapes, even into quite thin leaves, and it will retain these shapes on drying. During the drying process a shrinkage takes place: the dry material is hard and tenacious, and can only be broken or crumbled with difficulty. The shrinkage is considerable: a little brick was made of good modelling clay 7 inches long, and about 1 square inch in section; two marks were then made on this 6 inches apart; after a fortnight's drying in a room the marks were only 5·7 inches apart, showing a shrinkage of 5 per cent. Clay is further impermeable to water when in the moist puddled condition, for which reason it is used to line the bottoms of ponds in pervious soil, and is built up inside the retaining dams of reservoirs; quite a thin layer of clay will hold water indefinitely as long as it is not allowed to dry and crack, nor to be washed away by the action of running water.

From a chemical point of view, all clays are found to consist largely of kaolinite, the hydrated silicate of alumina which is formed by the weathering of felspar; the other materials present consist of extremely fine grains of quartz and other weathered minerals, together with more or less oxide of iron. "China clay" and the best "pipe clays" contain little or no iron; the deep-seated clay formations are generally coloured dark green or blue or black by the presence of ferrous silicates like glauconite; on weathering and exposure at the surface the clays become yellow or brown, owing to the oxidation of these ferrous to ferric salts.

Water in which a little clay has been rubbed up remains turbid for a very long time; days and even weeks elapse before the particles settle down to the bottom—indeed, however long the liquid may be at rest, a slight haze or cloudiness may be observed within it. Schloesing has drawn a distinction between the part of the clay, amounting to 1 or 2 per cent. only of the whole, which persists in remaining suspended and the portion which settles down; he has called it "colloid clay," and attributes many of the typical clay properties to the jelly-like medium of colloidal matter by which the other defined particles of the clay are surrounded. Schloesing associates this colloid clay with such typical colloids as the highly hydrated forms of silica and organic bodies like starch and gum which, though they appear to be truly dissolved, yet cannot diffuse through a membrane, and form, on drying, hard non-crystalline masses, with much shrinkage and a characteristic fracture. But later researches on colloids show that they are not essentially different from suspended matter; they consist of particles too fine to settle down in water, or to be arrested by a filter even of porous porcelain, but which are still sufficiently coarse to show their presence when a strong beam of light is passed through the liquid, as is not the case with bodies truly dissolved.   From this point of view the "colloid clay" would only represent the limiting state of fineness, differing in degree, but not in kind, from the other clay particles.

The question still remains whether we shall give to clay a physical or a chemical definition; in the first place, does the fineness of the material alone confer the characteristic clay properties of plasticity, impermeability to water, and shrinkage and tenacity on drying, or do these properties depend on the chemical composition of the substance making up the clay.   It is easy to show that fineness of division is a necessary factor in the existence of clay, because we can obtain material possessing the chemical composition of typical clays which yet behave physically as if they were sand.   A sample of crude kaolinite rock as dug in Cornwall from the surface of granite, was powdered and passed through a sieve retaining all particles above 0·2 mm. in diameter; the remainder, which consisted mainly of kaolinite with a little mica, was further separated by sedimentation from water into four fractions :—

Fraction.	Approximate Size of Particles in mm.	Per cent. of Original Material.
1	0·2 to 0·05	22
2	0·05 ,, 0·01	39
3	0·01 ,, 0·005	21
4	below 0·005	20

Of these fractions the first contained all the mica, the others were practically pure kaolinite, yet the second fraction showed none, and the third very little of the characteristic properties of clay; when dried they fell or could easily be rubbed into a fine powder, only the fourth and finest fraction dried into a hard coherent mass. Thus we can have material which consists entirely of kaolinite, and yet is not clay; such as we see in natural deposits of fuller's earth, which consists of kaolinite but possesses no plasticity, and falls on drying into a fine powder.

In the same way a natural soil contains particles of silicates of alumina of all sizes, though they only begin to predominate in the fractions of finest grain.

On separating one of the Rothamsted soils into fractions, according to their size by the method to be described later, and analysing them, the following results were obtained :—

Fraction.	Approximate Size of Particles in mm.	Per cent. of Original Soil.	Percentages in Material.		
			Silica.	Ferric Oxide.	Alumina.
I	0·2 to 0·04	24	94·6	1·1	3·4
2	0·04 ,, 0·01	35	92·0	1·2	6·2
3	0·01 ,, 0·004	11	88·3	1·8	8·5
4	0·004 ,, 0·002	6	61·7	7·0	23·4
5	below 0·002	24	45·9	12·2	30·9

Taking the mean of several analyses, the fifth fraction, which is to be regarded as clay proper, possessed the following approximate composition, if all the alumina is combined as $Al_2O_3, 2SiO_2, 2H_2O$—kaolinite 72 to 75 per cent.; ferric oxide, 11 to 12 per cent.; quartz, 9 to 10 per cent.; alkalis and alkaline earths, 4 to 6 per cent.

From these results we must conclude that kaolinite is not necessarily clay, but that fineness of grain is also an essential factor, the characteristic clay properties not being developed except in material the particles of which are less than one-fivehundredth of a millimetre in diameter.

But though fineness of grain is a factor, it is probably not the only factor, as may be seen from a consideration of another important property of clay—its power of flocculating or coagulating under the action of minute quantities of various salts. To illustrate this point, a few grams of good clay should be rubbed up with several litres of distilled water, and the supernatant turbid liquid poured off into a series of tall jars each holding from 300 to 500 c.c. of the liquid. To one of these jars nothing is added, to two others ·018 and 0·009 gram of hydrochloric acid respectively, to a fourth 0·028 gram of calcium chloride, and to the fifth 0·58 gram of sodium chloride. The contents of the jars are shaken up until solution is effected, and they are then put aside to stand. After some time the liquids to which the salts have been added will begin to clear, and the clay particles will clot together and fall to the bottom; the jar containing the larger quantity of hydrochloric acid will clear the first, the others will clear approximately together, but the pure clay water will remain turbid for many days. If a little of the turbid clay water be examined by a $\frac{1}{12}$-inch oil immersion lens under the microscope, it is just possible to see the clay particles in rapid " Brownian " motion, and if a little acid or salt be then introduced under the cover glass, they will be seen to move together and form into little clots or aggregates as soon as they experience the effect of the added acid or salt. By comparative experiments it can be shown that the flocculating power of any salt is proportional to its amount up to a certain limit, when the material is so completely flocculated that no further addition of salt has any effect; conversely, the flocculating power of a given amount of salt is inversely proportional to the quantity of clay suspended in the liquid. The flocculating power of a salt also varies with both the acid and the metal; the following table shows approximately their comparative effect :—

HCl	.	.	30	HNO_3	. .	28	H_2SO_4 .	. 20
$CaCl_2$	.	.	15	$Ca(NO_3)_2$	.	10	$CaSO_4$.	. >5
KCl	.	.	3	KNO_3	. .	>2	K_2SO_4 .	. <1
$NaCl$	.	.	>1	$NaNO_3$	.	<1	Na_2SO_4	. 0.5

The alkalis and salts like phosphate of sodium, which give rise to free alkalis on hydrolysis, instead of flocculating have the opposite effect, and keep the particles in their finest state of division without any tendency to settle.

It is, furthermore, possible to show that many substances, however finely divided, will not assume the condition of indefinite suspension in water so as to be flocculated by salts; in particular, suspensions of finely divided quartz, ferric hydrate, and hydrated alumina flocculate spontaneously and will not remain turbid for many minutes, though in their turn they can be deflocculated and made to remain in suspension by adding a trace of free alkali to the liquid.

Without going further into the details of a subject which is still very obscure, the condition of free suspension in water and the Brownian motion of the particles of clay seem to be associated with the presence of the zeolitic double silicates which contain atoms of potassium or sodium in their molecule, and which doubtless give rise to a little free alkali by their partial hydrolysis when in contact with a large bulk of water.

We may thus conclude that fineness of grain is not the only factor in the constitution of clay, but that the characteristic clay properties which are always associated with the power of flocculation depend also upon the nature of the material; in the soil they depend upon the presence of the zeolitic double silicates derived from the weathering of the felspars in the fundamental rocks.

The power of flocculation plays a very important part in the cultivation of clay soils. When such a soil possesses a good texture its finest particles are in a state of temporary aggregation or flocculation, so that they behave as if the soil, as a whole, were built up of much coarser particles. Just as a potter or a brick-maker brings his material into its highest condition of plasticity by repeatedly kneading and working it, by which process the naturally formed aggregates are resolved into their ultimate particles and the material is made as fine-grained as possible, so if a clay soil be in any way worked or disturbed when in a wet condition, it becomes apparently more clayey than before. It remains persistently wet and impervious to the percolation of water, and shrinks when dry into hard tenacious clods. But if the clay be exposed to the weather for some time, so that it undergoes alternations of temperature, freezing and thawing, wetting and drying, it will experience a certain amount of spontaneous flocculation and behave as though it were coarser grained, so that if caught in the right state of partial dryness it may easily be crumbled.

Flocculation may also be aided or otherwise by the use of certain artificial manures, as will be explained later; the incorporation again of humus much improves the texture, while the action of lime is particularly effective and is much employed in practice to ameliorate the working of clay soils.

Lime itself can be shown in the laboratory to possess little flocculating power, for though its base is calcium, a highly effective metal, it is combined as a hydrate, which has a deflocculating effect. However, as soon as lime is applied to the soil it becomes converted into carbonate, and some of it will be always going into solution as bicarbonate, a salt which possesses great flocculating power.

In practice, the application of such small quantities of lime as a ton or even half a ton to the acre have the greatest value in ameliorating the working of clay land; not only does it move more readily and fall more easily into a good tilth, but by becoming coarser grained it allows the rain to percolate more freely and thus dries earlier in the season, so that the limed land can often be worked several days before the unlimed land can be touched. Though the Rothamsted soil is by no means of the heaviest, it is only because of the repeated additions of carbonate of lime in former years that it can be retained under arable cultivation; portions of the same land without carbonate of lime lie so wet in the spring that they were laid down to grass in consequence of the repeated failures to secure a good seed bed.

Chalk, or carbonate of lime, is present in all soils, with the exception of a few extremely open sands and peaty soils that are practically of vegetable origin. The proportion varies enormously, according to the origin of the soil; on some of the thin loams derived directly from the great calcareous formations like the chalk or the oolite, the calcium carbonate in the soil may rise to as high a proportion as 60 per cent., but in the majority of the loams under cultivation the proportion is nearer 1 per cent., and it often falls much below this in clays and sands. Chalk in the soil is essentially a transitory substance, as it is constantly removed by the action of percolating water charged with carbonic acid, arising from the decay of vegetable matter in the surface soil. Many of the fermentation changes that also take place in this vegetable matter give rise to acids, which in their turn combine with the calcium carbonate. So rapid are these removals of calcium carbonate that it is difficult to understand how any of it persists in the surface layers of many soils, the subsoil of which shows that they must have been initially poor in chalk, were there not some compensating agencies at work. Amongst these agencies must be reckoned the calcium salts in plants, which in many cases are drawn up by deep-seated roots from the subsoil and become calcium carbonate on the ultimate decay of the plant tissues.

In a normal soil the particles of calcium carbonate are of all sizes, many of the finer particles of silt and clay are loosely cemented together by calcium carbonate, as may be seen by the increase in the finer fractions if a soil be washed with dilute acid before it is separated by sedimentation.

Humus.—On examining many rocks taken from such depths that they have undergone none of the weathering processes which convert them into soil, they are found to contain both carbon and nitrogen, occasionally in quantities comparable with those found in the soil itself. This is only the case with the sedimentary rocks and particularly the indurated clays, the carbon and nitrogen in fact only represent the organic matter in the original deposit in a more or less mineralised condition. But since these carbon and nitrogen compounds are only slightly affected by any of the weathering processes by which soil is made, they must pass into the soil and there become merged with the organic matter of more recent origin. Such material, however, plays a very unimportant part in the soil, and we may pass on at once to the débris of vegetation of recent origin or the humus which is characteristic of all soils proper.

The term humus is applied to the black or dark brown material of vegetable origin which gives to surface soil its characteristic darker colour as compared with the subsoil. It is essentially a product of bacterial action; there are a number of bacteria working in the absence of air and universally distributed, which attack the carbon compounds of plant tissues, especially the carbohydrates, with the production of marsh gas or hydrogen, carbonic acid, and humus. In the presence of air the characteristic humus-forming fermentation is replaced by one which results in the complete combustion of the organic matter to carbonic acid. For this reason more humus is found in a pasture than in a continually aerated arable soil, more again in clays than in the lighter soils through which air is always being drawn as the rain percolates, and the accumulation of humus reaches its maximum where considerable rainfall and an impermeable stratum combine to make the soil so water-logged that all access of air is cut off, as in swamps and bogs. The presence of chalk in the soil also assists in the destruction of humus, since it neutralises the acids which largely compose the humus, and which tend to inhibit the further action of bacteria.

The chemical composition of humus is indefinite; it is a variable mixture of several substances, themselves of very complex constitution; it always contains more carbon and less hydrogen and oxygen than the vegetable tissues from which it was formed. The following figures show the composition of grass and of the top brown layer of turf in a peat bog, also of the same peat of greater age at depths of 7 and 14 feet, the mineral matter and moisture being excluded in calculation in each case:—

	Grass.	Top Turf.	Peat at 7'.	Peat at 14'.
Carbon . .	50·3	57·8	62	64
Hydrogen .	5·5	5·4	5·2	5
Oxygen . .	42·3	36	30·7	26·8
Nitrogen .	1·8	0·8	2·1	4·1

Substances akin to humus can be formed from the carbohydrates (such as sugar, starch, and cellulose), by heating them for some time with water under pressure, the action being more rapid if a trace of mineral acid be present; the resulting substances are weak acids and form salts, so are generally termed humic acid :—

	HUMIC ACID.		
	From Sugar.	Natural.	
Carbon . .	63·9	56·3 to	59
Hydrogen .	4·6	4·4 „	4·9
Oxygen . .	31·5	32·7 „	36
Nitrogen . .	...	2·8 „	3·6

As a rule, the active humus of the soil is there present in the form of salts of calcium, which on treatment of the soil with dilute hydrochloric acid are decomposed, a little of the humic acids going into solution but the greater part remaining undissolved. By filtering off the acid and then treating the soil with a weak (4 per cent. by volume) solution of ammonia or other alkali, the liberated humic acids are dissolved and may be reprecipitated either as free acids by the addition of hydrochloric acid, or as calcium salts by the addition of a solution of calcium chloride. The humic acids thus going into solution are sometimes estimated as "soluble humus," they do not include the whole of either the organic matter or the nitrogen in the soil. The brown solution that is formed is akin to the dark liquid draining from a dung heap, which contains humus dissolved by the alkaline carbonates of the fermented urine.

Occasionally soils are found which naturally possess an acid reaction, and in which the whole or part of the soluble humus is uncombined with calcium, so that it goes into solution in ammonia without the preliminary treatment with acid. The portion of the natural humus of soils that is soluble in acids contains nitrogen, and seems to be of the nature of an amide.

Although dark brown humic substances can be prepared from carbohydrates, and therefore contain only carbon, hydrogen, and oxygen, yet the soluble humus of the soil, even when dissolved and reprecipitated, always contains some nitrogen, nor can it be obtained entirely free from phosphorus and mineral matter. The original vegetable matter is made up not only of carbohydrates, but of other carbon compounds containing nitrogen, and in some cases both nitrogen and phosphorus; these all break down under bacterial action into dark-coloured substances richer in carbon, and roughly classed as humus. The splitting-up process continues in the soil, so that humus becomes one of the great sources of nitrogen for the food of plants, and a soil well supplied with humus is generally regarded as fertile.

During the formation and continued decomposition of humus the carbohydrates appear to be first attacked, and the nitrogen-containing bodies, *e.g.*, the nucleins in particular, resist the action of bacteria. For this reason, where we find the proportion of humus in a soil is low, the proportion of nitrogen in the humus itself will be high, the decay of the humus falls more heavily on the purely carbonaceous part of the material.

This is seen in the figures obtained by Lawes and

Gilbert for the ratio that exists between the proportions of carbon and nitrogen in various soils :—

RATIO $\dfrac{C}{N}$.

Cereal Roots and Stubble	43
Leguminous Stubble	23
Dung	18
Very old Grass Land	13·7
Manitoba Prairie Soils	13
Pasture recently laid down	11·7
Arable Soil	10·1
Clay Subsoil	6

Hilgard and Jaffa also found that the humus of soils in an arid climate, where the deficiency of rainfall causes the soil to be very open, contains a higher proportion of nitrogen than is found in the humus of damper soils :—

	Number of Samples Examined.	Average per cent. of Humus in Soil.	Average per cent. of Nitrogen in Humus.
Arid Soils	18	0·75	15·87
Semi-arid Soils	8	0·99	10·03
Moist Soils	8	3·04	5·24

The following table (p. 47) gives the results of the determination of carbon, nitrogen, humus, and the percentage of nitrogen in the humus, in a selection of extremely rich virgin soils obtained from different parts of the world; the Canadian, Russian, and Monte Video soils were very similar uniform fine-grained grey or black soils found on the great plains.

These results would seem to indicate that the most valuable humus, *i.e.* that which will decay rapidly and yield nitrogen compounds available as food for plants, is that possessing a high ratio of carbon to nitrogen.

	Locality.	Description of Soil.	Carbon.	Nitrogen.	Ratio C/N.	Soluble Humus.	Nitrogen % in Soluble Humus.
1. Canada . .	Indian Head	Black Prairie	2·59	0·317	8·2	3·94	4·07
2. Canada . .	Wide Awake	,,	2·58	0·330	7·8	5·09	2·71
3. Russia . .	Ploty	Black Steppe	2·19	0·268	8·2	5·66	2·42
4. Rhodesia .	Salisbury	Black Vlei	20·15	1·89	10·7	21·3	2·40
5. Monte Video	... {	Black "Camp" Soil }	1·89	0·261	7·3	4·48	3·51
6. New Zealand	{ Tararua Mountains	Black Sandy Pasture	12·66	0·949	13·2	10·35	4·67

Against this, Berthelot and André have investigated the ratio of carbon to nitrogen in the different portions of the humus which can be dissolved by alkalis or acids, and they find that the most soluble portions contain the highest proportion of nitrogen. It does not, however, follow that the substances most soluble in acids or alkalis are necessarily those which will most readily be converted by bacteria into a form available for plants, and, on the whole, the evidence seems to show that a humus rich in nitrogen will yield it very slowly to crops.

Humus acts as a weak cement and holds together the particles of soil, thus it serves both to bind a coarse-grained sandy soil, and, by forming aggregates of the finest particles, to render the texture of a clay soil more open. In determining the sizes of the constituent particles of a soil, the "mechanical analysis," it is desirable to remove the humus as far as possible, and so break up these temporary aggregates.

Sampling of Soils.

The first step in the analysis of any soil, mechanical or chemical, consists in obtaining a sample that shall adequately represent the land in question.

In this country it is customary to take a sample down to a depth of 9 inches as representing the soil proper; it is, however, doubtful if this is not too deep, being below the depth to which cultivation is generally carried; probably a 6-inch sample would more truly represent the cultivated soil. In many cases it will be found that the true soil does not extend to a depth of anything like 9 inches, but that there is a sharp change into subsoil or even rock before this point: *e.g.*, on the chalk downs the soil is often not more than 4 inches deep, below which white broken chalk rock begins. In such cases the sample must only be taken to the depth at which the visible change begins.

To obtain the sample two methods are generally adopted. At Rothamsted a steel box, without top or bottom, 9 inches deep, and 6 inches square in section, is used; the sides are wedge-shaped, about $\frac{3}{4}$ inch thick at the top and tapering off to cutting edges below. The surface, if uneven arable land, is first raked over and gently beaten level, then the box is placed in position and driven down with a heavy wooden rammer till the top of the box is flush with the surrounding soil. The soil enclosed by the box is then carefully dug and scraped out into a bag for conveyance to the laboratory; two or three samples to the same depth being taken from the same field and afterwards mixed. Should samples of the subsoil be required, the box is left in position after its contents have been scraped out, and the surrounding soil is dug away to the 9-inch level, the box is then rammed down for the second 9 inches, and its contents removed: the process being repeated till the required depth has been reached.

A modification of the Rothamsted method consists in marking out on the surface a square 9 inches on the side, and digging away the surrounding soil until a

Fig. 1.—Photograph of Soil-sampling Tools.

[To face page 49.

9-inch cube of earth remains standing; over this a wooden box is slipped, and the cube is cut off by pushing a spade beneath at the 9-inch level.

On soils which do not contain many large stones, samples may be taken with an auger, both more rapidly and with greater security of obtaining an average sample. A convenient tool for the purpose consists of a cylindrical auger made of steel, about $\frac{1}{16}$ inch thick, of 2 inches internal diameter and 12 inches deep, with a slot $\frac{3}{4}$ inch wide running from top to bottom; the lower edge of the cylinder and the edges of the slot are sharpened; to the upper end of the cylinder a handle carrying a wooden crossbar is riveted. The auger is forced gently into the soil with a twisting motion until the required depth is reached, when the tool is withdrawn and the core scraped out into a bag. Six to ten cores at least are taken at regular intervals in the same field and mixed to secure an average sample. Each boring can be continued to obtain subsoil samples as deep as the length of the handle permits. It is impossible to obtain samples with the auger when the soil is dry. Fig. 1 shows a photograph of both types of soil-sampling tools.

When the samples reach the laboratory they are spread out on shallow trays to dry, which process may be accelerated by a gentle warmth, not exceeding 40° C. In dealing with stiff soils it is advisable to crumble all the lumps by hand while the earth is still somewhat moist. When the whole is sensibly dry the stones are separated by a sieve having round holes 3 mm. in diameter; the material that does not pass the sieve is gently worked up in a mortar with a wooden pestle, care being taken not to break the stones, chalk, etc., but only to crush the lumps of earth. Finally, the material upon the sieve is roughly weighed and well

D

washed in a stream of water till all the fine earth is gone, dried, picked over to free it from roots and stubble, and weighed as "stones." To get the proportion borne by the stones to the soil, the fine earth is also weighed, an addition being made of the weight lost by the stones in washing.

Of course the figure obtained for the proportion of stones is only approximate, for if the stones are of any size they will be very irregularly caught by the auger or even by the 6-inch square tool. The material passing the sieve is again spread out in a thin layer in an ordinary room, until the surface maintains the same colour as the lower layers; it is then bottled up as "air-dry fine earth" for analysis.

The Mechanical Analysis of a Soil.

The mechanical analysis that follows consists in dividing the fine earth into a series of fractions consisting of particles of known size; we can use sieves to sort out the coarser grades, but the finer ones must be separated by their relative powers of remaining suspended in water.

The methods in use depend on two principles: in one, the hydraulic method (Hilgard, Schöene, Nöbel), soil is washed by successive currents of water of velocities calculated to carry particles of the required size according to the table on p. 33: in the other, the sedimentation method of Osborne, Knop, and Schloesing, the soil is suspended in water and allowed to stand, the separation being effected either by the times required for the particles to settle down through a fixed distance, or by the distances fallen in a given time. The method to be described is based upon the latter principle. The hydraulic method requires special apparatus, and is only suited to laboratories entirely devoted to soil analysis.

Method of Analysis.

1. Ten grams of the air-dry fine earth are weighed out into a beaker or basin and treated with 100 c.c. of $N/5$ hydrochloric acid; the soil is well worked up with a rubber pestle (made by fixing a glass rod into a small solid rubber bung) until all the lumps of clay, etc., are broken up. If the soil contains much calcium carbonate, a further addition of acid may be required.

> The object of the acid is to dissolve the carbonates and humates, and thus loosen the particles in any aggregates where chalk or humus form the cement. Without this preliminary treatment the amount of clay found will be largely determined by the proportion of humus present; the soil of an arable field, for example, will show more clay than the soil of an adjoining pasture, when the sedimentation is made with water alone. But after the preliminary treatment with acid to remove the humus, both fields will show the same proportion of clay (as they should do, since they are of the same origin), and only differ in the amount of humus they have accumulated—a temporary factor.

After standing with the acid for an hour, the whole is thrown on a tared filter and well washed until all acid is removed. The filter and its contents are dried and weighed; the loss the soil has suffered represents the material dissolved and the hygroscopic moisture.

2. The soil is now washed off the filter with ammoniacal water (about 1 c.c. of strong ammonia solution in half a litre of water) on to a small sieve of 100 meshes to the linear inch, the portion passing through being collected in a beaker which is marked on the side at a distance of 8.5 cm. from the bottom.

> The ammonia completes the dissolution of the humates, and also masks the effect of any traces of soluble salts which may be left and would cause aggregation in the manner indicated earlier, p. 38.

The portion which remains on the sieve is dried and weighed. It is then divided into "fine gravel" and "coarse sand" by means of a sieve with round holes of 1 mm. in diameter, the portion retained by the sieve being designated "fine gravel."

3. The portion in the beaker is well worked up with the rubber pestle, ammoniacal water is added up to the 8·5 cm. mark, and the whole is put aside to stand for twenty-four hours. The turbid, supernatant liquid is then rapidly poured off into a large jar, and the residue is rubbed up again with the rubber pestle and more ammoniacal water, as before. The whole operation of filling to the mark, standing for twenty-four hours, and pouring off the turbid liquid is carried through as before, and repeated as long as any matter remains in suspension for twenty-four hours. Generally seven to ten decantations will be sufficient, after which the united turbid liquid is evaporated to dryness in a tared basin, and weighed. This fraction consists of the "clay" particles less than 0·002 mm. in diameter, together with all the soluble and some of the insoluble humus. The contents of the dish are ignited over an Argand burner for some time and reweighed, to obtain the weight of the "clay" after ignition.

4. The sediment from which the clay has been removed is worked up as before in the beaker, which, however, is now only filled to the depth of 7·5 cm. The contents are now allowed to stand for twelve and a half minutes only, when the liquid is poured off into a large jar as before. The operations are then repeated until all the sediment settles in twelve and a half minutes and the liquid above is left quite clear. The contents of the jar are now evaporated to dryness and weighed, as in operation 3, before and after ignition; this fraction is desig-

nated "fine silt," and lies between 0·010 and 0·002 mm.
in diameter.

5. The sediment remaining in the beaker is worked
up afresh just as in the previous operations, the mark
being now placed 10 cm. from the bottom of the beaker,
and the time of settlement fixed at one hundred seconds.
The sediment is dried and weighed as "fine sand," while
the portion that is poured off is obtained by evaporation
as in the previous operations, and is designated as "silt."
The soil has thus been divided into the following series
of fractions :—

		Diameter in Millimetres.		
		Maximum.	Minimum.	
1	Stones and Gravel .	...	3	⎫ Separated
2	Fine Gravel . .	3	1	⎬ by
3	Coarse Sand . .	1	0·2	⎭ sifting.
4	Fine Sand . .	0·2	0·04	⎫ Separated
5	Silt . . .	0·04	0·01	⎬ by
6	Fine Silt . .	0·01	0·002	⎬ subsidence.
7	Clay . . .	0·002	...	⎭

If there be much "fine gravel" in the soil, it is best to
make a separate determination of its amount on a
sample weighing 50 grams, treating with acid as before,
and then washing the whole on to the 1 mm. sieve.
The result obtained should be taken as the true
percentage, and the other percentages found in the
analysis of 10 grams only should be recalculated to agree
with it.

The sizes of the particles, the depth of the liquid, and the
times adopted above, are purely conventional. The time
of settlement required to obtain a fraction of any
given range of size can be determined by a series of
trials, the material remaining suspended in each case

is measured under the microscope until the right time is hit off to secure the desired range of size in the sediment. The relationship between the time of settlement, the height of the liquid column, and the diameter of the particles, is governed by the formula :—

$$v = \frac{2ga^2}{9} \frac{(\sigma - \rho)}{\eta}$$

where σ is the density of the particle, a its radius, ρ the density, and η the coefficient of viscosity of the liquid. The application of the formula, however, requires to be checked by observation with the microscope, because the particles are not spheres.

The hygroscopic moisture and the loss on ignition also require determination, which is described under the chemical analysis of a soil.

Interpretation of Results.

It is as yet impossible to predict the behaviour of a soil under cultivation from a consideration of its mechanical analysis; in a general way we can see whether a soil is heavy, whether it is likely to dry "steely," or whether it will crumble readily under proper cultivation, and whether it is more suitable for market gardening or wheat growing, but the more refined points of difference connected with the management of given soils, which become known by experience to a good practical farmer, cannot as yet be deduced from the analysis. It is necessary to accumulate more data, until we possess the mechanical analysis of a large number of soils whose texture and amenability to cultivation have been ascertained by long practice; then we shall be able to assign any soil by its mechanical analysis to a known type.

The power of a soil to retain moisture and resist moderate drought depends on a predominance of the

finer particles and of humus; good wheat land or
land that will form sound permanent pasture will
contain at least 30 per cent. of silt and clay. The
ease with which a soil suffers the rain to percolate
depends upon the relatively low proportion of silt and
clay rather than on the amount of coarse-grained
material; the fine particles pack in among the larger,
and the soil is equally resistent to the passage of water,
whether the finest material is diffused among coarse
sand and gravel, or among the finer grades of sand.
The shrinkage of a soil on drying, and its tenacity when
dry, are even more dependent on low proportions of
coarse sand, humus, and chalk, than on the actual
amount of clay and silt which cause the shrinkage.
The really difficult soils to work are those containing
less than 20 per cent. of sand above 0·1 mm. in
diameter.

The table on page 56 will serve to illustrate these
points.

Soil No. 1 represents one of the lightest of sands,
about the extreme limit of cultivation—a soil, indeed,
which had been found unfit for ordinary farming,
and had been planted with conifers.

It will be seen that more than 83 per cent. consists
of "sand," nearly all of the coarser kinds, while the clay
only amounted to 4·7 per cent., most of which was really
ferric oxide. Calcium carbonate is also entirely absent,
owing to which the soil accumulates more humus than
would be expected from its great aeration, and in the
hollows where water lies it often becomes peaty. Such
soils are rarely in cultivation, but are left as wastes,
carrying a natural vegetation of heather and pine.

Because, however, of their lightness and warmth,
they are sometimes valuable for market gardening on a
small scale, if they are so situated that large supplies of

farmyard manure or town dung are available, strawberries being a favourite crop.

Soil No. 2 was taken from the Stackyard field of the farm of the Royal Agricultural Society at Woburn, and represents a light sandy loam, early, and extremely easy

	1	2	3	4	5	6	7	8
	Coarse Barren Sand.	Light Sandy Loam.	Light Loam.	Light Loam.	Heavy Sandy Loam.	Heavy Loam.	Clay.	Very Stiff Clay.
Fine Gravel . .	4.1	1.0	3.0	1.2	1.9	1.9	1.3	0.4
Coarse Sand . .	70.3	49.9	33.8	5.3	3.3	6.2	21.2	0.8
Fine Sand . .	7.0	16.1	28.0	32.1	36.8	21.4	12.5	6.4
Silt . . .	1.5	11.1	5.6	33.3	21.0	32.5	15.0	18.6
Fine Silt . .	5.8	5.6	10.8	5.3	14.3	13.8	11.9	13.6
Clay . . .	4.7	9.7	6.6	11.8	13.5	17.6	28.3	42.2
Moisture . .	2.6	1.2	4.3	1.9	1.4	2.2	1.6	9.5
Loss on ignition .	3.0	3.8	6.9	4.5	4.5	5.8	7.8	9.1
Calcium Carbonate .	...	...	0.2	0.1	0.3	2.5	...	0.4
				SUBSOILS.				
Fine Gravel . .	6.5	1.0	4.1	0.3	2.6	1.7	0.7	0.2
Coarse Sand . .	75.5	50.1	36.8	2.1	2.8	4.3	11.6	0.5
Fine Sand . .	4.9	15.9	26.1	27.0	35.2	15.8	7.3	6.2
Silt . . .	1.7	12.5	5.4	40.8	19.9	24.0	9.8	15.9
Fine Silt . .	4.2	5.9	8.4	5.7	16.1	16.7	15.2	10.2
Clay . . .	2.2	8.6	9.5	16.4	16.2	28.7	42.7	48.9
Moisture . .	1.6	0.9	3.3	3.6	1.2	3.8	2.6	6.3
Loss on ignition .	2.7	2.7	5.7	2.8	4.1	4.6	8.1	7.3
Calcium Carbonate .	...	...	0.1	0.1	0.3	0.1	...	0.1

to work in any weather. Owing to the preponderance of coarse sand, it suffers somewhat from drought and rarely carries heavy crops; and though responding well to manuring, the soil is hungry and does not long retain organic manures. The soil contains enough silt to possess a distinct power of lifting the subsoil water by capillarity, and similar soils containing less coarse sand and rather more fine sand and silt are often among the most valuable, because they combine free working with a capacity to resist drought through capillary action. This soil is more suited to market gardening than to mixed farming, makes poor pastures, grows good barley and turnips, but is too light for wheat and mangolds.

Soil No. 3 is a light sandy loam from one of the most valued of the "red land" potato soils, near Dunbar. In the cool climate, with a fair rainfall here prevailing, this forms an excellent arable soil for all crops, specially prized as yielding potatoes which retain their colour and are mealy after boiling.

Soil No. 4 is a typical free working loam from the Thanet sand formation, but rather lighter than usual. It is easy to work, warm and early, stands drought well, and is grateful and fairly retentive of manure. This is a highly valued soil for all ordinary arable cultivation, but is rather too light for wheat and pasture in the south or east of England. No particular fraction of the soil is predominant, but the soil is a fairly uniform mixture of particles of all grades.

It should be noticed that in these first four soils of a sandy type soil and subsoil are of very similar structure, whereas as soon as the smaller particles predominate on the heavy lands, then the soil is coarser grained than the subsoil.

Soil No. 5 comes from the Hastings Sand in Sussex, and represents a light example of a type of soil which, with a certain amount of variation in the relative proportions of fine sand and silt, covers a considerable area in the high Weald country.

Generally it forms a sticky, heavy working soil, commonly described as a clay, though the sand and silt fractions predominate and no excessive proportion of

clay is present. The soil, however, is kept very close by
the lack of coarse sand and of any of the still coarser
gravel and stones, the absence of carbonate of lime also
makes it stickier and more difficult to work. If a good
tilth is obtained, as for instance a seed bed for roots, and
heavy rain follows, these soils are particularly liable to
run together and set on drying to a glazed caked surface,
very inimical to germination. When well supplied with
lime and organic matter, these soils are fertile and carry
magnificent crops ; but they are rather late and expensive
to work, so that they have in great measure been laid
down to grass. They carry good grass when well
treated, and particularly when dressed with lime and
basic slag.

Soil No. 6 is taken from the Broadbalk Wheat Field
at Rothamsted : it is a heavy loam, stubborn and
intractable to work, which would lie very wet were not
the land naturally under-drained by the chalk rock at a
depth of ten or twelve feet below. The surface soil also
contains a large number of flint stones, not shown in
the analysis, and these help to keep the soil more open
and assist the drainage. Heavy as it is, the soil is not
a true clay ; it is the silt and fine sand fractions which
predominate, and to these must be attributed the
tendency of the soil to run and dry with a caked surface,
if much rain falls after a fine tilth has been attained.
In the soil but not the subsoil there is a fair proportion
of calcium carbonate, of artificial origin, and this con-
tributes greatly to the workability of the soil, for it has
been found unprofitable to retain some of the fields,
in which the calcium carbonate is absent, under
arable cultivation. Land of this class is still largely
under the plough, and is good wheat, mangold,
and bean land, but is too heavy for barley or turnips.
An occasional bare fallow is desirable to clean the land

and bring it into tilth again; it also yields very fair permanent pasture.

Soil No. 7 is situated on the Kimeridge Clay formation in Cambridgeshire; it is heavy land, difficult to cultivate, and when under the plough requires a bare fallow from time to time to restore the tilth. This represents one of the heaviest soils which respond to arable cultivation, which indeed is only practicable because the soil, though containing so high a proportion of clay, also contains a good deal of coarse sand, which keeps it open and helps to render it friable.

Soil No. 8 is a heavy, undrained London Clay, which will carry nothing but poor pasture. At one time it would carry in favourable seasons heavy crops of wheat and beans, but the expense of cultivation and the danger of missing a season have rendered it quite unprofitable to farm under the plough. It will be noticed that the soil consists almost wholly of the finer fractions, nearly one-half being "clay"; nor is there any difference between soil and subsoil, except in the humus, which improves the texture of the surface.

CHAPTER III

THE TEXTURE OF THE SOIL

Meaning of Texture and Conditions by which it is affected—Pore
Space and Density of Soils—Capacity of the Soil for Water—
Surface Tension and Capillarity—Percolation and Drainage—
Hygroscopic Moisture.

IN the preceding chapter, the nature of the particles
composing the soil has been discussed; it now remains
to consider the manner in which they may be arranged,
and the structure that results from the interaction
of the soil particles, the water, and such salts as may
be dissolved in the water. On these factors depend
what the farmer knows as the "texture" of the soil,
the degree of resistance it affords to the passage of a
plough, etc., the ease or otherwise with which that prime
object of cultivation, the preparation of a seed bed, can
be attained.

It is clear that as a soil consists of particles there
must be between them a certain amount of space
which is occupied by air or water; this is known as the
"pore space," and on its amount will largely depend the
density of the soil. Taking the simplest theoretical
case, a soil made up of equal spheres in contact with one
another, it will be found that the pore space is dependent upon the method of packing, but not upon the

size of the spheres. If the system of packing shown in A and B, Fig. 2, is adopted, the pore space reaches its maximum and amounts to 47·64 per cent. of the whole volume occupied by the soil; this proportion is the same when the soil particles have a smaller diameter, as in B; as long as the spheres are uniform in size, whatever that may be, and are packed as shown in the diagram, the pore space will be at its maximum. The minimum pore space is attained by the packing shown in C and D; it amounts to 25·95 per cent., and is again independent of the size of the particles, provided they are uniform. If the spheres are, however, of very different sizes, so that smaller spheres lie wholly within the spaces between the larger spheres, as in the arrangement shown in E, the pore space may be indefinitely reduced. *Per contra*, if aggregates of particles exist in the soil, containing both pore space between the ultimate particles and between the aggregates which behave as single particles, as in F, the pore space may rise much above the maximum of 49 per cent. A soil *in situ* generally possesses a pore space larger than the proportions indicated above; various causes, such as the stirring due to cultivation, the decay of vegetation, etc., leave definite cavities in the soil: for example, if a hole be dug for any purpose in ordinary cultivated ground and afterwards filled up with its own soil, it is rarely possible to fill the hole completely, especially if a little pressure has been used to trample down each layer.

In ordinary soils the pore space varies from a little over 50 per cent. among the stiff clays, down to 25 or 30 per cent. in the case of coarse sands of uniform texture. The reason for the greater pore space with the finer grained soils lies in the fact that the weight of the small particles of clay is not sufficient to overcome the friction and move the particles into the arrangement

FIG. 2.—Diagram illustrating Pore Space between Spherical Particles.

giving the minimum pore space.   If some small shot are shaken into a graduated measure and the pore space determined by pouring in a measured volume of water, the indicated minimum will be found; but if the experiment be repeated with sand which has been sifted to get approximately a uniform size, a higher figure will result. In the one case the particles are too light to exert much force towards the rearrangement of the mass; in the former case the heavy smooth shot slip straightway into the most compact arrangement, because by it the shot attain their lowest position.   In consequence of the pore space, the density of a soil *in situ* will differ very much from that of the materials of which it is composed, nor will all soils possess the same apparent density when dry.   Perhaps the best way of ascertaining the apparent density of a soil or soil materials is to get a smooth metal pint pot or like measure, fill it with the material in question with gentle tapping, and then strike off the upper surface smooth with a rule.   The weight of the contents divided by the volume gives the apparent density, from which the true volume and the pore space can be calculated, if the true density of the material be known.   The following table shows the true and apparent density of the chief soil materials; as a mean figure for purposes of calculation, 2·65 can be taken as the true density of ordinary soils :—

	True Density.	Apparent Density when dry.
Humus	1·2	·34
Clay	2·5	1
Sand	2·6	1·45
Calcium Carbonate. .	2·75	...
Hydrated Oxide of Iron . .	3·4 to 4	...

The   following   table   shows   a few   determinations

made in the laboratory, of the apparent density of various soils in a roughly powdered state and without the stones, which, being solid, would add to the apparent density of the soil. The results are also recalculated to show the weight of a cubic foot of the soil, and the weight per acre of a layer 9 inches deep :—

	Apparent Density.	Weight per cubic foot.	Lbs. per acre to 9″.
Heavy Clay . . .	1·062	66·4	2,150,000
Sandy Clay . .	1·279	80	2,600,000
Sandy Clay Subsoil .	1·18	73·7	2,380,000
Light Loam . . .	1·222	76·4	2,480,000
Light Loam Subsoil .	1·144	71·5	2,320,000
Sandy Loam . . .	1·225	76·7	2,490,000
Sandy Peat . . .	0·782	49	1,580,000
Light Sand . . .	1·266	79·2	2,560,000

The figures given above are not exactly comparable with soils under natural conditions, because of the powdering, the exclusion of stones, etc., but they serve to show that the clay soils usually described as "heavy" are really less dense, and weigh less per cubic foot than some of the lighter soils, whereas pure sands are the densest of all. The farmer's terms of "light" and "heavy" land refer to the draught of the plough, the resistance the soil opposes to being torn asunder, and not to the actual weight of the portion moved; sands which he calls "light," being, as the table shows, heavier per cubic foot than the clays which the farmer calls heavy soils.

This point will be further elucidated by the following table, which shows the weight per cubic foot of the arable soils at Rothamsted and Woburn down to a depth of 3 feet. These results represent the real weights of the soil as obtained by cutting out a block 6 inches square by 9 inches deep, weighing it, and afterwards ascertaining the deduction to be made for water. The Rothamsted soil is a stiff clay with many flints, the Woburn soil is a loose, coarse-grained sand, containing only a little stone derived from the rock below. It will be seen that, if the stones are excluded, the density increases with the depth, because of the greater consolidation caused by the weight above and to some extent by the washing down of the finest particles, but the increase does not continue much below the depth of 3 feet, the limit of these measurements :—

				Weight per cub. foot.	Per cent. of Stones.	Weight per acre.
				Lbs.		Lbs.
Rothamsted Arable Broadbalk	0″	to	9″	95·4	16·8	3,116,000
	9″	,,	18″	93·0	12·0	3,037,000
	18″	,,	27″	92·0	7·1	3,004,000
	27″	,,	36″	92·2	7·5	3,012,000
Woburn Arable	0″	,,	9″	96·6	2·96	3,157,000
	9″	,,	18″	103·8	5·95	3,382,000
	18″	,,	27″	106·2	4·92	3,462,000
	27″	,,	36″	106·9	7·83	3,501,000

From the data thus obtained as to density and pore space, together with a mechanical analysis to show the proportion of particles of various sizes, it is possible to calculate for any given soil both the number of soil particles and the area of the surface they expose, on the assumption that the particles are spherical. Approximately with grains 1 mm. in diameter, there would be 700 grains in 1 gram of the soil, and the number of grains to the gram will vary inversely as the third power of the diameter, *i.e.*, if the diameter be divided by 10 and become 0·1 mm., there will then be 700,000 grains to the gram. The surface possessed by all the soil grains can be similarly deduced by calculation, and will be found to vary inversely as the diameter

E

of the individual grains; a sphere 1 inch in diameter
will have only half the surface of the eight spheres of
half an inch in diameter which possess the same volume.
Hence it follows that the surface of an ordinary soil
must be extremely extensive, and since many of
the properties of the soil are dependent upon the surface
it becomes important to arrive at some measure of
this quantity. By calculation only a very rough idea
of its extent can be formed, both because every
departure of the soil grains from the spherical form
will increase the surface without affecting the weight,
and also because the mechanical analysis of a soil
gives only a generalised statement of the distribution of soil particles of various sizes in the soil. But
the surface of the soil grains in the case of a sandy
soil where the grains are all free, may be calculated
from the observed rates of flow of fluids like air or
water through a measured portion of the sand; and by
using this method King has computed the surface of
the constituent particles of various types of soil with
the results set out below :—

	Pore Space, per cent.	Area of Surface in square feet, per cubic foot of Soil.
Finest Clay . . .	52·9	173,700
Fine Clay Soil . .	48	110,500
Loamy Clay Soil . .	49·2	70,500
Loam	44·1	46,500
Sandy Loam . . .	38·8	36,900
Sandy Soil . . .	32·5	11,000

As a rough figure to remember, the surface of the
particles in one cubic foot of an ordinary light loam
may be taken as about an acre; this will increase
as the soil approaches more and more to clay, and
diminish as the soil becomes increasingly sandy. The

extent of surface exposed by the soil particles is important because it is their active part; other conditions being equal, the amount dissolved from a solid body in a given time by any solvent will be proportional to the surface exposed.

Again, the water in a soil usually exists as a film, coating the surface of the soil particles, and the amount of water that can be held under particular conditions becomes a function of the extent of surface; even the power of a soil to remove certain substances from solution is likewise dependent on the surface.

Capacity of the Soil for Water.

So far, the structure of the soil in a dry state has only been considered, it is now necessary to consider its behaviour when fully saturated with water, before passing on to the more usual state when the soil contains both air and water.

The amount of water which a soil will hold when completely saturated will depend upon the pore space, will, in fact, be the pore space together with whatever water the material of the particles can imbibe without causing any swelling. Perhaps the best method for determining the water capacity of a soil is one devised by Hilgard. A small cylindrical brass box is constructed, 1 cm. deep and 6 cm. in diameter. The bottom is a sheet of perforated brass, and the whole is supported on three legs; the capacity of the box is about 30 c.c. The exact capacity is determined by waxing up the holes, weighing, filling with water, and reweighing. A circle of thin filter paper cut to fit the box is laid inside and wetted, any superfluous water that comes through being wiped away. The box is then weighed, care-

fully filled with fine earth, and gently tapped to settle
the soil down; finally, the surface is struck off level
with a straight-edge. The box is now weighed again
to find the quantity of dry soil taken, and placed in a
dish of distilled water, so that the water stands about
1 mm. above the lower surface of the soil inside the
box; the dish is then covered over to prevent evaporation. The water rises in the soil, displacing the air,
and in about an hour's time the soil will have absorbed
all the water possible. The box is lifted above the water
a little, allowed a few minutes to drain, the excess of
water clinging to the under-surface is wiped away with
a clean cloth or filter paper, and the whole is then
weighed. A previous determination of the moisture
present in the "air-dry fine earth" must also be made,
to provide all the data necessary for the calculation of
the water contained in the saturated soil. This calculation may be made in three ways: either the proportion the water in the saturated soil bears to the
dry soil, or the proportion of water in the wet soil
may be estimated, or again, the proportion by volume
that is occupied by water and soil respectively may
be calculated. The figures thus obtained will vary very
considerably, because the less dense the soils, because of
the clay and humus they contain, the more water they
will absorb; thus the proportion which the water
absorbed bears to the weight of the dry soil becomes
exaggerated in their case. Perhaps the soundest picture
of the state of affairs is attained by considering the
volume that is occupied by the water in the soil, and
expressing it either as a percentage by volume, or as
lbs. or inches of water per cubic foot of wet soil. The
following figures show the results obtained for four
distinctive soils, calculated out in the different ways
described above.

	Maximum.			Minimum.			
	Water absorbed per 100 of Dry Soil.	Per cent. of Water in Saturated Soil by Weight.	Per cent. of Water in Saturated Soil by Volume.	Per 100 Dry Soil.	Per cent. by Weight.	Per cent. by Volume.	Per cent. of Water when Air dry.
Coarse Sandy Soil	45	31	50·5	18	15·3	22·2	0·8
Light Loam . .	50·5	33·5	55·8	29·2	22·6	35·4	2·9
Stiff Clay . .	98·6	49·6	67·6	56·4	36·1	45·6	6·9
Sandy Peat . .	155	60·8	63·2	116	53·7	52·8	8·3

Under natural conditions a soil is rarely saturated to the extent indicated in the previous table; as the rain water enters from above, the surface of the soil is wetted first and the air within the soil finds a difficulty in escaping, so that even after long-continued rain the pore space does not become entirely filled with water.

The following table shows the water contained in a few field soils sampled a day or two after the cessation of long-continued rain, and calculated as percentages of the wet soil by weight :—

	Per cent. of Water in Wet Soil.
Sand at Water Level	18·4
Rothamsted Wheat Land, unmanured	23·0
„ „ manured with artificials . .	24·7
„ „ manured with dung for 26 years	37·6
Light Loam above Chalk	20·3

Hellriegel has shown that the optimum proportion of water in the soil for the growth of the plant is 40 to 50 per cent. of the maximum required for saturation.

Flow of Water through Soils.

The freedom with which water will move through soils under the action of gravity or other force will depend not only on the pore space, but upon the mean size of the channels formed between the soil grains. King made some experiments with sands graded by sieves and formed into columns 14 inches long and 1 square foot in section, above which the water was maintained at a head of 2 inches. He obtained the following results expressed in inches of water passing in twenty-four hours; the second column gives the number of meshes to the inch of the sieves which respectively passed and retained the sand :—

Medium.	Sieves.	Inches.
Sand	40 to 60	301
,, ...	60 ,, 80	160
,, ...	80 ,, 100	73·2
,, ...	100	39·7
Clay Loam . . .	...	1·6
Black Marsh Soil . .	...	·7

It will be noticed that there is a great diminution in the rate of flow as soon as a soil containing small clay particles is introduced; of course, one of the characteristic properties of clay is that it will not allow any flow of water through it when it has been puddled. In the puddled condition, the particles constituting the clay are no longer aggregated, the material is in its finest-grained condition, so that the pore spaces between them must have become extremely small. Not only is the flow diminished by the increase of friction in the narrow channels, but in the case of clay their dimensions have become so small that probably the contained water   wholly within the range

of the molecular forces to be described later; it is thus
prevented from flowing at all, and only moves by
diffusion. If we assume for clay particles a mean
diameter of 0·0002 mm., and a structure similar to A in
Fig. 2, p. 62, it is easy to show that no molecule in the
space between the spheres can be further than about $\frac{1}{5}$
of the diameter of a sphere, or 0·00004 mm. from one or
other surface, while the range of molecular forces as
calculated by Quincke extends to about 0·00005 mm.
from the surface. Spring has indeed shown that infiltration of water is impossible through clays or loams unless
they are first allowed to expand by taking up water.

Surface Tension and Capillarity.

The existence of attraction between the molecules
causes the free surface of any liquid to become a sort
of stretched elastic film, in tension itself, and exerting
a certain pressure inwards when free. The molecules
within the liquid are equally attracted in all directions
by the surrounding molecules, and are therefore in equilibrium; the molecules on the surface, having nothing on
one side, are only attracted inwards, and so, as a whole,
exert a pressure on the liquid similar to that which
would be caused by a stretched elastic skin over the
liquid.

The existence of this force of "surface tension," as
it is called, may be demonstrated by many simple experiments, *e.g.*, by the familiar fact that a clean needle
will float when placed carefully on the surface of water;
or, by the fact that any portion of a liquid which is so
small that the force of gravity on it is not large
compared to the molecular forces, immediately assumes
the spherical shape. Of all figures, a sphere has the
smallest surface in proportion to its contents, *i.e.*, the

stretched film on the surface of a drop of liquid shrinks as far as it can until the liquid is packed into the smallest possible compass, into the form of a sphere.

When a liquid and a solid are in contact, the form of the surface and the resulting pressure or tension depend on whether the liquid "wets" the solid or not. For

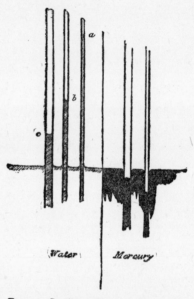

Fig. 3.—Capillary Rise and Depression
of Liquids in Glass Tubes.

example, if a series of very fine or "capillary" glass tubes are dipped into water and mercury respectively, the water will rise up the tubes in inverse proportion to their diameters, the mercury, which does not wet the glass, will be correspondingly depressed.

The water surfaces *a*, *b*, *c* (Fig. 3), are convex to the water, and become more convex the narrower the tube is; the pressure below the convex surface must

Fig. 4.—Photograph illustrating Liquid Film round Soil Particles.

be less than atmospheric, or the water would not stand higher within than without the tube; further, the pressure beneath *a*, the most convex and therefore most stretched surface film, is lower than the pressure beneath *b*, and still lower than that beneath *c*. *Per contra*, the mercury surfaces are convex outwards, and exert pressure on the liquid beneath, depressing it below the general surface of the liquid in proportion to the degree of convexity. These instances will help us to realise that the surface of a liquid may exert either a pull or a pressure on the liquid within, according to the curvature of the surface, and the greater the curvature the greater will be the force exerted. It is this tension of the surface film which causes movements of water in soil, other than those due to gravity; for example, if a flowerpot stands in a shallow dish of water, the whole of the soil within the pot is kept moist; or if water is poured on to dry soil, it is seen to work outwards through the soil, the water advancing from particle to particle as it wets them, just in the same manner as it rises up the capillary tubes. When a soil is saturated, the whole pore space is filled with water; if this soil be allowed to drain, some of the water is pulled away by gravity, but much remains clinging round the particles in the stretched film condition, the tension in the film balancing the pull due to gravity. Perhaps the best illustration of the state of affairs in a wet but drained soil may be obtained by linking a series of toy balls together, as shown in the photograph (Fig. 4), and then dipping the whole into oil. When the oil has ceased to drip it will be seen that every ball is covered by a thin film of oil, and that between the balls there is a layer of oil much thicker in the lower than in the upper layers. The whole surface film is equally stretched, but the stretching in the upper layers is largely due to the pull from the oil below, while in the lowest layer of all the whole tension exerted by the stretched film is devoted to holding up its own thick film of oil. If oil be taken away at any point, the curvature of the film, and therefore the tension of the surface in that region, is increased : a readjustment then takes place till the stretched film regains the same tension everywhere, which is effected by a motion of the oil to the place where the tension has been increased. If the withdrawal of the oil be continued, the film round the balls becomes thinner and thinner; the more it is stretched, the more closely it clings to the surface, so that the removal becomes progressively more difficult ; at last the film becomes so much stretched that it ruptures and reunites again over a smaller surface, hence with a diminished tension. The rupture naturally takes place where the film is thinnest, on the top layer of balls, which becomes more or less "dry" while the lower balls are still surrounded by their film.

Just in a similar way water will always move in a soil from a wet to a dryer place, till the film surrounding the particles is equally stretched throughout.

For example, if A, B, C (Fig. 5) represent three soil particles, of which A and B are surrounded by a thin, and C by a thicker, film of water : when the spheres are in contact the water will fill up part of the angle between the spheres, as shown in the diagram. But the water surface at a is more curved than at b, i.e., it corresponds to the surface at a in the fine capillary tube (Fig. 3) as compared with the surface at b in the wider tube. But the diminution of pressure caused by a is greater than that caused by b, as shown by the greater height to which water is raised in the tube ; hence in the same way the pressure inside the liquid at *a* (Fig. 5) will be lower than that at *b*, and there will be a flow of water from *b* to *a*, until the curvatures and corresponding surface tensions are equalised.

In a wet soil, then, surface tension is a force tending on the one hand to retain a certain amount of water round the particles, and on the other to equalise the distribution of water, by causing movement towards any point where the surface tension has been increased. For example, if the water in a soil is in equilibrium and evaporation begins at the surface, the film there is made

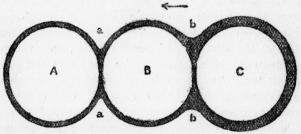

FIG. 5.—Diagram illustrating Liquid Film round Soil Particles.

thinner, and the curvature increased in the angles between the soil particles : hence the pull exerted by the film is increased, and water is lifted from below against gravity. *Per contra*, if rain fall on such a soil the films round the upper particles are thickened, their tension is lowered, and the pull of the film below now acts with gravity in drawing the water down into the soil.

Percolation.

The state of affairs illustrated by the model of balls dipped in oil is seen in the case of a soil which has been thoroughly saturated so that all the pore space is occupied by water, and then allowed to drain until the remaining water is held in the soil by surface tension only.

In the upper layers the film will be stretched to the utmost, or even broken by the pull of the water below; in the lower layers the film will be wholly engaged in holding the water immediately in contact with the particles of the layer: these layers may be saturated, while the upper layers hold an amount dependent on their distance from the saturated zone, and on the extent of surface exposed by the particles.

The accompanying diagram (Fig. 6) expresses the results of an experiment of King's, where columns of sand and soil, 8 feet and 7 feet long respectively, were saturated and then allowed to drain till they parted with no further water, which required a period of sixty days in the case of the soil columns, and of more than two years for the sand. The tubes were then cut up, and the proportion of water in the sand or soil in successive 3-inch lengths of the tubes was determined.

It will be seen that the sands retain very little water by surface tension in the upper layers, whereas the clay loam, with the enormous area its particles expose, holds practically the same proportion throughout.

If we also consider the following table, showing the time taken by the same sands and soils to part with their water, the difference of the texture of the soils will be even more evident :—

	INCHES OF WATER LOST IN				
	30 min.	31 to 60 min.	24 hrs. (?)	2 to 11 days.	12 to 21 days.
No. 20 Sand .	10·25	4·68	...	...	...
„ 60 „ .	5·67	4·52	...	...	...
„ 100 „ .	1·21	·84	...	...	...
Sandy Loam .	...	...	2·64	5·07	·9
Clay Loam .	...	...	1·96	2·11	·49

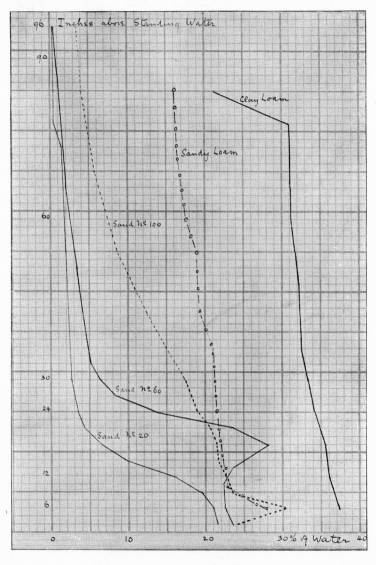

FIG. 6.—Water Content of Columns of wetted but thoroughly drained Sand and Soil.

[To face page 76.

The downward movement of rain water through soils is known as " percolation," and is distinguished from " flow " by the fact that the water is supposed to have free surfaces, so that surface tension comes into play. It takes place under the action of gravity through the pore space proper, and also through the cracks, the worm tracks, the passages left by decayed roots, and other adventitious openings in the soil. The percolation proceeds until the zone is reached where the pore space is completely filled; this is known as the " water table," and is the level at which water stands in the wells. Above the water table the soil will be more or less in the state represented in the diagram showing sands and soils in which percolation has ceased; though there will be most probably a more irregular distribution, with zones which contain an excess of water travelling downwards with greater or less rapidity, according to the texture of the soil. It is these temporarily saturated zones which cause the ordinary tile drains to run, although situated many feet above the permanent water table. A soil in which percolation has ceased, though it may still contain much water, will not part with it to a drain; the water cannot break away from the elastic film and run off down the drain, unless it be present in such an excess that the surface tension is insufficient to hold it against gravity. But in a clay soil, percolation is so slow that the upper few feet of soil may become saturated by the winter rains and remain so for months, if percolation has to proceed all the way down to the water table; by the introduction of drains, the percolating column is shortened to the distance between the surface and the drain. In a coarse-grained sandy soil percolation is very rapid, the land dries quickly after rain, and retains a minimum of water by surface tension; in fine-grained soils, which are, however, not too fine for percolation, the excess of rain will be removed rapidly enough to keep the soil below the saturated condition, yet enough water may be retained to supply the needs of the crop between the intervals of rain.

While the flow of water from a field-drain may be taken as a rough measure of the amount of percolation going on at any given time for that soil, the movement may be followed more closely by means of a lysimeter or drain-gauge. As a rule, the records of these instruments are vitiated by the disturbance undergone by the soil in filling them; but the drain-gauges at Rothamsted were constructed by building cemented walls round blocks of earth *in situ*, and then gradually introducing a perforated iron plate below to carry the soil. The following diagram (Fig. 7) shows the mean monthly records of rainfall and percolation through a depth of 20 inches and 60 inches respectively, over a period of thirty-five years.

It will be seen that of the total rainfall a little less than one-half percolates through 60 inches of the Rothamsted soil; it should be remembered, however, that the surface of these gauges is kept free from weed or any growth. The total drainage through 20 inches of soil is practically the same as that through 60 inches, but rather a greater proportion of the rainfall comes through the 60-inch gauge in the winter and through the 20-inch gauge in the summer. In the winter months the percolation reaches as much as 80 per cent. of the rainfall, in August little more than 20 per cent. of the rainfall finds its way through the layer of soil. When the ground has become dried to any depth in the summer, percolation may be much hindered by the air within the soil and the want of a

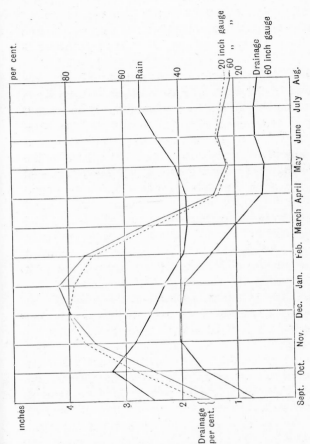

FIG. 7.—Diagram showing Rainfall and Percolation at Rothamsted, 1870-1905.

The two heavy curves show rainfall and percolation through the 60″ gauge in inches; the dotted and the lighter continuous curves show the percolation through the 20″ and 60″ gauges as percentages of the rainfall.

(Reproduced from the "Journal of Agricultural Science" by permission of the Cambridge University Press.)

[To face page 78.

continuous film of wetted surfaces to lead the water down by surface tension. The top layer of soil becomes thoroughly wetted and will not allow the air below to escape; only after some time are local displacements of the air set up, which enable the water above to make connection with the wetted subsoil below, so that percolation can begin. For this reason summer rains falling in a season of drought are often noticed to be of little benefit to the crop, because they are retained near the surface until wholly evaporated, instead of increasing the stock of moisture at the lower levels where the roots of the plant are then operative in obtaining water.

Minimum Capacity of Soil for Water.

The amount of water retained in a soil by surface tension alone, when percolation has removed as much as possible, is rather an important factor to determine, as upon it depends to some extent the power of the soil to resist drought by retaining water for the crop between intervals of rain. If short columns of sand and soil which have been saturated and then allowed to drain away into a state of equilibrium are considered, it is clear that very different proportions of water are retained by the various soils. Suppose, however, the column be of such a length that at some level the upper film of water cannot be further stretched, but the particles cease to be wet; the layer immediately below this dry soil contains the minimum amount of water consistent with a continuous film at all. Soil in this condition may be regarded as at the minimum of saturation; it will part with no more water by drainage, and will become drier only by evaporation. In order to obtain such a sample of soil for determina-

tion of its water content, much trouble would be
necessary, and a long time must elapse before equilibrium could be obtained in the long tube filled with
wet soil. Practically, however, the same result can
be reached with the apparatus previously described
for estimating the maximum capacity of the soil for
water, by constantly bringing the thin layer of soil
there used into contact with dry soil, until the
previously saturated soil no longer parts with water
to the new soil.

After the determination of maximum water capacity,
as previously described (p. 67), a little more fine earth,
which has been standing for some time over water in a
closed space so that it has acquired all the hygroscopic
moisture it can, is shaken lightly over the surface of the
wet soil in the box to the depth of $\frac{1}{4}$ inch or so. It
rapidly becomes wet, as will be evident by a change in
colour, whereupon it is struck off by drawing a fine
tightly stretched wire across the top of the box and
shaking the loosened layer off. More fine earth is then
shaken on and struck off as before when wetted, the
operation being repeated again and again, until a thin
dry layer remains on the surface for half an hour or so
without showing by change of colour any absorption of
water. During this wait the box should be in a closed
chamber over water. With fine-grained clays and loams
the process does not take long, with a coarse sand the
water moves slowly into the dry layer, and it is difficult
to hit off the exact end-point, when the soil particles
are still surrounded by water but the surface tension
is too great to allow this water to pass into dry soil.
Finally, the box and its contents are weighed, dried
in the oven, and reweighed. The second weighing
when dry is necessary, because the box will be found
to hold more dry soil than was originally filled into

it; a certain amount of consolidation has taken place through the addition of the dry earth and the subsequent striking off when wet. The numbers in the columns headed Minimum in the table on p. 69 were obtained in this way: they show that though the maximum capacity for water, or pore space, may not vary very greatly for different soils, there is a much wider and more important divergence between the amounts of water they will retain by surface tension alone, this latter being the important factor in judging of the power of the soil to retain a reserve of moisture for crops.

Variations in Surface Tension.

The surface tension of water is very high, but it is easily raised or lowered by the presence of small amounts of material in solution. The effect of altering the surface tension of a film at any point is to cause motion, as is seen in the well-known experiment of covering a plate with a thin film of coloured water and dropping a little alcohol into the middle of the film. The alcohol immediately weakens the surface tension of the film in the middle to such an extent that all the liquid runs to the outer edge and leaves the plate bare in the middle. Most of the salts which are used as artificial manures and are soluble in water increase the surface tension of the soil water, hence an application of salt or nitrate of soda may, by increasing the tension of the surface film, lift more water from the subsoil and maintain the top layer of soil in a moister condition. *Per contra*, solutions of organic matter, particularly of the many organic substances used as manure which have a little oil in them, extracts of dung, etc., have a surface tension below that of water. To this fact may be attributed the "burning" of soils which is sometimes

F

seen when organic manures are applied late in the
season and dry hot weather succeeds ; the soil water at
the top in contact with the manure has a lower surface
tension and consequently less lifting power for the
subsoil water ; hence any shallow rooted crop is deprived
of some of the subsoil water which would have otherwise
been lifted to it. A rise of temperature diminishes the
surface tension of water, and therefore lessens the
sustaining power of the film ; as it also lessens the
viscosity of water, it will often cause percolation to
begin afresh from soil that had apparently ceased to
yield any more drainage. This effect may sometimes
be seen in variations in the flow of land drains or in the
level of water in shallow wells. The following table
shows the comparative surface tension of water and
various solutions :—

Nature of Solution.	Density.	Surface Tension.
		Dynes per sq. cm.
Water	1·0	7·532
Common Salt	1·1	7·911
Kainit	1·1	7·9
Nitrate of Soda . . .	1·1	7·73
Dung	1·0013	7·464
Superphosphate . . .	1·0104	7·414
Soil Extract	1·0	7·244
Garden Soil Extract . . .	1·0	7·089

Cohesion caused by Surface Tension.

In certain cases the stretched film surrounding soil
particles will give them an apparent cohesion by
enclosing them and drawing them together. A handful
of wet sand can be moulded into shape, but falls in
pieces as soon as it is dry : just as in a camel-hair
pencil the bristles, which stand apart when dry or
wholly immersed in water, are drawn together to a

point if the brush be dipped in water and withdrawn. Or again, a flat sandy beach from which a smooth sea is receding will often show above tide-mark one stretch of sand quite dry and loose, in which the feet sink deeply, and another very soft stretch immediately left by the tide where the sand grains are completely surrounded by water. Between the two is a stretch of sand of the same character, but firm to walk upon; this is partly wet, and there is enough water to form a film round the grains and hold them in position with a certain amount of force. That this sand is really just as loosely arranged as the softer tracts that are either wetter or drier, may be seen by the fact that it will easily pack more closely together under repeated gentle pressure with the foot. The shrinkage of soils, especially of clays, as they dry, may be attributed to the surface tension of the films surrounding the groups of soil particles; as the water content is lessened the films exert more force in their effort to contract, and drag some of the particles closer together, especially the very small particles whose weight is trivial compared to the forces exerted by the film. Clay shrinks more than other soils because of the greater number of particles, their small size, and the higher proportion of pore space into which motion can take place. The tenacity of wet clay is due to the number of water films that have to be ruptured, the vastly greater cohesion of dry clay probably to the fact that many of the particles have been dragged within the range of one another's molecular forces. There is a stage in the drying of clay when it will fall to pieces when worked; probably this represents the stage analogous to the partly wet sand, when cohesion is due to the surface films. The clay is neither so wet that the particles just slip over one another when pressure is applied—the pasty condition; nor have they been drawn so closely together as to cohere without the aid of any water. It is not quite intelligible why a piece of dried clay becomes soft and swells again when wetted, nor why the particles should once more move apart.

Hygroscopic Moisture.

If the withdrawal of water from a soil by evaporation be continued, a point is at last reached when the soil becomes air-dry: it still retains some water, which will vary in amount with the degree of humidity of the atmosphere and the temperature. This last film of water is held very closely and in a somewhat different manner from the ordinary film held by surface tension, though the two shade off into one another. For example, the film of hygroscopic moisture can be produced by condensation alone, when perfectly dry soil is placed in an atmosphere containing water vapour: the surface of materials like glass, sand, etc., has sufficient attraction for water to condense it from a state of vapour. The amount of hygroscopic water retained by different types of soil when air-dried and then allowed to stand in a saturated atmosphere at ordinary temperature, is given in the table below; it will be seen to be more or less proportional to the surface possessed by the soil particles, clay and humus retaining the most.

This hygroscopic moisture cannot be of any service to plants: Sachs has shown by experiments in pots that tobacco plants will begin to wilt before the soil has parted with all its moisture. When wilting began with a sandy soil the sand in the pot still contained 1·5 per cent. of water, with a clay soil 8 per cent. of water; with a mixture of sand and humus there was as much as

12·3 per cent. of water retained by the soil. Heinrich
has further shown that wilting begins before the water
content of the soil has been reduced to the hygroscopic
water limit, as the following figures demonstrate—

	WATER PER 100 OF DRY SOIL.	
	When Plants Wilt.	Hygroscopic Water.
Coarse Sand . . .	1·5	1·15
Sandy Garden Soil . .	4·6	3
Fine Sand, with Humus .	6·2	3·98
Sandy Loam . . .	7·8	5·74
Chalky Loam . . .	9·8	5·2
Peat	49·7	42·3

This is easily intelligible in view of the fact that the
root hairs cannot be in contact with all the soil particles,
nor can the water move from particle to particle when
it has been reduced to so low a proportion. King has
made some observations of the amount of water still
present in soils in the field which had become so dry
that growth was at a standstill and the plants were
wilting.

Depth.	Nature of Soil.	Per cent. of Water under Clover.	Under Maize.
0″ to 6″	Clay Loam	8·4	7
6″ „ 12″	„	8·5	7·8
12″ „ 18″	Reddish Clay	12·4	11·6
18″ „ 24″	„	13·3	12
24″ „ 30″	Sandy Clay	13·5	10·8
40″ „ 43″	Sand	9·5	4·2

Under these conditions all the soils were about
equally dry, so far as any power to part with their
water went; if the estimates made previously of the
area of surface of the particles constituting various kinds

of soil be combined with these percentages to calculate
the thickness of film of the water on that surface, it will
be found that on all soils the film possesses approximately the same thickness, about 0·00003 inch.

Because of the quantity of water which some soils
will retain rather than give up to the plant, it is possible
that such soils may have less available water for the
plant than a much coarser grained soil which starts
with a lower initial amount of water.   For example, the
clay and sand in the table above contain when saturated about 26 per cent. and 18 per cent. of water
respectively; as the crop can reduce this to 12 per cent.
in one case, and 4·2 per cent. in the other, both sand
and clay yield about the same amount of water to the
crop.

A good example of the fact that only the water in
the soil which is in excess of the hygroscopic moisture
is available for the crop, is seen in F. J. Alway's studies
of soil moisture conditions in the "Great Plains" region
of north-western America.   There the rainfall is only
from 12 to 15 inches annually, and falls chiefly during
the summer months; because of its insufficiency for the
production of continuous crops, it is customary to take
a bare fallow one season in three in order to accumulate
the rainfall for the benefit of the two succeeding grain
crops.

The table shows the water content of the soil down
to the depth of 6 feet on two fields near Indian Head,
Saskatchewan, taken at the end of July 1904, field B.
having been fallowed, and C. having carried a crop of
oats which had shown the effects of drought.   Figures
are given for the total water in the soil as sampled, the
hygroscopic moisture as determined in the laboratory,
and the difference, which may be termed the free
water :—

Foot Section.	B, after Fallow. Water.			C, after Oats. Water.		
	Total.	Hygroscopic.	Free.	Total.	Hygroscopic.	Free.
First . .	29·4	12·0	17·4	20·0	12·7	7·3
Second . .	14·9	3·9	11·0	22·4	13·2	9·2
Third . .	16·4	4·7	11·7	21·6	13·5	8·1
Fourth . .	17·4	5·5	11·9	16·1	4·6	11.5
Fifth . .	21·8	7·6	14·2	15·1	4·2	10·9
Sixth . .	19·6	8·0	11·6	15·9	5·9	10·0
Mean .	19·9	...	12·9	18·5	...	9·5

In each field the upper layer of soil possesses a higher capacity for retaining hygroscopic moisture than does the lower layer, but in field C. this upper layer is thicker than in field B. It will be seen from the table that as regards total water there is no great difference between the two fields, but when the hygroscopic moisture is deducted, B. contains 3·4 per cent. more water available for the plant. This difference was manifested in the following season in the yield, which was only 2160 lbs. of grain and straw on C. and 9200 lbs. on B.

Though it is doubtful if the hygroscopic moisture gathered by the surface soil in the cooler and damper periods of the night, can be passed on to the subsoil and given up to the roots, yet by its evaporation the next day it may help to keep the temperature of the soil down, and so indirectly diminish the loss of water to the soil. Of course in certain conditions of air and soil temperature there is condensation upon the soil of visible water which can be available to the crops; for example, in some months drain-gauges yield more water than the rainfall, though a certain amount of loss by evaporation must also have taken place. This usually happens in

the early spring, and can be set down to the condensation of dews by the thoroughly chilled ground from
a warm and moist atmosphere. Warington has suggested that the persistent wetness of the soil in February
must be attributed to this cause. In a coarse-grained
soil mostly filled with air, the cooling of the surface that
comes by radiation at night may result in an upward
distillation of water from the wetter and warmer subsoil.
Hilgard has suggested this explanation to account for
the capacity of some Californian soils to maintain a
crop during a rainless winter, when the soil itself shows
only 3 per cent. or so of water.

A. Mitscherlich has made a number of determinations of the heat that is evolved on moistening dry soil
(benetzungs-warme), due to the condensation of the
hygroscopic water on the surface of the soil particles,
and regards the figure thus obtained as of great
significance in judging of the physical properties of a
soil, since it provides a measure of the total surface of
all the particles composing the soil. He obtained results
of the following order, in calories evolved per gram of
soil—sand 0·01, calcium carbonate 0·38, sandy soil 0·79,
sandy loam 2·37, strong clay 14·98, peat 22·66. Unfortunately the determination is by no means an easy
one to make, and no sufficient number of results have
been obtained for soils of known behaviour in the field
to enable one to form a judgment of the value of the
method.

CHAPTER IV

TILLAGE AND THE MOVEMENTS OF SOIL WATER

Water required for the Growth of Crops—The Effect of Drainage
—Effects of Autumn and Spring Cultivation, Hoeing and
Mulching, Rolling, upon the Water Content of the Soil—
The Drying Effect of Crops—Bare Fallows—Effect of Dung
on the Retention of Water by the Soil.

THE amount of water transpired by various plants
during their growth has been investigated by Lawes
and Gilbert at Rothamsted, by Hellriegel in Germany,
and Wollny in Munich, and by King in America. The
general principle upon which these observers have
worked, has been to grow the plants in pots and
measure the amount of water consumed during growth,
care being taken to eliminate or allow for losses by
evaporation from the bare ground, and also to render
the conditions of the plant's life as similar to those of
the open field as possible. Finally, the plant is washed
free of soil, dried, and weighed, so that a ratio is
obtained between the dry matter produced and the
water consumed during growth.

Some of the numbers obtained are given in the table
below: it will be seen that the same plant gives very
different results with the different observers.

	Lawes and Gilbert.	Hellriegel.	Wollny.	King.
Wheat . . .	225	359	...	...
Barley . . .	262	310	393	774
Oats . . .	...	402	557	665
Red Clover . .	249	330	453	...
Peas . . .	235	292	477	447

The divergencies in these results are intelligible, if we consider that the "transpiration" process by which the water is lost, and the "assimilation" process by which the plant gets heavier, have no necessary connection, though both become active under the same stimuli of light and warmth. Some leaves transpire rapidly as a means of maintaining a low temperature whilst absorbing large amounts of radiant energy from the sun; other plants which have to resist drought reduce the transpiration by a thickened cuticle, or by a more concentrated cell sap. Dr H. Brown has shown that of the radiant energy falling upon a sunflower leaf on a bright August noonday, about 95 per cent. was consumed in evaporating the transpiration water; of the energy falling upon the same leaf in bright diffuse daylight, only 28 per cent. was used up in evaporation. Comparing in these two cases the water transpired with the carbohydrate produced (and this will be about $\frac{9}{10}$ of the total dry matter) we find in the sunlight the ratio was 347 to 1, in the diffuse daylight 234 to 1. Further investigations are desirable; but, taking the whole group of observations, we shall be justified in assuming that our ordinary field crops transpire about 300 lbs. of water for each lb. of dry matter produced. It now remains to translate this approximate figure into tons of water per acre required to grow the ordinary crops. The following table shows the weight at harvest of a

fair yield of the crop in question, the percentage of
water contained in the crop, the weight of dry matter
produced per acre, then the water transpired as deduced
from the dry matter produced, and in the last column
this same amount of transpired water recalculated as
inches of rain.

Crop.	Weight at Harvest.	Per cent. of Water.	Weight of Dry Matter at Harvest.	Calculated Water transpired during Growth.	
	Tons per acre.		Tons per acre.	Tons per acre.	Inches of Rain.
Wheat . .	2·5	18	2·05	615	6·09
Barley . .	2	17	1·66	498	4·93
Oats . .	2·5	16	2·10	630	6·24
Meadow Hay .	1·5	16	1·26	378	3·74
Clover Hay .	2·0	16	1·68	504	(?)
Swedes .	17	88	2·04	612	6·06
Mangolds .	30	88	3·60	1080	10·69
Potatoes . .	7·5	75	1·87	561	5·55
Beans . .	2	17	1·66	498	4·94

It will be seen that in all cases the amount of water
transpired by the crop is a notable fraction of the total
annual rainfall, particularly so in the case of a root crop
like mangolds, which in the south and east of England
will often require a full half of the total rain falling
within the year. As much of the rainfall runs straight
off the surface into the ditches, and another portion
is lost to the land by percolation into the springs, as
again a considerable fraction is evaporated at certain
seasons from the bare surface of the soil, it is evident
that the water supply, even in our humid climate, is
far from sufficient for the maximum of production, and
may easily fall below that which is required for an
average crop. Indeed, we may take it as a truism that
the yield is more often determined by the water available than by lack of the other essentials of growth—

light and heat, manure, etc. Of this we can have no
better proof than the enormous crops grown by irrigation on sewage farms. Where the conditions are
favourable, and the farm is situated on a free draining
sandy or gravelly soil, so that the water can be often
renewed and drained away to keep the soil supplied
with air as well as water, the production of grass,
cabbages, and other green crops is multiplied five or
even tenfold by the unlimited supply of water. Speaking generally, over a great part of England, where the
annual rainfall is from 35 to 25 inches, a large proportion
of which falls in the non-growing season, it is necessary
to husband the water supply, and it will be found that
one at least of the objects of many of our usual tillage
operations is the conservation of the moisture in the
ground for the service of the crop. From this point
of view, the various operations dealing with the land
can now be considered, such as drainage, ploughing,
hoeing, rolling, and other cultivations.

The Effect of Drainage.

Drainage is usually regarded as a means of freeing
the land from an excess of water, but it also has an
important effect in rendering a higher proportion of the
annual rainfall available for the crop, so that drained
land will suffer less from drought than the same land
in an undrained condition.

Land may require drainage for various reasons : it
may possess a naturally pervious subsoil, and yet be
water-logged owing to its situation, or the subsoil may
be so close in texture that percolation is reduced to a
minimum and the surface soil remains for long periods
almost saturated with water, especially if the slope is
gentle and water lies after rain until very large amounts

soak in. The flat meadows adjoining a river are
often water-logged because their surface is little higher
than the water in the river and the general water table
in the adjoining soil. In these cases tile drains are of
no value because of the want of fall; open cuts and
ditches draw off the water best, and by exposing some
of the subsoil water both to aeration and evaporation,
lead to the improvement of the land. Another cause of
swampy water-logged land is the rising to the surface
of a spring or a line of soakage, such as is always
formed at the junction of a clay or other stiff soil
with an overlying pervious formation, "when the sand
feeds the clay," as the old rhyme runs. Such wet spots
can be drained by tiles or by an open ditch cutting the
springs or the line of soakage. Land lying on an
impervious subsoil at the foot of a slope is often very
wet because the water which has accumulated in the hill
and soaked downwards is forced to the surface by the
hydraulic pressure of the water above; such seepage
water rising to the surface from the subsoil is characteristic of many valley soils, and can best be dealt with by
a system of tile drains. But tile drains are most
generally employed and are of greatest value in dealing
with stiff impervious subsoils, which cannot get rid of
the rain falling upon them; indeed, one of the prime
improvements effected in English agriculture was the
drainage of something like 3,000,000 acres of heavy
land between the years 1840-70. A great portion of
the work was unfortunately of little avail, because at
first there was a tendency to set the drains too deep,
at 4 feet instead of the 2 to 3 feet which have been
found to answer best. The benefits conferred by
drainage depend upon the lowering of the permanent
water table to the depth at which the drains are laid,
so that instead of constantly stagnant water a movement

of both water and air is established in the soil above
the drain. In the first place, the introduction of the
air which follows the water drawn off by the drains
brings the whole depth of soil into activity, whereas
previously only the portion not water-logged was available. Plant roots cannot grow without oxygen from
the air, hence in a water-logged soil the roots
are confined to the surface layer only ; after drainage
the roots can penetrate as far as the air extends.
At the same time, all the fundamental chemical and
biological processes of the soil, such as nitrification and
weathering, are brought into action by the introduction
of the oxygen upon which they depend. Later it will
be seen that a water-logged soil results in the loss of
nitrogen to the land when such manures as nitrate of
soda are applied to it. It is the extended root range of
the crop resulting from the introduction of air by
drainage which enables the drained land to resist a
drought better than before. In an undrained soil
the roots are confined to a shallow layer, which
they soon deprive of all moisture ; further supplies
of water from the saturated soil move upwards very
slowly in a clay soil, so that the plant may suffer
greatly. In a drained soil, on the contrary, the roots
traverse the whole 3 feet or so into which air has been
admitted ; this mass of soil, even after it has given up by
percolation all the water it can, will still hold much more
than is contained in the shallow layer alone traversed by
roots before drainage. Following upon drainage, a slow
improvement in the texture of clay soil is always
manifest : by the drawing of air into the soil, by the
consequent evaporation and drying, a certain amount of
shrinkage and a clotting of the fine clay particles result,
which is never entirely undone when they are wetted
again. Roots, which afterwards decay and leave holes,

and deep worm tracks, are all brought into the soil by its aeration, and result in more rapid percolation. Again, the washing through the soil of soluble salts derived from the surface, especially the bicarbonate of lime which is so characteristic a constituent of drainage water, also induces flocculation of the fine clay particles. Lastly, there is a steady removal by the drains of the finest clay stuff, for whenever tile drains are running freely the water will be found slightly turbid with clay matter. All these causes contribute to establish a better texture in the drained soil, beginning at the tiles and spreading slowly outwards. The other result of drainage which may be noted here is the greatly increased warmth and earliness of a drained soil; the high specific heat of water, and the cooling produced by evaporation when the water table is near the surface, combine to hinder a water-logged soil from warming up under the sun's heat in the spring, so that undrained land is notoriously cold and late.

Effect of Autumn Cultivation upon the Water Content of the Soil.

In regions where the annual rainfall is not very high and occurs chiefly during the early winter months, it is important to get as much of it as possible into the soil for the use of the subsequent crop. Breaking up the stubbles after harvest is an important factor in catching the winter rain; all land which is to lie idle through the winter, previous to the sowing of roots or spring corn should be early turned over with the plough and left rough through the rainy season. On the old stubble which has been made solid by the weather and the trampling during harvest, the rain lies for some time and evaporates, and if the land be at all on a slope the water shoots off into the ditches. But the broken surface of a ploughed field both hinders the flow of the water and affords it many openings by which to sink in; at the same time the increase of pore space in the loose ploughed layer enables this portion to absorb more water before percolation begins. King has observed in May a difference of 2·3 per cent. of water in the top 3 feet of soil between land ploughed in the autumn and the adjoining land not ploughed; the gain in this case due to the ploughing was 110 tons of water per acre or rather more than 1 inch of rain.

The following table shows the effect of ploughing up a stubble in autumn on a thin chalky loam at Wye, Kent, where the soil is only about 2 feet deep. The samples were taken on 3rd March 1902; there had been but little rainfall except in the previous December. The figures show mean percentages of water in the wet soil exclusive of stones.

	Land Ploughed in Autumn.	Adjoining Land not Ploughed.
1st foot .	16·45	16
2nd foot .	15·8	14·6

Of course the autumn ploughing has many other beneficial effects in addition to the above-mentioned gain of water; the ploughed soil gets alternately frozen and thawed, wetted and dried, with the result that on the stiff lands the puddling effects of trampling, etc., are obliterated, and the soil acquires a loose, open texture, out of which a seed bed can be made. Again, the additional surface which is exposed to the action of frost and rain causes increased weathering, and some of the dormant mineral plant food is brought into a more available condition.

Spring Cultivation.

In such climates as prevail in parts of England, where it is necessary to retain as much of the winter's rainfall in the land as possible, and where spells of drying weather are apt to set in with the spring, it is desirable to cross plough or otherwise move any land that is destined for a summer crop at as early a date as it will bear cultivation. This spring working is necessary for two reasons: to obtain a mulch, or layer of loose soil, which will conserve moisture in the sub-soil during the dry periods that follow, and to give the surface soil an opportunity of drying gradually into a condition that will yield a good tilth. The land, even though ploughed in the autumn, will become consolidated again to a considerable degree by the beating rains of winter. In this closely packed material capillary water can move freely, and as the surface layer dries under the action of the sun and wind, fresh supplies of water are lifted from the subsoil by surface tension, with the result that there is a steady and continuous drain of subsoil water through its connection with the exposed and rapidly evaporating surface. But if the top layer of soil is broken up and left loose upon the land by the cultivator, there is no longer a continuous film joining the exposed surface and the subsoil water; surface tension can only lift water as far as the film is unbroken, *i.e.*, as far as the unstirred soil extends, and this layer is protected from evaporation by the loose soil above. Regarding it from another point of view—in the undisturbed land there exist fine passages and capillary spaces extending from the surface down to the subsoil; up these passages water will rise as long as it is withdrawn by evaporation at the top; in consequence, the surface soil is not allowed to dry, being fed with

G

subsoil water which is constantly withdrawn from below. But when the land is cultivated the capillary channels are broken, water cannot rise into the loose layer of surface soil, which in the main is separated from the firm soil below by large spaces across which water cannot rise; hence the surface soil can become dry, because it is cut off from the subsoil water, which in its turn is preserved for use later. The drying of the surface soil which ensues, through its severance from the water-yielding subsoil, is of the greatest possible importance in obtaining a tilth. At a certain stage the soil can be dragged and will fall in pieces, but if it be not detached from the subsoil it will either remain persistently wet, so that it cannot be harrowed down, or if it be forced to dry under the action of wind and sun, it will set very hard and "steely," should it contain any admixture of clay. The sudden forced drying of strong land always produces hard and intractable clods, which may defy all the efforts of the cultivator during the rest of the season, unless a fortunate succession of weather enable him to begin to make his tilth over again.

It may be thought that the amount of water lifted by surface tension cannot be so large as to result in any serious losses to the subsoil store, but in soils of suitable texture enough can certainly be raised to keep the crop alive during periods of drought. In some of King's experiments with a cylinder full of very fine sand, he found that the evaporating surface lost daily an amount of water equal to 0·46 inch if the permanent water level were 1 foot below, 0·405 if the water had to be lifted 2 feet, and 0·18 inch if the water had to rise 4 feet to the evaporating surface. When the sand was replaced by a clay loam, the lift of water to the surface was somewhat less, but in all

cases the amounts were probably less than would be
realised under field conditions, because the evaporation was not enough to dry the surface, and was
further checked by the formation of a saline crust on
the surface. Working in the field, King obtained a
daily loss at the evaporating surface of 1·3 lb. per
square foot, or 0·19 inch of water, the water table
being from 4 to 5 feet below the surface.

The relative powers of different soils to lift water by
capillarity alone is well seen during any long summer
drought, such as prevailed in the south of England
during 1899 and 1900. In the Thames valley, fields of
swedes grew till the roots were one or two inches in
diameter, and then died outright, although the water
table was not more than 16 or 20 feet below; yet the
coarse-grained gravel of which the subsoil was composed
could not lift the water in any appreciable quantity to
the surface. In the same seasons the crops upon the
chalk hills were quietly growing; though the water table
was as much as 200 feet below the surface, there was
still a steady capillary rise of water through the fine-
grained chalk. In a drought it is always the gravels
and coarse sands which suffer first, and this not because
they start with less water, for we have already seen
that what they absorb they can give up almost wholly
to the plant, whereas a clay, which absorbs much more,
can only hand over about the same proportion to the
plant as the sand did, so much being held as hygroscopic
moisture. The plant suffers because the small surface
of the soil particles gives the coarse-grained sand or
gravel a very limited power of lifting the subsoil water
to the roots of the plant. Should a drought continue,
the clay soils begin to suffer next, for though they start
with large supplies of water and have an extensive surface of soil particles, yet water can be moved so slowly

through the very fine pore spaces that the upward lift cannot keep pace with the loss by transpiration and evaporation. The soils which are least affected by drought are the deep loamy sands of very uniform texture, fine-grained enough to possess a considerable lifting surface, and yet not too fine to interfere with the free movement of soil water. The western soils which the American writers describe as capable of growing wheat with a winter rainfall of 10 to 12 inches and an unbroken summer drought of three months' duration, are deep, fine-grained, and uniform, with practically no particles of the clay order of magnitude to check the upward lift by capillarity.

The following table illustrates how the subsoil acts as a regulator to the amount of water contained in the surface layer, absorbing the water which descends by percolation during rainy periods, and giving it up again by capillarity to the surface soil during periods of drought. The first line shows the rainfall during the periods indicated, the second line the amount of evaporation during the same period, while the third line shows the changes in the water content of the top foot of soil. As this change is not represented by the difference between the rainfall and the evaporation, it is clear that water must have been in some cases passed down to the subsoil, in others lifted from it, in quantities shown by the last set of figures.

Water in inches.	30/iv. to 30/v.	30/v. to 9/vii.	9/vii. to 7/ix.	7/ix. to 27/x.
Rainfall	0·18	4·53	3·17	5·65
Evaporation	3·45	2·96	5·71	1·83
Gain or Loss of Water in top foot	−1·0	+1·4	−0·24	+0·61
Water furnished by (−), or passed on to (+) Subsoil . . .	−2·27	+0·17	−2·0	+3·21

During the first period, the month of May, a dry
spell prevailed, only 0·18 inch of rain fell, while the
evaporation amounted to 3·45 inches; despite this
loss the top foot of soil only contains 1 inch of water
less than at the beginning, so that the rest of the
excess of evaporation over rainfall must have come
from the subsoil, which had in fact to furnish 2·27
inches. In the second period more water fell as rain
than was evaporated; the surface soil gained 1·4 inch,
which did not account for all the excess of rain over
evaporation, a further ·17 inch must have descended
into the subsoil.

The following figures, obtained by King, illustrate
how a spring ploughing preserves the soil moisture
during a period of dry weather, by establishing a
loose protecting layer over the water bearing subsoil.
The upper line shows the water content of the top
4 feet of a certain piece of land on 29th April, on
which date part of it was ploughed and part left
untouched. On 6th May, no rain having fallen,
the soil was sampled again, both on the ploughed
and the unploughed piece, with the results set out
in the lower figures :—

Lbs. of Water in each successive cubic foot.	1st.	2nd.	3rd.	4th.
Land on 29th April	14·1	20·1	18	16·6
Land on 6th May, ploughed 29th April .	13·9	20·7	18·3	16
Land on 6th May, not ploughed . .	10·6	18	17·3	13·9

It is seen that the ploughed land practically lost no
water during the week ending 6th May, whereas
during the same period the land not ploughed lost
9·1 lbs per square foot of surface, a quantity equivalent
to 1¾ inch of rain.

A similar trial made on a light loam at Wye during a dry period in the spring of 1902, gave the following percentages of water in the wet soil.

	Land Ploughed Autumn and Spring.	Ploughed Autumn only.
1st foot .	16·7	15·9
2nd foot .	15·4	13·9

There can be little doubt that the earlier land which is intended for spring corn, or particularly for roots, can be moved in the spring, the more water will be saved for the use of the subsequent crop, and the easier will a good tilth be established. The chief danger lies on the very fine sandy soils which, when in a loose condition, are apt to run together under heavy rains and afterwards cake on drying.

Hoeing and Mulches.

The principles which have already been developed to explain the effect of an early spring ploughing in saving subsoil water, apply even more markedly to all the later spring and summer cultivations, hoeing and the like, which have for their object the maintenance of a loose tilth upon the surface. The loose soil becomes itself dry, but by reason of its discontinuity and coarse-grained condition, does not conduct the moisture from the firm subsoil to the surface exposed to sun and wind. Under these conditions the only loss will be of that water which evaporates from the moist soil into the air spaces of the loose upper layer and then diffuses into the atmosphere; the deeper the loose layer thus formed, the more effective will it be, and if it is destroyed by a fall of rain, which consolidates the ground and establishes a continuous liquid film from the subsoil water right up to the surface, it should be renewed by a fresh cultivation as soon as the land will admit of working. It is often noticed that a casual shower during a dry period, or watering a garden unless the operation is done very thoroughly, may result in a greater drying up of the soil than ever, just because a film of water is created able to lift water from the subsoil up to the evaporating surface. The loose hoed ground practically forms a mulch, though the protecting material is the soil itself instead of straw or kindred substances.

Of course, the conservation of soil moisture is not the only good effect brought about by the surface cultivation during the summer: the aeration of the soil, the mechanical distribution of the nitrifying bacteria that is effected, the warmth of the surface layers due to their dryness, all combine to render nitrification active, and to bring into a form available for the plant the reserves of nitrogen in the humus of the soil. This point will be dealt with more at length later: for the time, it will be sufficient to remind the reader how a turnip crop with its frequent spring and summer cultivations is almost independent of any nitrogenous manure, though it removes something like 100 lbs. of nitrogen per acre: whereas a wheat crop, removing less than half that quantity of nitrogen per acre, often requires the application of a nitrogenous manure, because it is grown on undisturbed soil in the cooler season of the year.

The saving of soil moisture which can be effected by hoeing is illustrated by one of King's experiments, when, during a dry period, the soil on a piece of land kept cultivated to a depth of 3 inches was sampled from time to time down to a depth of 6 feet, samples being taken simultaneously from an adjacent piece of land where the surface was kept smooth and firm. On the cultivated land there was a daily loss equivalent to 14½ tons of water per acre, which was increased on the uncultivated land to 17·6 tons per acre; the difference during the 49 days over which the trial was spread, amounting to 1·7 inch of rain saved by the cultivation.

The value of surface cultivation is well seen in other trials of King's, where the water content down to a depth of 4 feet was compared on two adjacent pieces of land, one stirred to the depth of 3 and the other to 1½ inches only. The 3-inch soil mulch, taking the whole season through, preserved more soil moisture than the shallower cultivation, but by keeping the soil immediately below the mulch more moist and therefore with a better developed water film, it also enabled this layer to lift more moisture from the 3 or 4 foot depth into the top or second foot, a position more available for the crop. Thus the average of three determinations of water content on 16th July gave the following results—

Per cent. of Water.	1st foot.	2nd foot.	3rd foot.	4th foot.
Soil cultivated, 3″ deep .	12·3	18·6	16·8	14·6
,, 1½″ deep .	11·2	17·6	17·8	16·2

On this occasion it is seen that the upper 2 feet of soil are being kept moister by their greater power of lifting water from the lower layers, which actually contain more water under the 1½-inch mulch than under the 3-inch mulch.

Although the gardener uses the hoe freely to establish soil mulches, he also employs dung, grass-clippings, and even straw to the same end, anything to break the connection between the water-bearing subsoil and the exposed evaporating surface. Such mulches of loose organic material are even more effective in conserving soil moisture than a fine tilth, there is less tendency to form any continuity of water film between subsoil and mulch; moreover, the evaporation of the water they themselves contain helps to keep the temperature down. The great drawback to their employment is that they prevent the continual stirring of the ground which promotes aeration and nitrification.

Stones serve almost the same purpose as a mulch, especially when they are impermeable, like flints, and cover the surface at all thickly. They shield the land below from evaporation; indeed, on picking a flint off an arable field the ground below will generally be found cool and damp. The vineyards of the Rhine, etc., are generally set on steep slopes very thoroughly drained and exposed to the sun; it will be noticed that the utmost care is taken to keep the surface of the soil covered with the broken slaty rock.

Effect of Rolling.

Though it has been pointed out that maintaining a loose tilth on the surface is the most effective means possessed by the farmer of saving the soil water and minimising losses by evaporation, yet one of the fundamental acts of husbandry in the spring consists in rolling and otherwise consolidating the land. Particularly is this the case on the chalk and similar light soils; whenever a spell of dry weather prevails in the early part of the year the farmer will be observed rolling his seeds, or his spring corn, or his newly sown turnip land, as the case may be; he will even take a heavy cart wheel down between the drills when the roller will not give him pressure enough. The result of the consolidation of the surface soil thus effected is to improve its power of lifting the soil water from below by capillarity, because the pore space is diminished and the wide intervals across which the water film cannot exist are largely closed up; just as the motion of water through surface tension almost ceases in a thoroughly loose soil, it is, *per contra*, increased when the particles are brought more closely together. Hence, on the rolled land there will be a greater lift to the evaporating surface and subsequent loss of water, but the farmer faces this loss in order to keep the upper few inches of soil supplied with moisture. Rolling is only done on land occupied by germinating seeds, young spring corn, or a young ley, where the roots, if any, are so close to the surface that the whole crop will perish if the top layer is allowed to dry. The effect of rolling is to increase the capillary lifting power of the top soil, so maintaining it in a moister condition, although the land as a whole is made dryer by the extra evaporation which must accompany the rise of subsoil water to the surface. It is a maxim in farming on the chalk, where there is always a store of subsoil water at some depth or other, and where also the surface soil is peculiarly liable to become open in texture through the action of worms and the rapid decay of dung, that the land will become moist if it can only be got "tight" enough. On any light cultivated land it is easy to notice how much moister the soil remains when it has been consolidated by a foot mark; a gardener again, whose rich and deeply-worked soil is apt to get very open, always treads the ground as solid as possible in preparing a seed bed for onions and other small seeds. The following figures given by King as mean values from a number of measurements show how rolling dries the soil as a whole when samples are taken down to 2

feet or more, but maintains the surface soil, sampled
only down to 18 inches, in a moister condition.

Depth of Sample.	Percentage of Water.	
	Rolled Ground.	Unrolled Ground.
Down to 18″ . .	15.85	15.64
Down to 24″ . .	19.49	19.85
Down to 36″-54″ .	18.72	19.43

Since rolling dries the soil as a whole, it is only desirable
when shallow-rooted crops must be kept supplied with
water at any cost; as soon as they get their roots down
hoeing should begin to diminish the inevitable evaporation from the firm surface.   Thus a tool like the old
broadsharing plough, still used on the chalk, is particularly valuable in preparing a tilth for roots, for, while
creating a loose surface tilth, it is consolidating the soil
below and increasing its power of lifting water from the
subsoil.

Similarly, in the semi-arid regions of Western
America and in Australia, where the rainfall is barely
sufficient for the needs of the crop, in the preparation of
the land great importance is laid on the two operations
of "subsoil packing," and "the establishment of a soil
mulch."   This is the equivalent of the English practice
of preparing a seed bed for roots; frequent cultivation
without inverting the soil to work it down to a fine
tilth, constant use of the ring roller or subsoil packer to
consolidate this crumb until it will lift water by capillarity,
and finally the production and continual renewal by
means of light cultivators or horse hoes of a very thin
skin of loose soil on the surface.

Valuable as the operation of rolling is on grass
land in the early spring, in order to consolidate the soil

round the roots of the grass after the surface has been lifted by the winter frosts and by the action of worms, it should be borne in mind that it is easy to do harm by injudicious rolling in wet weather on soils that are at all heavy. Even on grass land the clay may become so puddled or tempered that it dries round the roots with a very harsh caked surface, little permeable to air and water. This sort of damage is perhaps most often seen on lawns and cricket grounds which are often rolled repeatedly with heavy rollers when the ground is thoroughly wet; a smooth, pasty surface is produced to the ultimate great detriment of the growth of the grass. Of course upon arable land the greatest care must be taken never to roll when the top is at all wet or even damp, lest a pasty surface be developed, which will dry to a glazed baked crust. It is necessary even to wait until the dew has been dissipated before rolling strong land that has been well worked and drilled for roots.

The Drying Effect of Crops.

Since a crop transpires about 300 lbs. of water for each pound of dry matter produced, any land which is carrying a heavy crop must contain much less water than the adjoining uncropped land, unless there has been such an excess of rainfall as to saturate the soil in either case. Any summer growing crop, however, especially one of roots, transpires so large a proportion of the customary rainfall during the period of growth, that it must leave the soil much drier for its growth. As an example of this removal of water by the growing crop, the following figures obtained at Rothamsted during the very dry summer of 1870 may be quoted, showing as they do the water present in successive 9 inches of fallow and of adjoining land carrying a barley crop—

	Percentages of Water in fine Soil, June 27-28, 1870.	
	Fallow.	Barley.
First 9″ . . .	20.36	11.91
Second 9″ . . .	29.53	19.32
Third 9″ . . .	34.84	22.83
Fourth 9″ . . .	34.32	25.09
Fifth 9″ . . .	31.31	26.98
Sixth 9″ . . .	33.55	26.38

The total difference between the cropped and un-cropped land down to the depth of 54 inches, amounted to more than 900 tons of water per acre, or 9 inches of rain, which is quite half as much again as would be accounted for by the crop on the assumption that only two tons or so of dry matter had been grown at the date of sampling.

Another example of the withdrawal of water from the soil by the crop is seen in the proportions of water in the soil of certain of the permanent grass plots at Rothamsted, taken in July of the same year, 1870—

	PLOT 3.	PLOT 9.	PLOT 14.
	No Manure.	Mineral Manure + Ammonium Salts.	Mineral Manure + Nitrate of Soda.
Crop, 1870 . . .	5¾ cwt. of Hay.	29½	56¼
Per cent. of Water.			
First 9″ . . .	10.83	13.00	12.16
Second 9″ . . .	13.34	10.18	11.80
Third 9″ . . .	19.23	16.46	15.65
Fourth 9″ . . .	22.71	18.96	16.30
Fifth 9″ . . .	24.28	20.54	17.18
Sixth 9″ . . .	25.07	21.34	18.06
Means . . .	19.24	16.75	15.19

Down to the depth of 54 inches the plot receiving minerals and ammonium salts contained 200 tons, and the plot receiving minerals and nitrate 325 tons, less water than the unmanured plot, quantities in this case somewhat less than would be indicated by the amount of dry matter produced.

There are two important cases in which the drying effect of vegetation needs to be taken into account, in the use of catch crops and in the planting of fruit trees. On the lighter lands of the south of England catch crops are not uncommonly taken on the land before roots. The stubbles are quickly broken up, and vetches, trifolium, or rye, are sown in time to make a start while the land is warm, and to be either cut greer. or fed off before the land is wanted for turnips in the following spring. The advantages of the practice are that the summer-formed nitrates in the stubble-ground are saved from washing out, and that a valuable bite of early fodder is obtained: with the leguminous crops also, the farm is enriched by the nitrogen gathered from the atmosphere. The difficulty of getting catch crops lies in the fact that the stubble ground is left very dry by the preceding crop, so that a timely rainfall is needed to obtain a plant. The danger of their use is that they may so deplete the available soil water as to give the succeeding crop of roots a very poor chance of germinating or growing well. In America the practice has been suggested of sowing some leguminous crop like clover in the tillage orchards about the end of July, so that the new surface crop should so dry the ground as to forward the ripening of the apples on the trees; again, any second growth of the trees due to a late summer rainfall would be prevented, this moisture being dealt with by the catch crop.

The second illustration worthy of notice is that fruit

trees when newly planted in grass land often make a
very poor growth for a year or two. This is because a
fruit tree when planted is but indifferently supplied with
water-collecting roots ; inevitably they are few in number
and have a very restricted range. Hence they must be
in a soil well supplied with moisture if they are to provide
the tree with the necessary water, and they are very ill
fitted to compete with a crowd of fibrous grass roots
surrounding them, should the season turn out dry. In
one experiment the moisture in the top foot of a
pasture was found to be only half that present in the top
foot of neighbouring uncropped land.

The following table shows the percentages of water
in the fine earth of an orchard on heavy soil, part of
which was under grass and part kept tilled ; it will be
seen that in the winter the grass land carries as much
or even more water than the bare soil, but towards the
end of the summer the drying effect of the grass becomes
very pronounced, even down to the third foot.

	1st 9 Inches.		2nd 9 Inches.		3rd 9 Inches.	
	Grass.	Bare.	Grass.	Bare.	Grass.	Bare.
December 19/05	25·0	24·7	23·5	23·5	25·0	27·0
March 3/06	26·7	23·3	21·2	21·9	20·6	19·6
May 24/06	17·7	24·0	18·7	24·5	22·3	25·0
July 25/06	13·8	15·6	14·5	18·2	14·8	24·4
September 27/06	12·6	15·7	13·8	15·1	15·6	18·8
April 6/07	21·1	21·6	21·0	24·0	19·6	21·3
October 9/07	22·6	27·1	23·7	...	23·6	25·0

Few crops so effectually dry the surface soil as grass
does, because of the intimate way in which its roots
traverse the soil ; hence a fruit tree cannot compete
with grass for water as long as the two sets of roots are
confined to the same layer. The experiments at the

Woburn Fruit Farm of planting fruit trees and sowing the seed of coarse meadow grasses at the same time, show this competition at its highest degree, but even when trees are planted in old pasture care should be taken to keep a ring round the tree free from grass and well cultivated or mulched for at least two years. For similar reasons, when trees are planted in arable land weeds should be kept down, nor should crops like cabbages or mangolds be grown between the rows of trees; such crops are usually considered to "draw the land" and deplete it of plant food, but the harm they do lies in the water they withdraw just at the most critical season, when the tree is making its first start in its new quarters.

Bare Fallows.

The custom of fallowing land, of leaving it entirely bare for a season, during which the land is worked as often as possible, is one of the oldest in agriculture; a rotation of wheat, wheat, fallow, or of beans, wheat, fallow, being almost universal, until the introduction of turnips gave the farmer a chance of cleaning his land and yet growing a crop at the same time. The objects of a fallow were various: in the first place, the summer cultivations resulted in a thorough cleaning of the land and in a free development of nitrates for the succeeding crop; also on the heavy soils, which are the most suited to fallowing, a good tilth was obtained that was often impossible otherwise. Indeed, at the present day it is found desirable and even necessary to introduce an occasional bare fallow when farming on the heavy clays of the south and east of England, in order to obtain a satisfactory tilth in that dry climate.

One of the most notable effects of fallowing lies in the production of a stock of nitrates from the stores of combined nitrogen in the soil; these nitrates are at once available for the ensuing wheat crop if the autumnal rains are not too great to wash them out of the soil (see p. 116).

But in addition to the gain in available nitrogen due to fallowing, the land which does not carry a crop during a season will accumulate a store of water which may be of the utmost service to the succeeding crop. In the preceding section some figures have been given showing how much more water is present at the end of the summer in the fallow land than in the land which had carried a crop, so that in districts where the winter rainfall is small the fallowed land will start the next season with a great advantage. Indeed, in a semi-arid climate where the annual rainfall is insufficient, satisfactory crops may yet be grown in alternate years by using an intermediate fallow period in which to accumulate a reserve of subsoil water.

The following series of measurements will illustrate this point; it shows the percentages of water in spring and autumn on fallow and cropped land respectively, also the water present in the same land in the following spring and autumn, when both plots were in oats.

	SPRING.		AUTUMN.		FOLLOWING SPRING AND AUTUMN.			
	Fallow. 1.	Corn. 2.	Fallow. 1.	Corn. 2.	Oats. 1.	Oats. 2.	Oats. 1.	Oats. 2.
1st foot .	24 %	22 %	17 %	7 %	19 %	16 %	6 %	4 %
2nd foot .	20 ,,	19 ,,	20 ,,	12 ,,	21 ,,	18 ,,	10 ,,	5 ,,
3rd foot .	18 ,,	18 ,,	16 ,,	4 ,,	18 ,,	15 ,,	9 ,,	8 ,,

The effect of the fallowing in retaining more moisture in the soil is seen throughout the whole of the second season.

H

At Rothamsted portions of the wheat field were fallowed during the summer of 1904, and the following table shows the percentage of water in the fine earth on 13th September, 2·849 inches of rain having fallen since the crops had been cut.

	UNMANURED.		DUNGED.		MEAN OF 8 PLOTS.	
	Cropped.	Fallow.	Cropped.	Fallow.	Cropped.	Fallow.
1st 9″ . .	15·8	16·0	20·2	19·3	17·4	17·2
2nd 9″ . .	18·9	19·8	14·5	17·0	18·8	20·0
3rd 9″ . .	20·8	23·3	13·7	18·4	20·1	22·3
4th 9″ . .	23·1	25·2	15·5	19·7	20·9	23·1
Mean .	19·6	20·8	16·0	18·6	19·3	20·6

In the surface layer there is practically no difference, both having become equally wet by the rains after harvest, but in the lower depths the fallow soils are the wetter, and the differences are more pronounced for the unmanured plot where a small crop had been grown than for the dunged plot with its larger crop.

The way in which fallowed land is of benefit to the crop, both by making nitrates and particularly by saving water in a dry season, is easily seen in the superior plant always found on the outside rows or edges of an experimental plot divided from the others by a bare path; on one side the plant has the benefit of fallow ground as well as of extra space, light, and air, and flourishes accordingly. The Lois-Weedon system of husbandry, where the land was divided into alternate 5-foot strips of corn and cultivated fallow land, was nothing but an application of this principle on a large scale, as indeed is any system of growing a crop in wide rows to admit of some form of hoe or cultivator working regularly at the ground

between. In a humid climate or on a porous soil there
is great danger of losing the nitrates formed in the
summer by washing out during the autumnal and winter
rains, nor is there any advantage gained by storing water
where the usual winter rainfall is sufficient to saturate
the soil. For this reason, in the Rothamsted experiments, the plot growing wheat continuously has given a
greater crop per acre per annum than the plot fallowed
and sown with wheat in alternate years, though the
wheat crop following fallow has always been larger than
the crop grown the same year on the unmanured plot.

Average Crop.	WHEAT EVERY YEAR.		FALLOW AND WHEAT.	
	Grain.	Straw.	Grain.	Straw.
1856-1895 . .	Bushels. 12¾	Lbs. 1127	Bushels. 8⅝	Lbs. 798

Of course the average crop on the fallowed ground
was twice the above figures, *i.e.*, 17⅜ bushels of grain and
1595 lbs. of straw, but it was only grown every alternate
year.

That the autumnal rainfall is the great factor in
determining whether a bare fallow shall be profitable
or not to the following crop, may be well seen by a
further examination of the results obtained at Rothamsted on these plots, by comparing the crops with the
percolation which took place in the autumn previous.

The percolation through 60 inches of bare soil for
the four months, September to December inclusive, as
measured by the drain gauge previously described on
p. 78, amounted on the average to 6·45 inches for the
31 seasons 1870-1901. If, then, we divide the harvest
years into two groups according as the autumnal
percolation is above or below the average, and allot

to each year the crops on the continuous wheat and
wheat after fallow plots for the harvest following the
given percolation, we shall obtain the following
average results, which show in group 1 the mean
crops following autumns of less than average percolation, and in group 2 those following autumns of
comparatively high percolation. The percolation is
given in inches, the crops in lbs. per acre of total
produce, both grain and straw; and as further evidence
of the extent of percolation, the average number of
days are given during the four months on which
water ran from the tile drain underlying the continuous wheat plot.

		Rainfall.	Percolation through 60-inch gauge.	No. of days on which tile drain ran.	CROP, LBS. PER ACRE.		
					Wheat after Wheat each Year.	Wheat after Fallow.	Gain due to Fallow.
1.	15 Years of Percolation below average . .	8.94	3.99	4	1807	2677	870
2.	16 Years of Percolation above average . .	13.78	8.92	13	1627	1757	130

Thus the bare fallow which increased the succeeding
crop above that given by the continuous wheat plot
by nearly 48 per cent. in the seasons when a comparatively dry autumn succeeded the fallow, increased
it by less than 8 per cent. when there was much
percolation after the fallow.

It follows, therefore, that the practice of fallowing
land is only an economical one where the annual rainfall is low and where the land is too strong to admit
of free percolation; it is, however, admirably adapted to
the successful cultivation of clay land in dry, hot climates.

Effect of Dung on the retention of Water by the Soil.

A soil which has been enriched in humus through repeated applications of farmyard manure will resist drought better than one in which the humus is low ; the difference is seen not so much in the greater amount of moisture present in the soil containing humus, as in the way it will absorb a large amount of water temporarily during heavy rainfall, and then let it work more slowly down into the soil, thus keeping it longer within reach of the crop. Good examples are afforded by the Rothamsted plots ; samples of soil from the wheat land were taken on 13th September 1904, on the previous day 0.262 inch of rain had fallen, but for nine days before there had been little or no rain. The portions of the plots from which the samples were drawn had been fallowed through the summer, so that the drying effect of the crop is eliminated. Samples were also taken from the barley plots on 3rd October of the same year ; 0.456 inch of rain had fallen on the 30th September, before which there had been fifteen days of fine weather. The following table shows the water in the soil of the unmanured and the continuously dunged plots respectively, as percentages of the fine earth from which the stones had been sifted.

Percentages of Water in Rothamsted Soils.

Depth.	BROADBALK WHEAT.		HOOS BARLEY.	
	Unmanured.	Dunged.	Unmanured.	Dunged.
0″ to 9″	16.0	19.3	17.0	20.7
9″ „ 18″	19.8	17.0	22.5	17.7
18″ „ 27″	23.3	18.4	22.1	18.3

It is thus seen that in both cases the dunged soil, rich in humus, had retained more of the comparatively recent rainfall near the surface, so that the top soil was moister while the subsoil was drier. The difference in favour of the surface soil was about 3·5 per cent., which on that soil would amount to about 30 tons per acre, or approximately 0·3 inch of rain. It is thus seen that the surface soil of the dunged plot had retained practically the whole of the preceding rainfall; and the greater dryness of the subsoil was due to the way the soil had kept back the small rainfalls, which have been evaporated instead of passed on to the subsoil as they were on the unmanured plots. The same fact is illustrated by the behaviour of the drains which run below the centre of each of the wheat plots at a depth of 30 inches; below the dunged plot the drain very rarely runs, only after an exceptionally heavy and long‐continued fall, whereas the drain below the unmanured plot runs two or three times every winter. Putting aside the greater drying effect of the much larger crop on the dunged plot, the difference is mainly due to the way the surface soil rich in humus first of all absorbs more of the water, and then lets the excess percolate so much more slowly that the descending layer of over-saturation, which causes the drain to run, rarely or never forms.

The water-retaining power of the dung may also be seen in the superior yield of the dunged plots in markedly dry seasons. The following table shows a comparison of the yield on plot 2, receiving 14 tons of dung, and plot 7, receiving a complete artificial manure, for the years 1879, which was exceptionally wet and cold, and 1893, which was hot and dry throughout the growing period of the plant. The rainfall for this period, *i.e.*, for the four months March to June, was 13 inches in 1879 and only 2·9 inches in 1893.

WHEAT.   YIELD IN BUSHELS OF GRAIN.

Plot.	1879.	1893.	Average 51 Years.
2	16·0	34·25	35·7
7	16·25	20·25	32·9

The average yield on the dunged plot is about 3 bushels more than on plot 7, but in the dry year its superiority amounted to 14 bushels, whereas in the very wet year the two plots sank to the same low level. In a bad season the bacterial changes which render the plant food in dung available for the crop go on very slowly.

CHAPTER V

THE TEMPERATURE OF THE SOIL

Causes affecting the Temperature of the Soil—Variation of Temperature with Depth, Season, etc.—Temperatures required for Growth—Radiation—Effect of Colour—Specific Heat of Soils—Heat required for Evaporation—Effect of Situation and Exposure—Early and Late Soils.

THE life of a plant is practically suspended below a certain temperature, which is about 41° F. for the majority of cultivated plants; all the various changes which are essential to the development of the plant such as germination, vegetative activity, and the bacterial processes in the soil, show a similar dependence upon temperature.

These vital actions cease below a certain minimum, above which they usually increase with the temperature until an optimum is reached, when the action is at its greatest; beyond this point the action decreases until a superior limit is reached, which again suspends all change. It therefore becomes important to study the manner in which heat enters and leaves the soil, because upon the temperature acquired depend such practical questions as the suitability or otherwise of the land for particular crops, the season at which to sow, and the earliness or lateness of the harvest.

The surface soil receives heat in four ways:—

(1) By direct radiation from the sun, whose rays both of light and invisible heat are absorbed

and raise the temperature of the absorbing soil.

(2) By precipitation, as in the spring when warm rain enters the ground and brings with it a considerable quantity of heat, or when aqueous vapour in the air is condensed on the colder soil.

(3) By conduction from the heated interior of the earth a small amount of heat reaches the surface.

(4) By the changes which result in the decay of the organic material of the soil, when as much heat is developed as if the same material had been burnt in a fire.

The surface soil loses heat :—

(1) By radiation; like any other body possessing heat, the surface of the soil is always emitting invisible radiant heat, which may, or may not, be counterbalanced by the corresponding radiations it is absorbing.

(2) By conduction either to cooler layers of earth below or to cooler air above.

(3) By the evaporation of the water contained in the soil; at ordinary temperatures the evaporation of 1 lb. of water would absorb enough heat to lower the temperature of about 7500 lb. of soil by 1° F.

The actual temperature attained by a given soil at any time depends upon the relative effect of the heating and cooling actions set out above.

Soil Temperatures.

The accompanying curves (Fig. 8), show the monthly mean temperatures of the soil at 6 inches, 3 feet, and 6 feet respectively, as compiled from readings taken at 9 A.M. at Wye during 1896, the soil being a light well-drained loam under grass. It will be seen that the variations in temperature diminish with the depth: in fact a point is soon reached, about 50 feet down, below which the effect of the gain or loss of heat at the surface is inappreciable, and the temperature is constant from day to day, only increasing with the depth, according to the well-known law. Each curve cuts each other curve at least twice; for a certain period the upper layer is giving, and during the rest of the year, receiving heat from the layer above or below. The maximum temperature attained at a depth of 3 feet comes a little later in the year than the maximum for 3 inches, and the maximum at 6 feet lags still further behind, owing to the slowness with which the heat is conducted. It will be seen that the curve indicating the temperature at 6 inches (and the mean figures for 3 and 9 inches are almost identical) does not reach the 41° F. required for the beginning of vegetative growth until April; it is, however, constructed from monthly averages only, and from observations taken at 9 A.M., when the surface soil has been considerably cooled during the night. Much higher temperatures are obtained during certain parts of the day even in the early spring months, otherwise no germination could take place; these diurnal and hourly fluctuations are, however, chiefly confined to the surface soil. The following

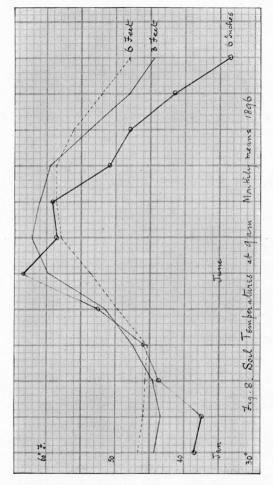

FIG. 8.—Soil Temperatures at 9 A.M., Monthly Means, 1896.

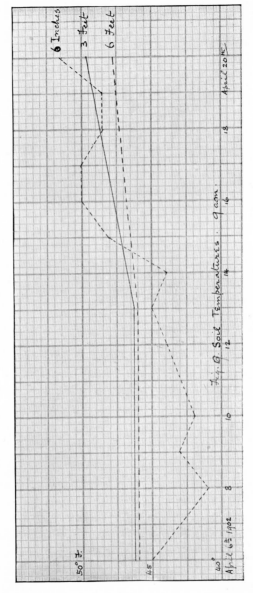

FIG. 9.—Soil Temperatures at 9 A.M., Daily Readings.

[To face page 123.

curves show firstly (Fig. 9), the daily results during a fortnight of April 1902, also (Fig. 10) certain hourly readings obtained in the same month, in this case beneath smooth, well-worked arable land. The diurnal variations die away before the depth of 3 feet is reached, nor are hourly variations perceptible at the depth of one foot, except in the case of heavy precipitation and a pervious soil. It will also be noticed from the last curves that during part of the day the temperature at the depth of 6 inches ran up to a point well above the minimum required for germination, although the mean soil temperature at 9 A.M. was near that limit.

Temperatures required for Growth.

Reference has already been made to the fact that a certain temperature is necessary before the vital processes involved in growth become active; this temperature is not always the same, but may be considered to lie between 40° and 45° F. for most of the plants grown as crops in this country.

The following table shows minimum, optimum, and maximum temperatures of growth for a few plants.

	Minimum.	Optimum.	Maximum.
Mustard	32° F.	81° F.	99° F.
Barley	41	83.6	99.8
Wheat	41	83.6	108.5
Maize	49	92.6	115
Kidney Bean	49	92.6	115
Melon	65	91.4	111

The next table shows the effect of soil temperature upon the growth of the root of maize.

ROOT GROWTH OF MAIZE IN 24 HOURS.

Temperature.	Millimetres.
63° F.	1·3
79	24·5
92	39
93	55
101	25·2
108·5	5·9

The osmotic absorption of water by the roots of a plant is much affected by the temperature of the soil; although some plants, like cabbage, will continue to take in a little water even near freezing point, others require a higher temperature; for example, Sachs has shown that tobacco and vegetable marrow plants will wilt even at night, when transpiration is very small, if the temperature of the soil falls below about 40° F.

The killing of plants like rose trees during frost is generally due to drying out from this cause rather than to the actual cold. As the air is often very dry during a frost, evaporation continues, especially if a wind be blowing at the same time; thus the exposed shoots of the plant are losing water which is not being replaced by the roots, whose action is suspended by the low temperature. A covering of snow or dead leaves, or even the protection afforded by a little straw, bracken, or spruce boughs, prevent the destruction of the plant, not by keeping it so much warmer, but by protecting it from evaporation.

The connection between soil temperature and vital processes is perhaps most apparent in the case of germination, for which not only is a certain minimum temperature requisite, but for several degrees above this minimum the germination is so slow and irregular that the young plant is very liable to perish while remaining

in such a critical condition. The following table shows
the range of temperatures for the germination of various
cultivated plants.

TEMPERATURES OF GERMINATION.

	FAHRENHEIT.		
	Minimum.	Optimum.	Maximum.
Wheat	32° to 41°	77° to 88°	88° to 110°
Barley	40°	77° to 88°	100° to 110°
Oats	32° to 41°	...	88° to 100°
Pea	38° to 41°	...	...
Scarlet Runner . .	49°	91°	115°
Maize	49°	91°	115°
Cucumber, Melon, etc. .	60° to 65°	88° to 99°	110° to 120°

The practical bearing of these figures is obvious;
it is necessary to sow some seeds, like the melon, in
heat, and to defer the seeding of other crops, like
mangolds or maize, until the ground has acquired not
only the temperature necessary for germination but
one that will ensure a subsequent rapid growth of
the seedling plants.

For example, turnips will germinate at almost as
low a temperature as barley, but the optimum temperature is higher for turnips; they are therefore sown much
later in the spring, when the ground has more nearly
reached this temperature, because the seed is small and
the young plant very susceptible to insect attacks, so
that the turnip seed must germinate and grow away
rapidly if it is to succeed.

Under ordinary field conditions much of the
nutrition of the crop depends upon the activity of
certain bacteria in the soil which break down organic
compounds containing nitrogen, and ultimately resolve
them into the nitrates taken up by the plant. Most

bacteria are active within about the same limits of temperature as have been indicated above for the higher plants; the nitrification bacteria, for example, cease their work below 41° F. and above 130° F., their optimum temperature being about 99° F.

The way a low temperature will check the production of nitrates until they are inadequate for the needs of the crop is often seen in spring, and may be connected with the yellow colour of the young corn during a spell of cold and drying east wind.

Radiation.

The main source of the soil warmth consists in the heat received from the sun by radiation; this, according to Langley, amounts to about 1,000,000 calories per hour per square metre of surface from a vertical sun in a clear sky. Supposing this energy were wholly absorbed by a layer of dry soil 10 cm. thick, its temperature would rise by as much as 90° F. in an hour. Of course in nature many other factors are at work to reduce this temperature; the sun is rarely vertical, the soil material does not completely absorb but reflects some of the sun's rays unchanged; at the same time it is always radiating in its turn rays of lower pitch than the majority of those received. The latter rays are easily caught by many substances, glass and water vapour in particular, which are transparent to the rays of higher refrangibility proceeding from the sun. A greenhouse, for example, is practically a radiant heat trap; the temperature inside runs up because the sun's rays of light and heat can penetrate the glass, whereas the obscure heat rays radiated back again from the warmed-up surfaces inside the house are not able to pass through the glass again. Just in the same way the temperature rises and the sun's heat becomes oppressive

when the air is laden with water vapour, because it
retains the radiations emitted by the surfaces heated by
the sun. *Per contra*, the temperature of the ground
falls more rapidly at night when the sky is clear and
the air dry, for then there is no blanket of cloud or
water vapour to arrest or reflect the radiations from the
surface.

The power of soils to absorb the sun's rays depends
very much upon colour : with black soils the absorption
is almost complete ; it is greater for red than for yellow
soils, least of all for those which look distinctly white or
light coloured. It has already been shown that the
colour of soils depends mainly upon humus and
hydrated ferric oxide, the latter accounts for all the
red, yellow, and brown shades, the former for the black
coloration of the soil. Deep-seated clays are often
blue or green, due to various ferrous silicates or to
finely divided iron pyrites, which afterwards oxidise
to brown ferric oxide. The more finely grained a
soil is the more surface it possesses, and the greater
amount of colouring matter that is required to produce a given colour ; a coarse sand is often quite
black though it contains but a small percentage of
humus.

Though the colour of a soil affects the rate at which
it absorbs heat, it does not follow that the dark soils
will lose with a corresponding rapidity when radiation
is taking place at night ; the emissive power of the
substance for rays of low refrangibility, such as are
emitted at ordinary temperatures, is not affected by
colour. Hence, the extra heat gained by a dark soil
is retained and not lost by a corresponding increase in
its radiating power.

The curves in the accompanying diagram (Fig. 10),
show the temperatures of the soil at a depth of 6

inches during an April day with a bright sun and a
strong drying wind. The land was a light loam of
a grey-brown colour when dry; it had been cultivated, rolled, and the surface hoed over before the
thermometers were inserted; on plot 1 the bare
ground was left untouched, plot 2 received a dressing
of soot until the surface was black, plot 3 was
similarly whitened over with lime. It will be seen
that the covering of soot warmed the soil until at 3
P.M., when the maximum temperature was attained,
the difference was 2·4°; this superiority is also retained during the later cooling stages; even at 9 P.M.
the blackened soil was still 2·5° warmer than the bare
ground. The whitening with lime had caused so considerable a reflection of the radiant heat that the soil
beneath was always 2 to 3° cooler than the bare ground.
In carrying out this experiment it is necessary to use no
more lime or soot than will distinctly colour the soil;
the results will be disturbed if an excess of either loose
powder acts as a mulch.

Specific Heat.

The specific heat of the substances of which soil
is composed is comparatively low, ranging from 0·1
to 0·2, *i.e.*, only from one-tenth to one-fifth as much
heat will be necessary to raise the temperature of 1
lb. of dry soil by 1°, as would be required to produce
the same rise of temperature in an equal weight of
water. The humus possesses the greatest specific heat
and the sand the least; against this must be set off the
fact that the densities of these soil constituents vary
in the opposite sense, so that the amounts of heat
required to bring about a given rise of temperature to
a certain depth in different soils are more nearly equal.
The specific heats are, however, small in every case

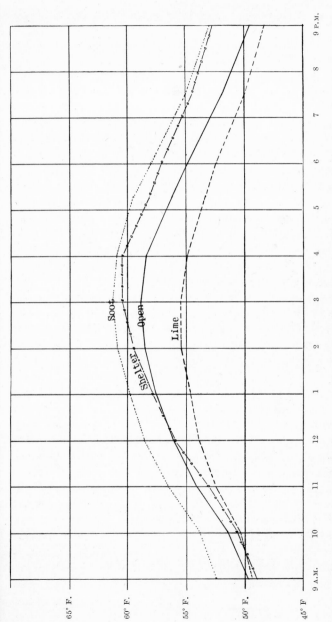

FIG. 10.—Soil Temperatures at 6 in. depth, as affected by the state of the surface. Sun with strong N.E. wind. 27/iv/02.

[To face p. 128]

when compared with that of water; hence soils which retain much water will require far more heat to raise their temperature than dry soils would. In consequence, clay and humus soils are cold because the water they retain gives them a high specific heat, they require more of the sun's rays in spring to bring them up to the proper temperature for growth, while sandy and other open-textured soils are warm because of their dryness.

If the figures given by Oemler for the specific heats of various soils be combined with their approximate densities and with their minimum capacity for water, the following results are obtained for the specific heats of certain typical soils in a saturated but completely drained condition—

	SPECIFIC HEAT.		
	Equal Weights.	Equal Volumes.	
	Dry.	Dry.	Wet.
Water . . .	1·0	1·0	1·0
Humus . .	0·21	...	...
Sandy Peat . .	0·14	0·11	0·72
Loam . . .	0·15	0·18	0·53
Clay . . .	0·14	0·15	0·61
Sand . . .	0·1	0·125	0·34

The sandy soil only requires about half as much heat to raise its temperature by a given amount as would be needed by the peaty or clay soil, when all the soils are in a wet but thoroughly drained condition; of course if the clay or peat were inadequately drained, so that a higher proportion of water was retained, their specific heats would approximate still nearer to that of water.

Just as a clay soil is slow to warm in the spring, its high specific heat causes it to cool correspondingly

I

slowly after the heat of the summer. On clay soils growth will be noticed to continue later into the autumn than on the lighter lands.

Heat required for Evaporation.

The coldness of a wet and undrained soil is due, not only to its high specific heat, but to the fact that so much of the heat it receives is spent in evaporating some of its retained water, without causing any rise in temperature. The evaporation of 1 lb. of water at 62° F., *i.e.*, its conversion into water vapour at the same temperature, requires as much heat as would raise the temperature of 1050 lbs. of water by 1° F., and, if there be no source of external heat bringing about the evaporation, the substance from which the water is evaporated must become cooled to a corresponding extent. The cooling effect of evaporation is well known, but its application to the soil is not always realised; clays and even more so undrained soils are cold and late, not only because of their high specific heat, but because they retain so much water which can be evaporated. The drying winds of early spring exercise a great cooling effect whenever the soil moisture is allowed to evaporate freely, hence the importance of establishing a loose tilth, if the seed bed is to warm up the temperatures requisite for germination.

Anything providing a little shelter to check evaporation and break the force of the wind in the spring will have a considerable effect in raising the soil temperature. The dotted curve in Fig. 10 shows the effect of enclosing a plot of the same land with a slight hedge made of spruce fir boughs about 2 feet high. In the morning the temperature of the sheltered plot was below that of the open ground because of the shading from the direct rays of the sun, but as soon as this effect was over

it will be seen that the wind break, by checking evaporation, maintained the soil temperature more than 2°
above that of the open ground. Sufficient attention is
not given in practice to the value of even slight wind
breaks for checking evaporation and so raising the
temperature of the soil in early spring. The raisers of
specially early vegetables, radishes in particular, on a
strip of light land close to the sea in Kent are, however,
in the habit of breaking the sweep of wind across their
fields by erecting temporary fences of lightly thatched
hurdles.

Even the stones upon the surface of the land help.
In the *Journal of the Royal Agricultural Society* for
1856, an experiment is described in which the flints
were picked off the surface of one plot of ground and
scattered over an adjoining plot, with the result that the
plot with double its usual allowance of stones was three
or four days earlier to harvest than the rest of the field,
while the plot without stones was a week later still. It
will always be noticed how the grass upon a field coated
with dung starts earlier into growth, because the loose
manure acts as a mulch and protects the soil from the
cooling due to evaporation.

Land which is protected from evaporation, and to
some extent from radiation, by a layer of vegetation, is
always both warmer and less subject to fluctuations of
temperature than bare soil.

The warming up of a well-tilled surface soil is
increased by the fact that the conduction of heat into
the soil below is much checked by a loose condition. A
solid body will always conduct heat far better than
the same substance in the state of powder, and the
more compressed the powder is the better it will conduct,
simply because there are more points of contact. Hence
a rolled and tightened soil will conduct the heat it

receives more rapidly to the lower layers than one which is loose and pulverulent. King has shown that, despite the increased evaporation, there is always a higher temperature below a rolled than an unrolled surface.

A few observations may be given showing the effect of drainage in enabling the sun's heat to raise the temperature of soil. The curves (Fig. 11) show the hourly temperatures of the drained and undrained portions of a peat bog during two last days in June (Parkes, *J. R. Ag. Soc.*, 1844, 142), at depths of 7 inches and 13 inches respectively; the sudden rise of temperature between 3 and 4 P.M. on the second day was due to a thunderstorm, during which heavy rain at a temperature of 78° F. was falling.

The figures in the table below are derived from observations made by Bailey-Denton in 1857 (*J. R. Ag. Soc.*, 1859, 273), on a stiff clay soil situated on the Gault at Hinxworth, the drains being 4 feet deep and 25 feet apart in the drained part. It is noteworthy that the temperature of the air 9 inches above the surface is higher for the drained than for the undrained land, thus supplying further evidence of the cooling effect of evaporation.

MEAN TEMPERATURE °F. AT 9 A.M.

	A.—Land Drained.			B.—Land Undrained.		
	Air.	At 18″.	At 42″.	Air.	At 18″.	At 42″.
March	39.4	40.6	41.7	39	38.2	40.3
April	43	46	44.8	42.4	44	43.8
May	52.9	51	48.4	52.7	48.8	47.1
Mean excess over B.	0.4	2.2	1.2	...	...	...

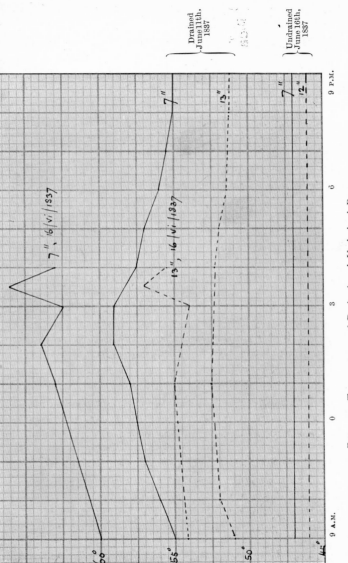

9 A.M.

60°

55°

50°

45°

9 P.M.

7″, 16/vi/1837

13″, 16/vi/1837

7″

13″

7″

12″

Drained
June 11th,
1887

Undrained
June 16th,
1887

FIG. 11.—Temperatures of Drained and Undrained Bog.

[To face page 132.

Effect of Situation and Exposure.

Other conditions being equal, in the northern hemisphere the soil temperatures will always be higher on land sloping toward the southern quadrant than with any other aspect. King found a difference of about 3° F. down to the third foot between a stiff red-clay soil with a southern slope of 18° and the same soil on the flat; Wollny obtained a mean difference of 1°·5 between the north and south sides of a hill of sandy soil inclined at 15°. The chief cause of these differences is the fact that in this country the sun is never vertical, hence a beam of sunlight represented by *xy*, Fig. 12, is spread

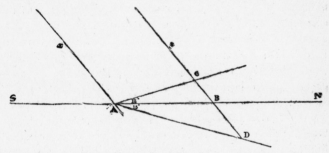

Fig. 12.—Distribution of the Sun's Rays on Southerly and Northerly Slopes.

over an area represented by AB when the ground is flat; if the ground slopes to the south, the same beam is spread over the smaller area represented by AC; if the ground slopes to the north, it is spread over the larger area represented by AD. During the winter half-year, also, the southern slope will have a longer duration of sunlight than the northern slope.

Though in a general way the temperature both of the air and the soil decreases with elevation above

sea-level, yet it is well known that the severest frosts
occur locally at the bottom of valleys and hollow places.
This is particularly noticeable in the sudden night frosts,
characteristic of early autumn and late spring, which
are so dangerous to vegetation; it is usual to find the
tenderer plants of our gardens, such as dahlias, cut
down by frost on the lower levels long before the
gardens on the hill are affected. Spring frosts, again,
will often nip the early potatoes in the valleys when
the higher lands are untouched.   Fruit plantations
should not be set in the valleys, for no crop suffers
more from these unseasonable snaps of cold; so clearly
is this fact recognised, that in some fruit-growing
districts only land above a certain elevation is regarded
as suitable for fruit, and commands a higher rent in
consequence. Two causes co-operate in producing the
excess of cold at the lower levels. The night frosts
in question are always the result of excessive radiation
when the sky is clear and the air still. The ground
surface loses heat rapidly and cools the layer of air
above; the cold air thus produced is denser, and proceeds to flow downhill and accumulate at the lower
levels. There is thus a renewal of the air above the
higher slopes, and the effect of radiation is mitigated
by the inflow of warmer air; at the bottom no change
of air is produced and the radiation proceeds to its
full effect.

At the same time the vegetation in the valley
is generally more susceptible to a frost; the greater
warmth by day, together with the extra moisture and
shelter, induce an earlier and a softer growth.

The other cause that operates to produce severer
frosts in the valleys arises from the fact that frosts,
and radiation weather generally, accompany the distribution of pressure known as an "anti-cyclone," during

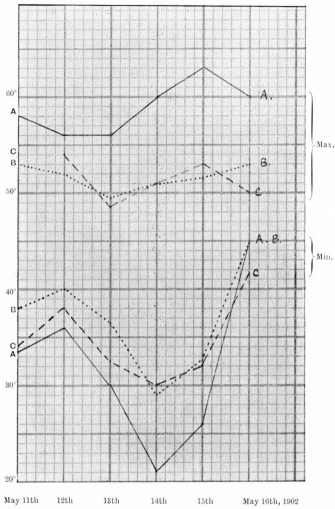

FIG. 13.—Temperatures (Maximum and Minimum) at Various Altitudes.

A = 100 feet.　　B = 150 feet.　　C = 500 feet.

[To face page 135.

which there is always a gentle downdraught of cold
air from the clear sky above. But the circulation of
air in an anti-cyclone is always reversed at a certain
elevation, so that as one ascends, the downdraught of
cold air becomes less and eventually ceases; the mean
temperature at the same time rises instead of falling
with the elevation.

Observations of the minimum temperature on the
grass made at two stations on a gentle slope of the downs
at Wye, about a mile apart and differing in level by
100 feet, showed during a period of thirty-six days
in February and March 1902 (which was exceptionally
calm and mild), a mean difference of 1° in favour of
the upper station, but on two occasions the lower
thermometer fell to 24°·5 and 21°·5, when the upper
thermometer was 30°·5 and 29°·5 respectively.

The accompanying curves (Fig. 13) show the daily
maxima and minima of the air temperatures of 4 feet
from the ground for a few days before and after the
occurrence of a disastrous late spring frost in May 1902.
One station, A, was in a river meadow about 100 feet
above sea-level, the second, B, was on a terrace about
50 feet higher and half a mile away; the third, C, was on
the flat summit of the down, 500 feet above sea-level
and about 1½ mile from the first station. It will be
seen that the river-side station gave always the highest
maxima during the period and the lowest minima,
showing on the one occasion 11° of frost.

Early and Late Soils.

From all the considerations developed above it will
be seen that an early soil is essentially a coarse-textured
and well-drained one. Such a soil retains little water,
thus possessing a low specific heat, and is easily warmed;

at the same time the low water content gives rise to less evaporation at the surface, and this great cause of cooling is minimised. The dryness of the soil permits of early cultivation, which, by cutting off the access of subsoil water and diminishing the conduction of heat from the surface, quickens the warming up of the seed bed. The early aeration and warming of the soil promotes the nitrification which is also necessary to growth. If, further, the soil be stony, the conduction of heat from the surface layer into the soil is more rapid, solids being better conductors than powders. Such soils, again, are generally dark coloured, because on the comparatively small surface exposed by the coarse grains the same proportion of humus has a greater colouring effect.

These conditions are generally fulfilled by the alluvial soils bordering the larger rivers; in the neighbourhood of large towns, which are generally situated on a river, they form the typical market-gardening soils, especially as their natural poverty can be alleviated by the large supply of dung which is easily obtainable from the town.

At the same time these soils have their disadvantages; from both their nature and their situation they are subject to rapid changes of temperature; they suffer much from night frosts both in spring and autumn, and dry out easily in the summer, so that some crops do not come to their full growth. Autumn planted vegetables grow away rapidly, and are apt to become "winter proud" and killed by severe weather.

Of course, to ensure the maximum of earliness and freedom from spring frosts, the geographical situation and the climate must be considered as well as the nature of the soil. The neighbourhood of the sea or any large body of water has a great effect in equalising the temperatures and preventing severe frosts; in the British Islands, for example, the earliest potatoes are grown in Jersey, near Penzance, and on other light land along the southern coast of Cornwall, and again a little later near the sea in Ayrshire. Light land round the coasts of Kent and Essex, which borders, and in some cases is almost surrounded by the sea, is also specially valued for the growth of early vegetables.

The soils naturally retentive of water are late, both because they dry slowly and are rarely fit to work early in the year, and because the high water content keeps their temperature down. Except in long-continued droughts they maintain a supply of water to the plant, their high specific heat keeps them at a comparatively equable temperature and prevents them from cooling down so soon when the summer heats are past. In consequence, the crop is neither forced early to maturity nor is growth checked so soon in the autumn, the period of development is prolonged until in some cases the season becomes unsuitable for ripening. Many subtle differences may be noticed between the quality of produce grown upon early and late soils; for example, a comparison made by the author of the same variety of apple grown upon adjoining clay and sandy soils showed that the apples from the clay land were smaller and greener, but contained a greater proportion of sugar and acid, and possessed a higher aroma than the apples grown upon the lighter and earlier soil. Wheat grown on the clays is generally of better quality and "stronger" than that yielded by the lighter soils; whereas the lighter soils yield the finer barley, in which carbohydrates and not nitrogenous materials are characteristic of high quality. On a light soil, becoming both warm and dry early in the season, the plant ceases the sooner to draw nutrient material from the soil; assimilation, however, continues after the plant has ceased to feed; finally, maturation — the removal of the previously elaborated material into the seed—begins earlier and can be more thoroughly accomplished. Hence grain from an early soil is, on the whole, characterised by a higher proportion of carbohydrate to albuminoid, always provided that no excessive or premature drying-out has taken place, for that ripens off the grain before the transference of starch has been completed

CHAPTER VI

THE CHEMICAL ANALYSIS OF SOILS

Necessary Conventions as to the Material to be Analysed—
Methods Adopted — Interpretation of Results — Distinction
between Dormant and Available Plant Food—Analysis of
the Soil by the Plant—Determination of "Available" Phosphoric Acid and Potash by the Use of Weak Acid Solvents.

THE chemical analysis of a soil aims at ascertaining the
amount which the soil contains of the various elements
necessary to the nutrition of the plant, with a view of
either making good the general deficiencies of the soil or
of adjusting the supply of plant food to such special
requirements of a particular crop as may have been
indicated by previous experiment.

The analysis of plants grown under ordinary conditions shows that a comparatively limited number of
elements enters into their composition; in the main they
are composed of water and certain combustible compounds of carbon, hydrogen, nitrogen, and sulphur. In
the mineral residue that is left after the combustible
material has been burnt off, will be found potassium,
sodium, calcium, magnesium, and a little iron among
bases; and phosphorus, chlorine, sulphur, and silicon
among non-metallic elements. Manganese in very small
quantities occurs in nearly all plants: other elements
like lithium, zinc, copper, are found in traces under

special conditions of soil. By pot cultures in the laboratory it can be shown that of the above elements, the carbon, hydrogen, and oxygen are drawn from the atmosphere or the water, and that nitrogen, chlorine, sulphur, phosphorus, among non-metals, and potassium, calcium, magnesium and iron, among metals, are elements indispensable to the plant, and are derived by way of the root from the soil. In view of the above facts it is clearly unnecessary to make an ultimate determination of all the elements present in the soil, which has already been shown to consist largely of sand and various silicates of alumina, etc. These materials constitute the medium in which the plant grows, but do not themselves supply it with any food; they need not, therefore, be estimated chemically.

The chemical analysis of a soil, then, resolves itself into determinations of the nitrogen, phosphorus, potassium, calcium, and (of less importance) of sodium, magnesium, iron, aluminium, chlorine, and sulphur. To these must be added the determination of the carbon compounds of the soil, which have already been touched on under the head of humus, and of the carbonates of calcium and magnesium, which in most soils constitute the bases available for neutralising any acids that may be produced. Having decided upon the elements to be determined it would then be possible to proceed as in an ordinary mineral analysis: the sample of soil would be reduced to such a state of division as would admit of drawing an accurate small sample, and then entirely disintegrated by some such reaction as fusion with ammonium fluoride. But results obtained in this way would give very imperfect information about the soil, for the procedure draws no distinction between material present in the unweathered interior of the stones and coarser particles, which could not reach the plant for generations, and that which exists as very small particles or as a coating on the larger ones, and is therefore open to attack by the water in the soil. The nutrient material of the soil can only reach the plant in the dissolved state, and in dealing with slightly soluble substances such as constitute the soil, the amount which goes into solution is practically proportional to the surface exposed. But the surface exposed increases as the material is subdivided, one gram of soil in pieces 1 mm. in diameter would only expose one-thousandth of the surface exposed by the same amount of soil in particles 0·001 mm. in diameter, so that to all intents and purposes the stones and coarser particles contribute such a small proportion of the surface of the soil that the material dissolved from them can be neglected.

For these reasons—the small surface exposed by the larger particles and the unweathered nature of the compounds within them — the stones above a certain size are not included in the analysis, nor is any attempt made to bring into complete solution even the selected material. Hence it becomes necessary in soil analysis to accept certain "conventions" as to the preparation of the soil for analysis, the nature of the acid used for solution, and the duration and temperature of the attack; all of which factors so affect the mineral matter going into solution that results are only comparable when obtained in the same way. It must always be remembered that soil analysis is only a relative process, by which soils that are unknown can be compared with others whose fertility has been tested by experience; no means exist of directly translating the results into terms of the crop the soil will carry. The methods of analysis that are indicated below are those adopted by the members of the Agricultural Education Association in this country: unfortunately, there is no uniformity in the methods pursued even among chemists in the same country, wide as are the variations introduced by the different processes in vogue. For example, an acid such as hydrochloric will dissolve very different amounts of potash from a given soil, according as the soil is treated directly with the acid or first ignited, nor is there any constant relation between the amount dissolved from ignited and from raw soil.

Method of Analysis.

The soil sample is taken, passed through the 3 mm. sieve, and air-dried, exactly as previously described for the mechanical analysis. From the large air-dried sample of "fine earth" a portion of about 100 grams is drawn, and either ground in a steel mill or broken in a steel mortar till it will all pass through a sieve with round holes 1 mm. in diameter. This is done to enable the analyst to draw a fair sample weighing only a few grams: if the "fine earth" which passes the 3 mm. sieve were itself used, it would be impossible to adjust the relative proportions of coarse and fine to correspond with the bulk. It is not uncommon to find coarse particles of carbonate of lime sparsely scattered through the soil when the land has been limed; only by grinding and mixing can this matter become evenly distributed through the soil. On the ground material the following determinations are made:—

(1) Moisture lost at 100° C.
(2) Loss on ignition.
(3) Nitrogen.
(4) Earthy carbonates.

(5) Phosphoric acid and potash soluble in strong hydrochloric acid. If necessary, soda, lime, magnesia, oxides of iron, alumina, and sulphuric acid can be determined in the same solution.

(1) About 5 grams are weighed out into a platinum dish or porcelain basin and dried in the ordinary steam oven, the temperature of which is never quite 100° C. If the soil contains much organic matter, it will be difficult to bring it to a constant weight, the material will slowly lose water for weeks. An arbitrary limit of twenty-four hours drying should be taken.

(2) The loss on ignition should represent the organic matter which is burnt to carbon dioxide and water when the soil is heated in the air, but it is impossible to avoid at the same time driving off some of the water of constitution in the zeolites, kaolinite, and similar hydrated silicates in the soil. It is difficult even to obtain consistent results, because of variations in the temperature and time of the operation. The best plan is to heat the soil, as dried in the previous operation, at as low a temperature as possible, to a barely visible redness, preferably in a platinum dish, for some hours with occasional stirring.

The loss on ignition is wanted as a measure of the organic matter of the soil, but we have no means of estimating the varying part, great with clay soils, that is played by the water of constitution. It is possible to get a better measure of the organic matter by estimating the total carbon in the soil and assuming that the organic matter of the original soil contained about 55 per cent. of carbon. The combustion of a soil by the ordinary method for determining carbon is rather a tedious process even in skilled hands; in dealing with soils it is convenient to effect the oxidation by means of a mixture of sulphuric and chromic acids, taking care to interpose a tube of heated copper oxide between the flask containing the soil and acids and the apparatus used for absorbing the carbon dioxide, in order to complete the oxidation of some of the products formed. This process can be made to follow the determination of the carbon dioxide evolved by the action of acid alone, the same apparatus and the same portion of soil serving for both.

(3) The nitrogen in 10 to 20 grams of the ground "fine earth" is estimated by Kjeldahl's process. Though there is some nitrate present in the soil, no special precaution need be taken on its account, the proportion it bears to the total nitrogen is so small as to be negligible.

(4) The earthy carbonates of the soil are estimated from the quantity of carbon dioxide, which is evolved on treating the ground "fine earth" with an acid. When the proportion of calcium carbonate is high the determination can be made by the usual gravimetric methods. Scheibler's apparatus for measuring the volume of carbon dioxide evolved is suitable when the proportion of calcium carbonate does not fall below 1 per cent.; below that point some other method must be employed, because all the carbon dioxide evolved goes into solution in the reacting acid. The most exact and convenient method for determining calcium carbonate, especially when the quantity involved is very small, consists in absorbing the carbon dioxide evolved by dilute caustic soda in a Reiset tower, and estimating the carbon dioxide by titrating the alkali first with phenol-phthalein and then with methyl orange as an indicator (see *Amos. Jour. Agric. Sci.*, 1, 1905, 322). Certain acid soils rich in humus contain other organic substances which yield carbon dioxide on boiling with dilute acid,

in which case the soil should be attacked with a boiling dilute solution of ammonium chloride. It is not sufficient in such cases to estimate the calcium dissolved by dilute acids from the soil, because there are always present other compounds of calcium, *e.g.*, silicates and sulphates, which are soluble in the acid and would be reckoned as calcium carbonate. The factor that is required is not the calcium, but the amount of carbonate which will serve as a base in the soil and combine with the acids liberated by decay, nitrification, or from some of the artificial manures. To this end it is not necessary to discriminate between the carbonates of calcium and magnesium, accordingly the carbon dioxide evolved is calculated back to calcium carbonate. In a few soils ferrous carbonate may be present; this is oxidised to ferric hydrate when the powdered soil is boiled with water, and may be so removed before determining the carbon dioxide. In temperate climates, however, it is only a few bog soils that need be examined for ferrous carbonate.

(5) For the determinations of soluble constituents 20 grams of the powdered soil are placed in a flask of Jena glass, covered with about 70 c.c. of strong hydrochloric acid, and boiled for a short time over a naked flame to bring it to constant strength. The acid will now contain about 20.2 per cent. of pure hydrogen chloride. The flask is loosely stoppered, placed on the waterbath, and the contents allowed to digest for about fortyeight hours. The solution is then cooled, diluted, and filtered. The washed residue is dried and weighed as the material insoluble in acids.

The solution is made up to 250 c.c. and aliquot portions are taken for the various determinations. The analytical operations are carried out in the usual

K

manner, but special care must be taken to free the
solution from silica and organic matter. For phosphoric acid a portion of the solution is evaporated to
dryness and ignited, the residue is taken up with
hydrochloric acid, filtered, again evaporated to dryness, and heated in an air - bath for half an hour at
105°. This residue is then taken up with dilute
nitric acid, filtered, and made up to about 50 c.c.
Five grams of ammonium nitrate are added, and 50
c.c. of a solution of ammonium molybdate containing
60 grams molybdic acid per litre. The mixture is
put aside in a warm place for twenty-four hours, the
precipitate is filtered off, and, after washing with
ammonium nitrate solution, is dissolved by ammonia
into a tared porcelain basin, evaporated to dryness,
and gently ignited over an Argand burner. The
resulting material contains 3·794 per cent. of phosphoric acid. For the determination of potash the
same procedure is followed, but the residue after the
second evaporation is taken up with dilute hydrochloric instead of nitric acid. To the solution 25 c.c.
of a solution of chloroplatinic acid containing 0·005
gram platinum per c.c. is added, and the whole gently
evaporated over a water-bath till almost dry. It is
then thrown on to a filter and washed with alcohol,
then washed again with a solution of ammonium
chloride which has been saturated with the double
chloride of platinum and ammonium, and finally dissolved off the filter paper with a little hot water in a
tared basin, evaporated, and weighed. A Gooch crucible
is most convenient for handling both the phosphoric
acid and potash precipitates.

The other determinations which may be made in
this solution consist of soda, lime, magnesia, iron,
alumina, manganese, and sulphuric acid, but in most

cases these may be omitted. It is occasionally desirable to examine the soluble salts in the soil; about 200 grams of the fine earth should be successively washed with small portions of hot water by the aid of a filter - pump. In the solution the total solids are determined; they consist, in the main, of the nitrates, sulphates, and chlorides of sodium, potassium, magnesium, and calcium, which can be determined by the usual methods. Of course, the amount of soluble salts to be found in the surface soil at any time is largely regulated by the previous weather; after considerable rainfall the soluble salts are washed down into the subsoil, after long evaporation they are concentrated in the surface layers. The amount of nitrates that is present is further affected by the previous cropping, temperature, and working of the soil, and by the manipulation the soil receives after it reaches the laboratory. Thus the determination of the soil constituents that are soluble in water does not enter into the ordinary routine of analysis, their presence is affected by so many temporary factors which prevent the comparison of one soil with another.

As, however, the determination of the amount of nitrate present in a soil is often required for other purposes, it will be convenient here to indicate the method to be followed. In the first place, the soil must be analysed either immediately after it has been sampled and after rapid drying with the aid of heat, for the manipulation a soil sample usually receives in the drying, sifting, and other preliminary operations, will cause the production of large quantities of nitrates in ordinary soils.

A funnel with a large filtering surface, at least 2 inches in diameter, must be taken; Warington originally made use of the inverted upper portion of a Winchester

quart bottle with a disc of copper gauze, 2 inches in
diameter resting in the neck, but this may be replaced
advantageously by a Buchner funnel 6 inches in
diameter.   In either case the funnel is connected with
an exhaust - pump, the disc is covered with a good
filter paper wetted, then at least 500 grams of the soil
are packed carefully into the funnel and pressed down a
little, care being taken to avoid plastering if the soil is
clayey.   The soil sample as it comes from the field is
spread out, roughly crumbled, and mixed ; from this the
500 grams or so are taken and weighed before putting
on the funnel.   Another portion is weighed out and
dried in the steam oven, to ascertain the proportion of
water in the sample.   50 c.c. of hot distilled water are
now poured on the soil, allowed to stand a few minutes,
and the pump started.   When the liquid has been drawn
through, successive small portions of hot water are put
on, and the pump started afresh ; it will be found
possible to wash out practically the whole of the nitrate
with 100 c.c. of water.

If the liquid shows any tendency to come through
the filter turbid, this can be obviated by adding a few
drops of sulphuric acid to the water.   In the filtered
liquid the nitrates may be determined by reducing with
the zinc copper couple, distilling off the ammonia and
determining it either by Nesslerising or by titration,
according to its amount.   The couple is prepared by
dipping half a dozen strips of thin sheet zinc, 6 inches
long by $1\frac{1}{2}$ broad, successively into dilute caustic soda,
very dilute sulphuric acid, and then into a 3 per cent.
solution of copper sulphate, in which it is allowed to
remain until it has acquired a good black deposit of copper.
They are washed by immersion in water, and finally in
ammonia - free distilled water, and placed in a bottle
with 200 c.c. of the soil extract and a crystal of oxalic

acid.   The bottle is kept in a warm place or an incubator at 25° for twenty-four hours before distilling off the ammonia.

The table (Appendix I.) shows the analyses by the method above described of a few typical soils.

It will be seen, as a rule, that the water retained by the soil when air dry, the loss on ignition, and the nitrogen, rise and fall together, because the humus which contains the nitrogen is the most hygroscopic constituent of soils.   Clay soils which tend to conserve humus also contain the most constitutional water; this further tends to increase the loss on ignition in their case.

The proportion of nitrogen found ranges from 0·5 per cent. in very rich pasture soils down to below 0·1 per cent. on light arable soils, it is rarely up to 0·2 per cent. in arable soils, and the warmer, the more open, and more worked the soil is, the less will be the proportion of nitrogen.   In the fertile hop-gardens of East Kent the percentage of nitrogen is rarely as much as 0·2 per cent., despite the great dressings of nitrogenous manure that are annually applied.

The proportion of phosphoric acid in soils is not so variable as the proportion of nitrogen; it ranges from about 0·06 per cent. to 0·2 per cent.; the lower amounts occur generally on the sands and clays, the higher on loams and soils well provided with calcium carbonate.

The proportion of potash shows extreme variations, a clay soil may yield one per cent. of potash to strong hydrochloric acid, a sand only one-tenth as much.   It has already been pointed out that "clay" is chiefly the result of the weathering of felspars and kindred minerals containing potash; this weathering is never chemically complete, so that all soils containing any considerable admixture of clay are necessarily rich in potash.   The amount dissolved out by hydrochloric

acid is also somewhat of an accidental figure, as it
depends very much on how far the previous treatment
of the soil has forwarded the weathering process, for
there remains in all soils rich in potash much material
that will not yield potash to strong hydrochloric acid
even after forty-eight hours' digestion. For example,
the soil from one of the plots in the Broadbalk wheatfield at Rothamsted only yielded 0·5 per cent. of potash
to hydrochloric acid, but when completely broken up
by ammonium fluoride it was found to contain 2·26 per
cent. of potash.

Of all the soil constituents calcium carbonate shows
the widest fluctuations ; it may constitute 40 or 50 per
cent. of some of the thin soils resting on the chalk,
or it may sink on some of the sands and clays to such
small proportions as only to be detected by the most
refined analysis.

The importance of the calcium carbonate lies not
in the calcium that it supplies for the nutrition of
plants, but in that it acts as the chief base, maintaining the neutrality of the soil. Many plant diseases,
like the slime fungus which causes "finger-and-toe"
in turnips, etc., are only prevalent when the soil is
losing its neutral condition, and are not found when a
sufficiency of calcium carbonate is present. The normal
changes in a soil are brought about by bacteria, which
only flourish when the medium is neutral or very faintly
alkaline ; as soon as the soil becomes acid the bacterial
actions are largely suspended, and in their place moulds
and other micro-fungi become predominant. It is for
this reason always desirable to test the reaction of a
soil by putting a little on litmus paper, moistening
it, and after a few minutes washing away the soil.
What proportion of calcium carbonate is required for
fertility and health is difficult to say, probably an

inferior limit of 0·5 per cent. is the lowest that is safe. In the case of soils containing about this proportion much will depend on how finely it is disseminated, 0·5 per cent. in visible pieces will not be so effective as 0·1 per cent. of the amount in particles of the same order of size as the clay or silt particles. For this reason it is advisable when analysing a doubtful soil of this kind, to make a rough separation of the finer particles, by pestling up 10 grams of the soil with water, and pouring off the supernatant liquid after one minute's standing, as in a mechanical analysis. Having washed away the finer portion of the soil two or three times in this way, the residue is dried and the carbonates which remain are estimated as before, thus a rough idea is obtained of their distribution among the finer or coarser sets of soil particles.

Interpretation of the Results of a Soil Analysis.

Though much may doubtless be learnt by a comparison of the analysis of a given soil with the analysis of others whose fertility has been proved by experience or by actual manurial experiments, there are yet many considerations which prevent much weight being attached to the results thus obtained.

A comparison of the total amount of any of the elements of plant food in the soil with the amount that is withdrawn by an ordinary crop shows at once that even in the poorest soils there is sufficient material for something like a hundred average crops.

The density of the surface soil has already been discussed; it will be sufficiently accurate for our purpose if we consider that the top 9 inches of one acre of an ordinary arable field weighs 2,500,000 lbs. On this basis, and without taking into account the fact that the roots of most cultivated plants range far deeper than 9 inches, there is yet present about 2500 lbs. per acre of nitrogen, potash, and phosphoric acid in a soil containing only 0·1 per cent. of these constituents, which is about the lower limit usually found. The following table shows the amounts of these food materials— nitrogen, phosphoric acid, and potash—which are taken from the soil by an average crop grown in rotation.

Lbs. per acre.	Wheat.	Swedes.	Barley.	Clover.
Nitrogen . .	41·7	94·0	49·0	159·3*
Phosphoric Acid .	20·5	24·1	20·7	28·2
Potash . . .	3·56	93·5	35·7	102·4

* Partly derived from the atmosphere.

It is clear from a comparison of this table with the quantities previously specified, that even the poorest soil contains the nutrient material required by any ordinary crop many times over, yet we know that crops respond vigorously to dressings of manure which only add a fraction to the plant food already stored in the soil. For example, a wheat crop on poor soil would often be doubled by the use of 2 cwt. of nitrate of soda per acre, *i.e.*, by the addition of 35 lbs. of nitrogen in nitrate of soda to a soil that already contained in the top 9 inches more than 2000 lbs. per acre. Again, 4 cwt. per acre of superphosphate, containing about 60 lbs. of phosphoric acid, will be necessary in the usual rotation to secure a good swede crop, though there may be already 2000 to 3000 lbs. of phosphoric acid in the soil. We are then driven to conclude that the nitrogen, potash, and phosphoric acid are present in the soil in some other mode of combination than the form in which they exist in manures: so that although they may be in the soil

they are in such a state as to be very partially of service
to the growing plant.   Further evidence of the enormous
stores of plant food in the soil and the comparative slowness with which they can be utilised may be obtained
by considering the results obtained at Rothamsted,
where on one plot wheat has been grown continuously
without manure for sixty-four years (to 1907).   The
average yield from this plot was for the first twenty years,
1844-63, 16·3 bushels of grain and 15·1 cwt. of straw;
11·6 bushels of grain and 9·3 cwt. of straw for the next
twenty years, 1864-83; and 12·3 bushels of grain and
8·7 cwt. of straw for the third period of twenty years,
1884-1903.   It is calculated that during the last fifty years
there have been removed from this plot about 900 lbs.
per acre of nitrogen, 470 of phosphoric acid, and 760 of
potash, *i.e.*, about 18, 9, and 15 lbs. per acre per annum
respectively; yet from analyses of a sample taken in 1893
the surface soil to a depth of 9 inches still contained
0·11 per cent. of nitrogen, 0·114 per cent. of phosphoric
acid, and 0·38 per cent. of potash soluble in strong
hydrochloric acid, or 2750, 2850, and 9500 lbs. per
acre respectively.   The soil must therefore be regarded as possessing most of its plant food in states
of combination that cannot be utilised by the plant,
and these forms slowly pass, by weathering and other
changes, into material which is available for the crop.
The plant food of the soil represents so much capital,
and, as in many another business, but a small proportion
of the capital is liquid at any given time: it is largely
the object of cultivation to effect such a turnover of the
capital as will liquidate some of it in a form available
for the nutrition of the crop.

In the old systems of agriculture, before the land was
enclosed, the whole crop was grown out of capital,
nothing but labour was put into the soil: in which con-

nection it is interesting to note that the original meaning of manure was to work by hand.*

It becomes important, then, to attempt to discriminate between the various forms in which the nitrogen, potash, and phosphoric acid may be present in the soil, according as they are soluble, or likely in a short time to become sufficiently soluble to reach the crop. In the case of nitrogen we know that of the various compounds such as proteins and protein residues, amides, ammonia salts, and nitrates which can be detected in the soil, only the latter can enter the plant, but that, by processes of fermentation, all of the other compounds will eventually pass into the state of nitrate. Of the immediately soluble nitrogen compounds—nitrates, nitrites, and ammonia— a very small amount, varying from 5 to 200 lbs. per acre, is ever present in the soil at any given time, though it is constantly being renewed by fermentation processes.

Phosphoric acid also exists in the soil in many distinct compounds : in combination with carbon, etc., it is found in nuclein and lecithin, which in a more or less humified condition are found among the plant and animal residues : it also occurs as phosphate of the sesquioxides of iron and alumina ; as tribasic, and probably also as dibasic phosphate of lime. Of these compounds the latter are undoubtedly the most soluble in either pure water or the carbonic-acid-charged water of the soil, but much must depend on the physical condition, as well as on the chemical combination, in which the material exists. For example, when using tribasic phosphate of lime as a manure, the softer phosphates, such as steamed bone flour, are more effective than the chemically similar but harder material in ground rock phosphate.

* *Cf.* Defoe, *Robinson Crusoe* (1719)—" The ground that I had manured or dug up for them was not great."

It is not so easy to classify the various compounds of potash existing in the soil: we know that as felspar passes into kaolinite there are intermediate stages of weathering in which the potash is gradually becoming more soluble in soil water, but it is impossible to isolate or classify the various hydrated silicates containing potash that must exist. Potash, again, which has once been dissolved, is caught and retained by the soil in various ill-defined compounds, some of which must reach the crop more rapidly than others.

The work, then, of soil analysis must be extended to include some investigation of the condition of the plant food in the soil, as well as its absolute quantity: it is not enough to determine what constituents are present with the view of making good the deficiencies, because there is always more than enough for many crops; inquiry must be rather directed towards finding how much is likely to reach the crop. The attempt to discriminate between the total and what may be termed the available plant food in the soil, *i.e.*, that which is in a form the crop can immediately utilise, has been made in two ways — by using the growing plant as an analytical agent, or by attacking the soil with very dilute acids, whose action is akin to the natural solvent agencies at work when the plant is growing. The former process proceeds upon the assumption that any given plant has a certain average composition which it will acquire when freely supplied with all the elements of nutrition; if this plant be grown upon a soil deficient in one particular, that deficiency will be reflected in the analysis of the plant when fully grown. It is thus necessary to select a standard plant and grow it under normal conditions of manuring to ascertain the proportion that nitrogen, phosphoric acid, and potash usually bear to the ash.

The selected plant is then grown upon the soil in question, gathered at the appropriate stage and analysed, when the composition of the ash, as compared with its composition under normal conditions, should give indications of the state of the soil. Various disturbing factors come into play; for example, the presence in the soil of large quantities of a non-essential material like calcium sulphate or sodium chloride lowers the proportion that potash bears to the total ash without necessarily indicating any want of potash; again, a deficiency of nitrogen is more seen in a general stunting of the whole development of the plant than in a comparative poverty of nitrogen in the final growth. But by selecting suitable test plants, valuable indications can be obtained as to the need or otherwise for specific manuring. As a rule, cereals are unsuitable test plants, since they are well able to satisfy their requirements for mineral nutrients from comparatively impoverished soils; the straw of barley, however, shows considerable variations from which the condition of the soil as regards its supply of phosphoric acid and potash can be interpreted. The phosphoric acid in the ash of barley straw will vary between 2 and 4 per cent. and the potash between 6 and 24 per cent., and as the straw of barley grown without special manuring can readily be obtained, it forms a convenient test plant. The most sensitive test plants are provided by roots— swedes for estimating the phosphoric acid, and mangolds for estimating the potash in the soils on which they have been grown. The phosphoric acid in the ash of swedes has been found as low as 9 per cent. when the soil was one that responded readily to phosphatic manures, rising to 16 per cent. when the soil was one that required no phosphatic manure. Similarly, the potash in the ash of mangolds will vary between 12 and 40 per cent.

The method which is now very largely employed to determine the mineral plant food in the soil that may be regarded as immediately "available" for the crop, consists in attacking the soil with a very dilute acid, whose action shall be comparable with the natural solution processes bringing nutriment to the plant. The mineral matter finds it way by osmosis into the plant in two ways: either from the natural soil water, or from the more concentrated solution formed in immediate proximity to the root-hairs by the attack of the excreted carbon dioxide upon the soil particles.

The natural soil water is constantly dissolving small quantities of phosphoric acid, potash, and other materials, in which it is aided by the carbonic acid it also contains; as this water passes by osmosis into the root-hairs it will carry with it the dissolved material, with the exception of any particular ion or radicle which has already attained in the cell sap a higher concentration than it possesses in the external soil solution. But if the soil water alone brought the mineral matter with it, not enough enters the plant to account for the observed facts. For example, the growth of a crop of a ton and a half of clover hay requires the transpiration through the leaves, and therefore the absorption at the root, of about 400 tons of water (see p. 91); the same crop would also contain about 50 lbs. of potash. If, then, the crop derived all its mineral matter by the simple inflow of the soil water into the root, the 50 lbs. of potash must have been originally dissolved in the 400 tons of water that passed through the crop, which means that the soil water contained as much as 0·006 per cent. of potash, a greater concentration than is observed in humid climates. In fact, the particular ions or radicles concerned in nutrition enter the root faster than the water does; they diffuse through the cell wall because the sap within is maintained in a less concentrated state as far as they are concerned than the external soil water, because they are constantly being withdrawn from solution by the living protoplasm of the cells.

It has been supposed that solvent action of the soil water is also assisted by the cell sap of the root-hairs, which is always distinctly acid in its reaction; these root-hairs are always very closely in contact with soil particles, and some of the acid has been supposed to diffuse outwards through the cell wall. Sachs has shown that a polished slab of marble is etched wherever the fine roots of a plant came in contact with it, and on the strength of this and similar experiments, the cell sap has been regarded as a factor in bringing the minerals of the soil into solution for the plant. All the solvent actions, however attributed to the cell sap, can be brought about by the carbon dioxide which is always being excreted by the root, and more critical experiments seem to negative the opinion that any fixed acids pass outwards through the cell wall of a living plant, at any-rate after it has passed the seedling stage.

Whatever the theories which have been formed as to the manner in which the mineral constituents of the soil pass into solution for the plant, it is improbable that the conditions can be reproduced in the laboratory, and for the practical purposes of analysis the desideratum is a solvent that will dissolve the class of material which is found by experience to reach the immediate crop, but which will not touch the same material should its state of combination or physical condition be such as to render it unavailable for the plant. Various solvents have been proposed: for example, Dehérain showed that dilute acetic acid, while dissolving some phosphoric acid from ordinary soils, was incapable of extracting any from a

particular soil which yielded very poor crops unless manured with superphosphate, though it contained 0·1 per
cent. of phosphoric acid soluble in strong hydrochloric
acid. Hence he concluded that dilute acetic acid
forms a solvent only capable of attacking the available phosphoric acid. A solution of carbonic acid has
been suggested as akin to the natural soil water;
other solutions have been employed because they will
dissolve certain of the compounds of phosphoric acid
in the soil, but not all—the calcium phosphates, for
example, but not the phosphates of iron and aluminium; other solvents, again, are recommended as
akin to the acid cell sap. However, experience seems
to show that the 1 per cent. solution of citric acid proposed by Dyer in 1894 gives results that are most in
accord with what is known of the soil, either from its
past history or by cropping experiments.

The method of conducting the analysis is as follows:
—200 grams of the "fine earth" that has passed the 3
mm. sieve, in its air-dried state, is placed without any
further grinding in a dry Winchester quart bottle with
20 grams of pure crystallised citric acid and 2 litres of
water. The bottle should either be one previously used
for the storage of strong acids or should have a preliminary soaking in dilute hydrochloric acid. The
mixture of soil and dilute acid is thoroughly shaken from
time to time, as often as may be convenient, during the
seven days the solvent action is allowed to proceed.
After seven days the solution is filtered, and two aliquot
portions of 500 c.c. each are evaporated to dryness and
ignited to get rid of the citric acid and other organic
matter. The residues are dissolved in hydrochloric acid,
again evaporated, and heated for a time to 105° C. to
render all the silica insoluble. In one portion the
phosphoric acid, and in the other the potash, are deter-

mined by the processes previously described. The time of extraction may be shortened to twenty-four hours if the bottle be put in a good end-over-end shaking machine which will keep the soil and the solvent thoroughly agitated.

An examination of the citric acid solution shows that all the compounds of phosphoric acid that have been indicated as existing in the soil are more or less attacked; at any rate, the resulting solution contains organic matter and salts of aluminium and iron, in addition to calcium. It has been suggested that the varying amounts of calcium carbonate contained by soils will much affect the material dissolved by the citric acid, some of which becomes neutralised by the calcium carbonate. But though the amount of phosphoric acid dissolved from a given soil by the citric acid solution will be diminished if the calcium carbonate in the soil is increased, a very similar reduction will be effected in the natural processes of solution of the soil phosphates under field conditions. No attempt should be made to add an extra amount of citric acid to combine with the calcium carbonate; secondary solvent actions are set up both by the carbon dioxide evolved and by the calcium citrate formed, moreover, the real comparative basis of the method of analysis is destroyed.

It must not be supposed that the citric acid solution, nor indeed any of dilute acid solvents that have been proposed for this purpose, are real differential solvents, which extract the material in the soil which is available for the plant and leave untouched whatever is combined in some other form. In reality, as soon as the acid has been for a sufficient time in contact with the soil a state of equilibrium is attained between the phosphoric acid, for example, that has gone into solution and that which remains in the solid state. The precise equilibrium attained depends not only upon the strength of the acid solution and the nature and amount of the phosphoric acid compounds in the soil, but also on the nature and amount of the bases that are there present. If, for example, the citric acid solution is filtered off after it has extracted all the phosphoric acid it can, and a second portion of solution is added and the soil extracted afresh, then more phosphoric acid will go into solution, the amount being smaller than before but still considerable. A third, a fourth, and even a fifth extraction does not remove from the soil all the phosphoric acid that will go into solution in the dilute citric acid solution. Thus it is impossible to say that the dilute citric or any other acid dissolves out and measures the "available" phosphoric acid or potash; it does, however, provide a figure indicating the comparative rate at which the soil is likely to yield up its nutrient constituents to the normal solvent actions going on in the soil. The results, then, of this method of analysis are not to be regarded as absolute amounts, but as empirically obtained figures which must be interpreted in the light of experience. The type of the soil plays a part; for example, a quantity of citric acid soluble phosphoric acid that would indicate poverty in a strong loam or in a soil rich in organic matter like an old pasture, would be ample for ordinary crop purposes if the soil were light and sandy. Again, the crop must be taken into account; a percentage indicating enough available phosphoric acid in the soil for wheat or mangolds would indicate deficiency when the swede crop came round.

In certain cases, by continuing the extraction with citric acid until the amount going into solution at each extraction becomes approximately constant at some low figure, it is possible to differentiate between the phosphates in the soil that are easily soluble and may

L

therefore be termed "available," because they possess a comparatively high solubility factor, and other phosphates which would yield, under natural conditions, solutions too dilute to nourish the crop efficiently.

For example, the following table shows the amounts of phosphoric acid dissolved by successive extractions of certain Rothamsted soils with 1 per cent. citric acid solution, from which it will be seen that at about the fifth extraction the quantity dissolved begins to approach a constant.

PHOSPHORIC ACID, MGMS. PER 100 GRAMS SOIL.

Field.	Plot.	Treatment each Year.	EXTRACTION.					
			1st.	2nd.	3rd.	4th.	5th.	6th.
Broadbalk	3	Unmanured . . .	6·4	6·8	3·9	3·0	2·5	...
"	5	64 lbs. P$_2$O$_5$, no Nitrogen	69·0	28·0	11·3	7·3	4·5	2·3
"	7	64 lbs. P$_2$O$_5$, 86 lbs. N. .	56·1	22·8	8·9	6·5	4·4	4·4
"	8	64 lbs.P$_2$O$_5$, 129 lbs. N. .	46·3	18·9	7·8	5·3	4·0	3·0
"	10	86 lbs. N. only . .	7·7	5·2	3·3	2·7	2·7	2·7
"	2	Dunged	49·3	15·3	7·5	6·0	4·4	...
Hoos	1AA	43 lbs. N. only . .	6·3	3·5	2·2	1·9	2·0	1·2
"	2AA	64 lbs. P$_2$O$_5$, 43 lbs. N. .	52·2	21·2	8·9	6·5	3·8	2·9
"	3AA	43 lbs. N. and Potash .	6·3	2·7	2·3	2·1	1·9	1·5
"	4AA	64 lbs. P$_2$O$_5$, 43 lbs. N., Potash . . .	53·5	10·6	6·4	4·9	4·5	3·8

The successive amounts going into solution in the first four or five extractions of the soil from the plots which had received soluble phosphoric acid every year are found to be decreasing in a logarithmic series, and this may be supposed to indicate that the solvent is dealing with only one class of material, which is entirely removed at about the fifth extraction. After the fifth extraction there only remains the more insoluble classes of phosphates which form the main stock in

the soil.   The unmanured plot and that which has
received dung do not show the same regular decrement,
indicating that the solvent is each time dealing with a
more complex mixture of phosphates successively going
into solution.   This conclusion is strengthened when the
total amount of phosphoric acid dissolved in five extractions is compared with the amount known to have been
applied to the land during the period the plots have
been under experiment, after deduction has been made
of that which is also known to have been removed in the
crop.

PHOSPHORIC ACID IN ROTHAMSTED SOILS.

Field.	Plot.	Dissolved in Five Extractions.		Supplied in Manure.	Removed in Crop.	Surplus.
		Per cent.	Lbs. per acre.			
Broadbalk	3	0·0226	565	0	550	− 550
,,	5	0·1201	3000	3960	790	3170
,,	7	0·0987	2470	3810	1370	2440
,,	8	0·0823	2055	3810	1520*	2290
,.	2	0·0825	2060	4780	1650	3130
Hoos	1AA	0·0159	400	0	555	− 555
,,	2AA	0·0926	2315	3390	1200	2190
,,	4AA	0·0799	2000	3390	1240	2150

* Approximate estimate, since the crop has rarely been analysed.

It will be seen from the above table that the amount
of phosphoric acid dissolved by the five extractions
agrees closely with the surplus left by the manuring in
all the cases where the phosphoric acid has been put on
as soluble mineral superphosphate.   This is not the case,
however, for the plot manured with dung, which contains
a considerable proportion of difficultly soluble phosphate.
   It should not be supposed that the whole of the
so-called "available" phosphoric acid or potash will be

removed by the crop; even the minimum of 0·01 per cent., soluble in citric acid, which has been suggested, as marking the limit of fertility, means about 250 lbs. per acre in the surface layer 9 inches deep: and few crops will take away as much as 50 lbs. per acre of phosphoric acid or 150 lbs. per acre of potash. No crop searches the soil so thoroughly for food as does the solvent acid : if we assume that the roots themselves by their excretion of carbon dioxide effect some of the solution, it is obvious that they come in contact with but a small proportion of the soil particles ; nor can the soil water, limited in amount and moving slowly, attack the soil with the vigour displayed by an acid which is continuously shaken with a comparatively small proportion of soil.   Even in the case of material so essentially "available" as a manure soluble in water, the whole of the manure applied is never recovered in the crop; *e.g.*, in the experiments with wheat at Rothamsted, only 73 per cent., and with mangolds 78 per cent., of the nitrogen supplied as nitrate of soda has been recovered in the crop, though there was an abundant supply of the other manurial constituents.   In the same way, on the plot with an excess of nitrogen there was recovered only 36 per cent. of the phosphoric acid supplied as super-phosphate, and 50 per cent. of potash supplied as sulphate of potash.

In other words, the "available" plant food in the soil represents not that which the succeeding crop will remove, but that which it can draw upon : how much it will acquire will depend on a variety of factors, such as the nature of the plant, the texture of the soil, the supply of water, and other necessaries of nutrition.

No method akin to solution in dilute citric acid has yet been devised for determining what proportion of the nitrogen reserves in the soil is likely to be avail-

able.   The conversion of the nitrogenous matter of
the soil into soluble nitrates, in which form nitrogen
enters the plant, is a biological process which is influ-
enced by a number of conditions, such as temperature,
degree of moisture and aeration of the soil, the mechanical treatment it receives, all impossible to predict.

Some idea of the condition of the organic matter
and the readiness with which it is likely to change, may
be obtained by a determination of the humus soluble in
dilute ammonia and the percentage of nitrogen in this
humus, or again by a study of the ratio of carbon to
nitrogen in the organic matter as previously indicated
(p. 46).   In order to determine the soluble humus, 20
grams of the soil are digested with enough 1 per cent.
hydrochloric acid to dissolve all the calcium carbonate,
thrown upon a filter, washed with a little more of the
hydrochloric acid and then with water until neutral.
The soil is then washed off the filter into a bottle with a
4 per cent. solution of ammonia and shaken for twenty-
four hours, after which the bottle is left to stand until
the bulk of the inorganic matter of the soil has settled.
150 c.c. are pipetted off and evaporated to dryness over
the water-bath, weighed and ignited, a deduction being
made of the inorganic matter remaining after ignition.

To determine the nitrogen content of the humus a
second 150 c.c. are placed in a Kjeldahl flask.   Two or
three grams of magnesia are added and the whole
evaporated to dryness to get rid of the ammonia in the
solution, after which the contents of the flask are
digested with sulphuric acid in the usual manner.

Valuable as these determinations may become in
judging a soil, a sufficient body of data do not as yet
exist to enable them to be interpreted with precision.

In the analysis of a soil, without doubt the most
important figure is the proportion of calcium carbonate,

for on that must be based the decision not only of whether liming is necessary, but what class of artificial manures should be employed. Where the calcium carbonate is scanty, manures like superphosphate and sulphate of ammonia should never be employed, but basic slag or some neutral phosphate on the one hand, and nitrate of soda as a source of rapidly acting nitrogen on the other. The texture of the soil, the rapidity with which decay and nitrification of organic matter take place, freedom from fungoid diseases, all depend on an adequate proportion of calcium carbonate in the soil, say from half to one per cent.; so that of all the determinations this is the most important.

The determinations of the loss on ignition, the nitrogen, and possibly the humus, give the analyst an idea of the reserves of organic matter in the soil; judged in conjunction with the mechanical analysis and the proportion of calcium carbonate, an opinion can be formed as to the condition of the soil and how far these reserves are likely to be brought into play by cultivation. An opinion may, again, be formed as to the need for organic manures to increase the humus content of the soil, or whether fertility is likely to be maintained with purely mineral manures.

A consideration of the available phosphoric acid and potash will give the analyst an idea of the immediate need or otherwise of mineral manuring; the proportions these bear to the "total" phosphoric acid and potash give him grounds for deciding whether the lack is only temporary or real. In the former case measures may be taken to liberate some of the reserves, as by the judicious use of lime or of organic manures which will generate carbonic and other acids within the soil.

Such further questions as the presence of harmful substances, or even of an excess of more normal constituents of the soil, must be considered by the analyst, but will be dealt with in a later section.

In some cases it will be possible by a chemical analysis to pronounce a given soil to be unsuited to a particular crop: as a rule, however, it is not its chemical composition which fits the land for a particular crop, but its mechanical texture, water-bearing power, drainage, etc. In most cases the soil can be adjusted to the crop by manure, though the process may be unsound from an economic standpoint, but no expenditure can ever rectify unsatisfactory texture, *e.g.*, convert a light sand into good wheat land.

Even in considering the chemical analysis of a soil, no hard-and-fast rules can be laid down, the judgment and experience of the analyst must come into play in deciding how far the deficiency or excess of one constituent is likely to affect the action of some of the others: and again, how far the texture, the aspect, and other factors that can only be ascertained *in situ*, will exercise an influence upon the enormous reserves of plant food contained in every soil.

CHAPTER VII

THE LIVING ORGANISMS OF THE SOIL

Decay and Humification of Organic Matter in the Soil—Alinit—
The Fixation or Free Nitrogen by Bacteria living in Symbiosis with Leguminous Plants—Soil Inoculation with Nodule
Organisms—Fixation of Nitrogen by Bacteria living free in the
Soil — Nitrification — Denitrification —Iron Bacteria — Fungi
of Importance in the Soil : Mycorhiza, and the Slime Fungus
of "Finger-and-Toe."

THE soil is the seat of a number of slow chemical
changes affecting the organic material it receives:
residues of an animal or vegetable nature, when applied
to the soil, are converted into the dark-coloured complex
known as "humus," which becomes eventually oxidised
to carbonic acid, water, nitric acid, and other simple
substances serving as food for plants. These changes,
at one time regarded as purely chemical, are now
recognised as dependent upon the vital processes
of certain minute organisms, universally distributed
throughout cultivated soil, and subject to the same
laws of nutrition, multiplication, life and death, as
hold for the higher organisms with which we are more
generally familiar.

The microscopic flora of the soil, roughly classed
as fungi and bacteria, is vast, and has been very inadequately explored as yet: certain types of change

in the soil materials have, however, been associated with particular organisms or groups of organisms, and many of these changes are of fundamental importance in the ordinary nutrition of plants. The organisms in the soil which so far have received the chief attention are those concerned with the supply of nitrogen to the plant. Certain organic compounds of nitrogen, chiefly of a protein nature, become gradually broken down by the action of soil bacteria into simpler compounds, *e.g.*, into amino-acids, and then into ammonia, which latter substance is seized upon by other organisms and oxidised successively to nitrous and nitric acid. As nitric acid is almost the only form in which the higher plants obtain the nitrogen they require, the fertility of the soil is wholly bound up in the maintenance of this cycle of change. Under certain conditions the work of other organisms intervenes, and the nitrogen compounds, instead of becoming nitric acid, are converted into free nitrogen gas, and are lost to the soil. *Per contra*, another group of organisms possesses the power of "fixing" free nitrogen, *i.e.*, of taking the gaseous element nitrogen and combining it with carbon, hydrogen, oxygen, etc., into forms available for the higher plants. Such organisms sometimes act when living in "symbiosis" with plants possessing green carbon-assimilating tissue: the two form a kind of association for mutual support, the bacteria deriving the carbohydrate which they must consume from the higher plant supplied by them with combined nitrogen.

Other symbiotic processes have been traced in the soil, and may yet be made to play an important part in the nutrition of field crops. Indeed, a number of tentative trials have already been made with the view of increasing the productiveness of the soil by introducing either useful organisms that were wanting, or

no. of bacteria
kept down by protozoa

improved types to replace already existing kinds of less effective character.

The Changes of Organic Matter in the Soil.

The surface layer of soil is constantly receiving additions of organic matter, either leaves and other débris of vegetation covering the ground, together with the droppings of animals consuming that vegetation, or dung and other animal and vegetable residues which are supplied as manures to cultivated land. These materials rapidly change in ordinary soil, losing almost immediately any structure they possess, becoming dark-coloured humic bodies, or even burning away as thoroughly as if placed in a furnace. That these changes are due to micro-organisms is seen by their immediate cessation if the soil be treated with antiseptics like chloroform or mercuric chloride: or if the mixture of soil and organic matter be sterilised by heating. Attempts have been made to estimate the number of bacteria contained in the soil: the prodigious numbers obtained, 2 up to 50 millions or more per cubic centimetre of the upper soil, show little beyond the fact that the soil is tenanted much as any other decaying organic material would be. The soil bacteria are always associated with a certain number of fungi and yeasts, especially when the reaction of the medium is at all acid: the organisms are most numerous in the surface layer, though they are still to be found in the deepest subsoils. Below a certain depth they must disappear, because deep well water often comes to the surface in an absolutely sterile condition. The changes which organic materials undergo in the soil may be roughly grouped into two classes; according as there is free access of oxygen or not, either decay (eremacausis) with eventual resolution into the simplest inorganic oxidised compounds, or "humification" will set in. These changes can be best indicated by the fate of a dead branch when it falls either upon the ground, or into a pond or swamp where it becomes buried in the mud at the bottom.   In the latter case the fermentation changes cause the wood to darken even to blackness; gases like carbonic acid and marsh gas are split off, so that the material becomes proportionally richer in carbon and poorer in oxygen.   Eventually, however, the process slackens, the losses practically cease, and a large proportion of the original material persists.   On the other hand, the branch exposed to the air, without darkening very much, becomes slowly resolved by the action of fungi and bacteria into carbonic acid and water, ammonia, nitrogen gas, and mineral salts, with much the same final result as though it had been placed in a furnace.   In soil, both these types of change may go on, and the conditions of the soil as regards aeration, drainage, temperature, and cultivation, determine which will predominate.

Practically, the whole group of aerobic bacteria, *i.e.*, those which require free oxygen for their development, and fungi are capable of bringing about the oxidation changes which result in the production of carbonic acid, the combustion of some carbohydrate being essentially the means by which they derive their energy.   As an intermediate step between the carbohydrate and the carbonic acid, a certain amount of humus is produced—"mould," or the "mild humus" of the German writers.   Examples of this material can be seen in the leaf-mould collected by gardeners from woods, or the fine, brown powder which can be scraped out of the inside of a hollow tree, particularly of a willow; this mould differs from the peaty humus,

to be described later, in its neutral reaction and in
the readiness with which it can be further oxidised.
Neutral in its reaction, it yields but little soluble
"humic acid" to the attack of an alkali.

Besides carbohydrates, most aerobic bacteria require
some carbon compound of nitrogen, and will begin to
break down protein and other nitrogen-containing
materials. The products of their attack are successively peptones, bodies like leucin and tyrosin, eventually ammonia, and probably free nitrogen, but the
ultimate production of ammonia is perhaps the most
characteristic feature of the aerobic fermentation of
protein bodies. Other amides are also resolved into
ammonia, of which a characteristic example is afforded
by the change of urea into ammonium carbonate.
This process [which is one of hydrolysis, not of oxidation, being represented in the gross by the equation
$CO(NH_2)_2 + 2H_2O = (NH_4)_2CO_3$] is brought about by
more than one organism, universally distributed and
abundant in such places as stables and cattle stalls.
In warm weather the conversion of the urea of the
urine into ammonium carbonate is very rapid, and as
the resulting product dissociates into gaseous ammonia
and carbonic acid, to this cause is due the smell of
ammonia which is always to be noticed in such places.
These changes to ammonia are the necessary prelim-
inaries to the final oxidation process or nitrification,
which, as the means by which the higher plants receive
their supplies of nitrogen, will be discussed separately.
The various oxidation processes in the soil are, like
all other bacterial actions, promoted by a certain
warmth, the optimum temperature being about 25°-30°,
by a sufficiency of moisture, and by the presence of
mineral food, like phosphates and potash salts. In
any great quantity, however, salts are harmful,

particularly sodium chloride; an acid reaction also diminishes considerably the rate of decay. Speaking generally, bacteria do not thrive as soon as the medium passes the neutral point, and all the decay processes must be carried out by the development of fungi when the medium is acid. The presence of chalk, or any form of carbonate of lime, by neutralising any acids as fast as they are formed, promotes the destruction of organic matter. Wollny has also shown that calcium humate will oxidise much more rapidly than uncombined humic acid placed under similar conditions. To the absence of carbonate of lime and mineral salts generally, may be ascribed the tendency of humus to accumulate and persist on the very light, sandy heaths, where the soil is dry and hot in summer, and also well aerated. It has already been indicated, in treating of humus, that the various organic compounds of nitrogen show very different susceptibility to the breaking-down process which eventually renders the nitrogen available for the crop— amongst the most resistent substances being the nucleo-proteins in the undigested portions of food which form dung, and the humus residues from poor, cropped-out land. As in all cases much of the nitrogen of both soil and manure seems to pass into obstinately persistent compounds yielding slowly, if at all, to oxidation, and hence wasted to the farmer, an attempt has been made to increase the preliminary breaking down of nitrogen compounds in the soil by the introduction of certain very active bacteria. Stoklasa has shown that various organisms—*B. megatherium, B. fluorescens*, etc.—when seeded into soil manured with bone-meal or similar materials, increase both the nitrogen and the phosphoric acid obtained by the plant. A pure cultivation of some such organism, *B. Ellenbachensis*, was for a time sold

commercially under the name of *alinit*, and though
the power of fixing nitrogen was claimed for it, its
chief action was probably such as was described above. It
has been found to cause increased crop returns on peaty
or other soils rich in humus, or where slow-acting
nitrogenous manures have been applied.

The fermentation which goes on in absence of
oxygen, is brought about by a large number of bacteria,
some of which are only active in the absence of oxygen,
others are aerobic, but will continue their work when
deprived of free oxygen. Carbohydrates are decomposed
with formation of carbonic acid and other gases like
hydrogen and marsh gas, butyric and other fatty acids,
a residue of humus being always produced at the same
time. The protein bodies readily undergo putrefactive
change, with the production of tyrosin and various
amino-acids, fatty acids, ammonia, phenol, and other
bodies containing an aromatic nucleus, gaseous compounds of sulphur, etc. In the main, however, the
changes of organic material in the soil fall upon the
cellulose; it loses carbonic acid, marsh gas, hydrogen,
etc., and becomes humus with a gradually increasing
proportion of carbon; the nitrogenous materials resist
attack more than the carbohydrates, and hence tend to
accumulate, so that an old sample of deep-seated peat
is richer in nitrogen than a more recent sample taken
from nearer the surface. Finally the humus thus produced, which may be called peat, is essentially an acid
product, and even when aerated and supplied with
mineral materials will oxidise with extreme slowness.

The Fixation of Free Nitrogen.

In the earliest theories regarding the nutrition of the
plant which were accepted after chemistry had become
an exact science, it was considered that the plant

derived its nitrogen from the humus of the soil, as, for example, in de Saussure's statement that "Plants receive their nitrogen almost entirely by the absorption of the soluble organic substances." This view was displaced by the so-called "mineral theory" of Liebig, who, in laying down the broad principle that the plant only derived certain necessary mineral constituents, its "ash," from the soil, and the whole of its carbon compounds from the atmosphere, was led to regard the nitrogen as well as the other combustible matters of the plant as due to the atmosphere, largely because of the exaggerated estimate which then prevailed as to the amount of ammonia from the air that was brought down in the rain. Boussingault had already shown, by weighing and analysing the crops on his own farm for six separate courses of rotation, that from one-third to one-half more nitrogen was removed in the produce than was supplied in the manure. The gain of nitrogen was little or nothing when cereal crops only were grown, but became large when leguminous crops were introduced into the rotation. Liebig, however, considered that cereals, as well as the other plants, were able to draw their ammonia from the atmosphere, and that, provided sufficient mineral plant food were forthcoming, there was no need of ammonia compounds in the manure.

This view of Liebig's, though modified later, when he admitted that cereals must obtain their nitrogen from a manurial source in the soil, led to considerable investigation of the source of the nitrogen in the plant. Boussingault himself carried out a long series of laboratory experiments, in which weighed seeds containing a known proportion of nitrogen were grown in artificial soils containing no nitrogen, but supplied with the ash constituents of the plant. Care was

taken to remove all ammonia from the air in which
the plants were grown, and from the water and
carbonic acid supplied to them ; finally, after growth
had ceased, the amount of nitrogen in the plant and
in the soil was determined. In some cases a known
quantity of nitrogenous compounds was supplied as
manure ; but all the results went to show that there
was no gain of combined nitrogen during growth ; the
seed and manure at starting contained as much nitrogen
as was found in the plant and soil at the end.

Similar experiments were carried out with the
utmost precautions by the Rothamsted investigators,
who likewise found no gain of nitrogen by the plant
from the atmosphere. The following results, obtained
by Lawes and Gilbert in 1858, will serve to show
the agreement between the nitrogen supplied and
recovered :—

	Nitrogen in Seed (Grams).	Nitrogen in Soil and Plants.	Gain or Loss.	Nitrogen in Seed and Manure.	Nitrogen in Soil and Plants.	Gain or Loss.
Wheat .	0·0078	0·0081	+ 0·0003	0·0548	0·0536	− 0·0012
Barley .	0·0057	0·0058	+ 0·0001	0·0496	0·0464	− 0·0032
Oats . .	0·0063	0·0056	− 0·0007	0·0312	0·0216	− 0·0096
Beans .	0·0750	0·0757	+ 0·0007	0·0711	0·0655	− 0·0056
Peas . .	0·0188	0·0167	− 0·0021	0·0227	0·0211	− 0·0016
Clover .	...	...	...	0·0712	0·0665	− 0·0047
Buckwheat	0·0200	0·0182	− 0·0018	0·0308	0·0292	− 0·0016

It has sometimes been objected that the plants in
these experiments made such a poor growth as compared
with their normal development in the open air that they
never attained their usual power of fixing nitrogen.
However, Hellriegel's experiments on plants which
were supplied with limited amounts of nitrogen showed
that growth is practically proportional to the supply of

nitrogen as long as that is below the maximum required by the plant. Field experiments at Rothamsted with leafy crops like mangolds, to which a very small amount of nitrogen was supplied in order to give them a start, showed that the increase thus produced was only proportional to the nitrogen supplied, so that there is no evidence that even a plant which has begun to grow vigorously can then continue its development by taking nitrogen from the atmosphere.

From all these experiments the conclusion was drawn that cultivated plants are unable to "fix" atmospheric nitrogen, but obtain this indispensable element in a combined state from the soil together with the ash constituents; and such was the opinion that prevailed for something like thirty years.

Notwithstanding the conclusive nature of all the laboratory experiments, there was still a residuum of facts obtained under field conditions which were inexplicable on the theory of the non-fixation of nitrogen, and these facts were chiefly connected with the growth of leguminous crops.

Boussingault's crop statistics have already been referred to; the following table gives a short summary of the kind of results he obtained :—

Rotation.	NITROGEN. Kilos per hectare.	
	Supplied in Manure.	Removed in Crop.
Wheat, Wheat, Fallow	87·2	82·8
Potatoes, Wheat, Clover, Wheat or Turnips, Oats	202·2	268·5
Potatoes, Wheat, Clover, Wheat . . .	182	339
Lucerne, 5 years	...	1035

The amount of nitrogen removed was equal to

that supplied only when wheat was grown, but became progressively greater the more frequently leguminous crops occupied the ground.

At Rothamsted the following average quantities of nitrogen were removed per acre per annum in the crop, when mineral manures only were applied :—

Wheat (24 years)	22·1
Barley (24 years)	22·4
Roots (30 years)	16·4
Beans (24 years, only 21 years in Beans)	45·5
Red Clover (22 years, only 6 years Clover)	39·8

In this case also the amount of nitrogen in the produce was much increased when a leguminous crop was grown.

Another of the Rothamsted experiments showed still more strikingly the accumulation of nitrogen by a leguminous crop. A piece of land which had been cropped for five years by cereals, without any nitrogenous manure, was divided into two portions in 1872, one being sown with barley alone, and the other with clover in the barley. In 1873 barley was again grown on the one portion, but the clover on the other, three cuttings of clover being obtained. Finally, in 1874, barley was grown on both portions. The quantities of nitrogen removed in the crops of 1873 and 1874 are shown in the table.

NITROGEN IN CROP—LBS. PER ACRE.

1873	Barley	37·3	1874	Barley	39·1
1873	Clover	151·3	1874	Barley	69·4

Thus, the barley which followed clover obtained 30·3 lbs. more nitrogen than the barley following barley though the previous clover crop had removed 114 lbs. more nitrogen than the first barley crop. An analysis of the soil was made in 1873, after the clover and barley had been removed; this showed down to the depth of 9 inches an excess of nitrogen in the clover land, despite the larger amount which had been removed in the crop.

In Soil after Barley	.	0·1416 per cent. Nitrogen.
In Soil after Clover	.	0·1566 „ „

In another experiment, land which had previously grown beans and then been fallow for five years, was sown with barley and clover in 1883, the clover being allowed to stand in 1884 and 1885. At starting the soil was analysed; the surface 9 inches contained on an average 2657 lbs. per acre of nitrogen, while of nitrogen as nitric acid the soil only contained 24·7 lbs. per acre down to a depth of 6 feet. As a result of the three years cropping with barley and clover, and then with clover only, an average amount of 319·5 lbs. of nitrogen was removed, yet the soil contained, on analysis at the end of the experiment, 2832 lbs. of nitrogen per acre in the top 9 inches, or a gain of 175 lbs. per acre in the three years, making a total, with the crop removed, of nearly 500 lbs. of nitrogen per acre to be accounted for.

The consideration of field trials of this description led many observers to think that there still might be some fixation of free nitrogen, particularly by leguminous plants. Voelcker, in England, when discussing the power of a clover crop to accumulate nitrogen, expressed the opinion that the atmosphere furnishes nitrogenous food to that plant; in France, it was maintained by Ville; Berthelot also brought evidence to show that the soil itself, by the aid of its microscopic vegetation, assimilated some free nitrogen. Even in the laboratory experiments, some of Boussingault's results, and others of Atwater, in America, showed a

gain of nitrogen.   But the clearing up of the whole
subject came with the publication, in 1886, of the
researches of Hellreigel and Wilfarth.   These investigators found that when plants were grown in sand
and fed with nutrient solutions, the Gramineæ, the
Cruciferæ, the Chenopodiaceæ, the Polygonaceæ, grew
almost proportionally to the amount of combined
nitrogen supplied; and, if this were absent, nitrogen
starvation set in as soon as the nitrogen of the seed
was exhausted.   With the Leguminosæ, however, a
plant was observed sometimes to recover from the
stage of nitrogen starvation, and begin a luxurious
growth which lasted until maturity, though no combined nitrogen was supplied.   In such cases the root
of the plant was always found to be set with the little
nodules characteristic of the roots of leguminous plants
when growing under natural conditions.   Further experiments were made in which the plants were grown in
sterile sand, but as soon as the stage of nitrogen hunger
was reached, a small portion of a watery extract of
ordinary cultivated soil was added; whereupon, the
plants receiving the extract recovered from their nitrogen
starvation and grew to maturity, assimilating considerable quantities of nitrogen.   The renewed growth and
the assimilation of nitrogen were always found to be
attendant upon the production of nodules on the roots.
The nodules were found to be full of bacteria, to which
the name of *Pseudomonas radicicola* has been given.
They could only be produced by previous infection either
by an extract of the crushed nodules or of a cultivated
soil; in some cases (lupins, serradella) only by soil which
had previously carried the same crop.

These results, though not at first accepted by Lawes
and Gilbert, led to a repetition of the experiments,
which brought out the fact that in their earlier

trials with leguminous plants the necessary inoculation had always been wanting because of the great care that had been taken to prevent the entry of any accidental impurity. Eventually, both at Rothamsted and by other investigators, the conclusions of Hellreigel and Wilfarth were confirmed, that when leguminous plants are grown under sterile conditions, without a supply of combined nitrogen there is very limited growth, no formation of nodules, and no gain of nitrogen. But when the culture is seeded with soil extract there is luxuriant growth, abundant nodule formation, and coincidently, great gain of nitrogen, many times as much in the products of growth as in the seed sown. Gilbert also showed that there is a gradual accumulation and then withdrawal of nitrogen from the nodules. Lastly, Schloesing *fils* and Laurent, by growing Leguminosæ in closed vessels, and analysing the air before and after growth, found an actual disappearance of nitrogen gas, agreeing with the amount gained by the plant during growth. Thus, a conclusion was reached that the leguminous plants can assimilate and fix the free nitrogen of the atmosphere by the aid of bacteria living symbiotically in the root nodules,—a conclusion which served to explain, not only the discrepancies in the previous experiments, but the long-accumulated experience of farmers that crops like clover and lucerne enrich the soil, and form the best preparation for cereals like wheat, which are particularly dependent on an external supply of nitrogen. The mechanism of the fixation of free nitrogen is still incompletely understood. It has been found possible to grow these bacteria apart from the leguminous plants, if they are cultivated on a medium containing only a trace of nitrogen but supplied with the ash constituents of the plant and also with some carbohydrate like dextrose or maltose. The quantities of nitrogen fixed in this way are always, however, very much smaller than are fixed by a leguminous plant on whose root the nodules are well developed. To fix the nitrogen, some expenditure of energy is required, and this is derived from the combustion of carbohydrate supplied to the bacteria by the higher plant; indeed it has been observed that the nitrogen fixation and general growth of the Leguminosæ is stimulated by a supply of sugar or other carbohydrate to the soil. The organism, *Pseudomonas radicicola*, appears to be capable of considerable modifications; in the nodules it forms rather large rod or Y-shaped organisms, but if an active subculture be obtained by inoculation from a nodule into a non-nitrogenous medium as described above, excessively minute rod-shaped organisms appear, generally in rapid motion. It is in this minute unspecialised form that they exist free in the soil, and it has been shown that they infect the leguminous host by getting through the thin walls of the root hairs. The characteristic Y forms have also been obtained in artificial cultivations by introducing certain substances into the medium. Much investigation has also been applied to the question of whether there is only one kind of bacterium living in symbiosis with all the Leguminosæ, or whether there is not a definite race appropriate to each species of leguminous plant, with which it alone can bring about nitrogen fixation to the full extent. The earliest investigations had already shown that lupins and serradella did not develop nodules when infected with an ordinary garden soil, but only when an extract was added from a sandy soil on which these plants had been previously grown; and Nobbe brought further evidence to show that, though there is very widely distri-buted in the soil an organism which will cause some nodule formation and fixation of nitrogen, yet it becomes so modified by growing in symbiosis with the different leguminous plants, that the best results are only obtained when each species is directly infected from nodules taken from the same kind of plant.

Accordingly, he proceeded to the introduction, on a commercial scale, of pure cultivations on a gelatine medium of the races of bacteria appropriate to each of the leguminous plants grown as field crops. The jelly, which was called "Nitragin," was to be dissolved in a large bulk of water and sprinkled over the seed before sowing; thus ensuring inoculation with the appropriate organism, which might not happen to be present in the soil. Nitragin failed to fulfil the expectations which were formed at its introduction, partly because of the nitrogenous character of the medium, in consequence of which the organisms possessed very little vitality or power of fixing nitrogen. Since that time, however, several other methods of cultivating the organism for inoculation purposes have been introduced, either by growing it on an agar jelly, which contains practically no nitrogen (Hiltner), by drying up cotton wool which has been soaked in an active liquid culture (Moore), or by drying soil which has been treated in the same way. The culture thus obtained is added to a large bulk of water, containing a little separated milk to protect the organisms from substances excreted during germination, and the seed is dipped into it and allowed to dry before sowing. The culture may also be sprayed over the ground or absorbed by a large quantity of earth which is afterwards sown. The results of such inoculation are very conflicting; where the land has been regularly under cultivation and has carried the leguminous crop in question many times previously, nodules are practically always formed whether the seed be inoculated or not. In such cases inoculation can only be beneficial if the bacteria introduced either belong to a more vigorous race of nitrogen fixers than those normally present in the soil or are more specifically adapted to that particular crop. It has not as yet been conclusively demonstrated that such improved races can be cultivated in the laboratory, or that they can maintain themselves in the soil in competition with the kindred organisms already present. It should, moreover, be borne in mind that even if such improved races of the nodule-forming organism can be introduced to the plant, the improvement they can produce in the yield is likely to be something of the order of a ten per cent. increase, a gain which is only really perceptible after careful and continued field experiments, and one not to be detected by the ordinary farmer's eye. Of a very different order are the results attained by inoculation when the land contains none of the appropriate organisms; inoculation will then change a stunted, sickly looking growth into a profitable crop. It is only in special cases that land devoid of the nodule organisms is to be met with, most commonly when land is being brought under cultivation for the first time, as in breaking up a virgin soil or in reclaiming heath and bog land. Such peaty and heathy soils, which are devoid of carbonate of lime, rarely carry any leguminous plants the nodules of which could supply the necessary bacteria to farm crops like clover and lucerne; when such land has been reclaimed and limed an inoculation is advisable before sowing a leguminous crop.

Similarly when the cultivation of such leguminous crops as lucerne or even sainfoin is being extended into districts where they have not been grown previously, an inoculation is often necessary before the roots will nodulate freely and the plant make its proper growth. Lucerne

grown for the first time on heavy land in a new district
has been observed to fail completely, the failure being
attended by a complete absence of nodules from the roots.

Inoculation with soil from a field which has previously grown the crop about to be sown has often
proved a signal success in reclaiming the poor heath
lands of East Prussia, by the system of green manuring
worked out by Dr Schultz at Lupitz. Very large
areas of barren sandy heath land have been reclaimed and rendered fit for the cultivation of the
ordinary crop by a system of growing lupins and
ploughing in the green crop. Mineral manures alone
are employed, latterly basic slag and the Stassfurt
potash salts; the lupins accumulate nitrogen from
the atmosphere, thus gradually there is built up both
humus to bind together the loose sand and make it
retentive of moisture, and also a store of nitrogen for
the nutrition of succeeding crops. The soil of a field
growing lupins every year from 1865 was found in
1880 to contain 0·087 per cent. of nitrogen in the
surface 8 inches, as compared with 0·027 per cent.
in an adjoining pasture. By 1891 the proportion of
nitrogen had increased to 0·177 per cent., despite the
annual removal of the lupin crop and the fact that
the manuring had been with phosphates and potash
only. It is in reclaiming these heath lands which
have not previously been under cultivation, nor, in
many cases, carried any leguminous vegetation whatever, that soil inoculation from land previously cultivated
has given successful results. Dr Salfeld of Hanover has
recorded several cases of the successful cultivation on a
large scale of various leguminous plants, beans, clover,
serradella, lupins, only after previous inoculation with
soil. The experiments were made on both peaty (moor)
and sandy soils, on which, without inoculation, legumin-

ous plants made but little growth and developed no
nodules.   Success followed when about 8 cwt. per acre of
soil from a field which had previously carried the crop in
question were sown broadcast over the land in April,
and harrowed in just before seeding.   In one case, over
7 tons per acre of green serradella were grown where
the land had been treated with 8 cwt. of soil from an
old serradella field, whereas the crop failed after germination where no inoculation had been practised.

Fixation of Free Nitrogen by the Soil.

As already indicated, Berthelot attributed to the
soil itself the power of fixing a small quantity of atmospheric nitrogen, a power which was lost when the soil
was sterilised and maintained under conditions preventing infection.   This gain of nitrogen was independent
of the small amount of ammonia absorbed by soil from
ordinary air, which always contains a trace of ammonia ;
and at first it was attributed to the microscopic green
algæ which clothe the surface of ordinary moist soil.
The experiments of Kossowitsch, and of Krüger and
Schneidewind, have, however, shown that the growth of
pure cultures of these algæ is dependent on a supply
of combined nitrogen, and that no fixation of free
nitrogen takes place whether the algæ growth be small
or large.   It is possible, however, that they may live
in symbiosis with nitrogen-fixing bacteria and supply
the carbohydrate, by the combustion of which the
energy needed for the fixation of nitrogen by the bacteria
is obtained.   More recently, however, several organisms
have been isolated from the soil which are capable when
growing in a free state of fixing nitrogen drawn from the
atmosphere, and it is to these that the gains of nitrogen
observed by Berthelot must be attributed.   Winogradsky
was the first to isolate an organism of this type, which,

when grown under anaerobic conditions and supplied
with soluble carbohydrate, breaks the latter down with
the formation of butyric and other acids, and at the same
time draws some of the gaseous nitrogen present into combination. This particular organism *Clostridium Pastori-
anum* is very widely diffused and can readily be isolated
from pond mud and similar material, where organic matter
is decaying under comparatively anaerobic conditions.
The extent of the nitrogen fixation is, however, small;
in the laboratory not more than 2 to 3 mg. of nitrogen
are brought into combination for each gram of carbohydrate oxidised. By far the most effective of the
nitrogen-fixing bacteria that are free in the soil is a large
organism, named by its discoverer, Beijerinck, *Azotobacter
chroococcum*. It may be easily isolated from most soils
by adding a small portion of soil to 50 c.c. of a culture
medium containing per litre 10 grams of mannite or
glucose, 0·2 gram each of potassium phosphate, magnesium sulphate, and sodium chloride, and 0·1 gram of
calcium sulphate, half a gram of calcium carbonate being
also added to each flask. The solution and its flask
and plug of cotton wool are previously sterilised by heat.
After inoculation, the flask is placed in an incubator,
and after a week's time a considerable fermentation will
be observed to have taken place, attended by the
evolution of gas and the formation of a brown scum upon
the surface. By making a subculture in a similar
medium, inoculated with a trace of the brown scum, a
fairly pure growth of the *Azotobacter* can be obtained
for examination, or the amount of nitrogen fixed may
be determined by Kjeldahling the contents of the
flask.

Azotobacter chroococcum is a large oval organism, 4 to
5 μ in length and 3 μ in width, which differs from most
bacteria in containing glycogen, so that it stains a deep

brown colour with a solution of iodine, a method which is convenient for the observation of the organism. It is aerobic, and is, in fact, a strong oxidising agent, the dextrose or other carbohydrate which it requires being converted by it into carbon dioxide and water, together with small quantities of lactic and acetic acids, alcohol, and sometimes butyric acid.

A very characteristic bye-product is the dark brown or black pigment from which the organism derives its specific name, a pigment which may play its part in the usual coloration of humus.

As a rule, about 9 or 10 mg. of nitrogen are fixed for each gram of carbohydrate oxidised, but the ratio obtained varies considerably under different conditions; cultures which have been repeatedly transferred, being, as a rule, less effective than the impure culture derived directly from the soil.

Azotobacter chroococcum and its kindred forms are widely distributed in soils from all parts of the world; it has been found in most cultivated soils, and the author has observed it in virgin soils from East Africa, India, New Zealand, Egypt, Russia, Monte Video, Ohio, and Sarawak.

It is, however, not to be discovered in acid soils; the presence of calcium carbonate appears to be essential to its development. Certain minor differences are to be seen in the *Azotobacter* organisms present in the soil from different parts of the world. From tropical and semi-tropical soils in East Africa, for example, a form has been isolated which is a very effective fixer of nitrogen, but which differs from the normal in not giving rise to the brown pigment; another form, again, from Monte Video gives rise to a green fluorescence in the culture medium.

The amount of nitrogen fixed by *Azotobacter* may

easily be rendered evident by an increased yield of crop. Koch treated soil in pots with large quantities of sugar, 2 per cent., 4 per cent., and even more of dextrose, and then sowed oats, buckwheat, etc. At first the sugar was injurious, and the first crop suffered in consequence; but the proportion of nitrogen in the soil increased, and the second and third crops were far greater than those in the check plots of untreated soil. When the soil, after the application of the sugar, was placed in an incubator for a month, in order to complete the oxidation of the sugar, the increased yield due to nitrogen fixation was also seen in the first crop.

To the *Azotobacter* and kindred organisms must certainly be ascribed a large part in preparing and maintaining the world's stock of combined nitrogen. It is customary to regard such virgin soils as the black soils of the Russian Steppes, of Manitoba, and of the Argentina, as rich in nitrogen because of the accumulation of the vegetable débris of many epochs; but since plants other than the Leguminosæ do not fix nitrogen themselves, there could in this way be no addition to the original stock, which would only circulate from the soil to the plant and back to the soil again. Under such conditions, however, there is a continual addition to the soil of the carbon compounds which the plant derives from the atmosphere, and this is material which the *Azotobacter* can oxidise, and so derive the energy required for the fixation of nitrogen. It is the constant return to the soil of oxidisable organic matter which differentiates the wild from the cultivated land, and renders possible the long-continued storing up of nitrogen in the virgin soils.

Interesting evidence on this point may be derived from the Rothamsted experiments; on the Broadbalk wheatfield the unmanured plot has, during the fifty years 1844-93 yielded a crop containing on the average

17 lbs. of nitrogen per acre per annum. Analyses of the soil at the beginning and end of the period showed a decline in the amount of nitrogen equivalent to a removal of 12 lbs. per acre per annum, and the rainfall is known to bring down between 4 and 5 lbs. per acre per annum. The annual withdrawal in the crop would thus be closely balanced by the loss experienced by the soil and the additions, were there not other unknown withdrawals in the weeds which are removed from the plot, and in the nitrates which are washed down into the subsoil and the drains. Doubtless, neither of these two withdrawals are large, but because of their existence, un-balanced by any corresponding falling off in the nitrogen content of the soil, it must be concluded that even on the arable land some small restorative action is going on. A portion, however, of the same field has been covered with a wild vegetation of weeds and grasses for the last twenty-five years, and this is never cut or harvested, so that all the débris fall back on the land just as it would on a virgin soil. Analysis of samples of this soil taken in 1881, when it ceased to be under cultiva-tion, and in 1904, showed an annual accumulation of nitrogen of more than 100 lbs. per acre. The enormous difference in the fixation on this plot as compared with the unmanured plot carrying wheat, must be set down to the difference in the supply of non-nitrogenous carbon compounds to the two plots; in the one case the wheat is all removed except a small portion of root and stubble; in the other the whole of the vegetable growth falls back on the land. The wild vegetation on this plot did include a considerable proportion of leguminous plants, but a similar, though smaller accumulation of nitrogen was observed in another plot of land which had been allowed to run wild in the same manner, but which carried no leguminous vegetation in consequence of the small

amount of calcium carbonate in the soil.   These two plots present a very close parallel to the actions which must have been taking place in all virgin soils where the soil similarly contains the *Azotobacter* organism.   Doubtless also some of the value of laying down land to temporary pasture must be due to the accumulation of nitrogen by the same agency, because we know that land under grass accumulates carbon compounds from the roots and stubble that is not removed during grazing.

Nitrification.

It has long been known that when any organic compound of nitrogen is applied to the soil it becomes eventually oxidised to a nitrate, which is practically the only compound of nitrogen taken up by cultivated plants, the Leguminosæ excepted.   The potassium nitrate collected from Indian soils, the calcium nitrate made artifically in nitre beds in Europe, owe their origin to this oxidation of organic compounds of nitrogen.   That the process was a biological one was first indicated by Müller in 1873, but any widespead recognition of the fact did not take place before the work of Schloesing and Muntz in 1877.   These investigators showed that the formation of nitrates in the soil ceased at temperatures below 5° and above 55° C., that it could be stopped by chloroform vapour and similar antiseptics, and that the soil lost entirely its power of nitrification if it were heated to the temperature of boiling water.   The investigations of Warington confirmed these results, and brought to light the further fact that there were two stages in the oxidation process, one being the formation of a nitrite, followed by the conversion of this nitrite into the completely oxidised product.   It was found possible to obtain cultures which would only push the oxidation to the nitrite stage, thus indicating that there must be at least two organisms concerned in the complete nitrification process. The further study of the organisms was for a long time hindered by the fact that they could not be got to grow upon the gelatinous media employed in the ordinary methods of isolating specific bacteria; and though P. F. Frankland, by a dilution method, succeeded in isolating and describing a nitrifying bacterium, it was not until 1890 that Winogradsky cleared up the problem. He prepared a solid nutritive medium containing no organic matter but with silica in its gelatinous form as a basis, and thus was able to separate nitrifying bacteria from the large number of other species simultaneously present in the soil. Winogradsky was able to isolate two species of bacteria capable of transforming ammonia compounds into nitrites. One of these, termed *Nitrosomonas europœa*, was obtained from all the soils of the old world he examined; the other, ascribed to the genus *Nitrococcus*, was peculiar to the soils of America and Australia. The former occurs both as a single, free-swimming form, and clustered together in a colony or zooglœa state.

Finally, there appears to be one type of organism only, included in the genus *Nitrobacter*, which oxidises the nitrites to nitrates. Winogradsky and other observers have worked out the conditions of life of these nitrifying organisms—the limits of temperature for their growth, 5° and 55° C., have already been given, the optimum temperature is about 37° C. Their action is much restrained by the presence of organic matter, or any quantity of alkaline carbonates or chlorides; at the same time, some base * must be present to combine

* Instruction sur la fabrication du nitre :—Par *les régisseurs généraux des poudres et salt pêtres*, 1777, " Elles doivent l'être toujours avec une addition de terre calcaire qui puisse servir de base à l'acide nitreux."

with the nitrous or nitric acids produced, for nitrification ceases as soon as the medium becomes at all acid. While calcium carbonate is the substance which, as a rule, is effective to this end, many organic salts will also supply the necessary base. Ammonium salts of the strong acids will not nitrify directly in the absence of a base, and the function of the calcium or magnesium carbonate is usually added to form, by double decomposition, ammonium carbonate, which the nitrifying organisms can attack. The complex salts formed by the interaction of the zeolites of clay with ammonium salts can be nitrified directly, but not, however, the ammonium humate formed by the corresponding interaction of ammonium salts and humus. Humus itself does not inhibit nitrification, and, indeed, the organisms can be brought to tolerate considerable quantities of other organic matter, by transferring them into successively stronger solutions. The organisms are able to obtain the carbon necessary to their growth from carbonates in the culture medium or carbonic acid in the air; the energy necessary to decompose the carbon dioxide and fix the carbon is derived from the oxidation of the ammonia, about 35 parts of nitrogen being oxidised for each part of carbon that is fixed. The nitrifying organisms are chiefly confined to the cultivated surface layer of the soil. Warington found that, in the close-textured Rothamsted soil they were by no means uniformly distributed below the top 9 inches, and that they were never present, except accidentally, in the subsoil below a depth of 2 feet. It has also been shown that they are entirely absent from many heath and moor soils, even in the surface layer. They are abundantly found in the water of shallow wells and rivers.

Summing up the above facts, it is seen that for the

N

active production of nitrates from the organic compounds of nitrogen present in the soil—and this is necessary if the crop is to be kept supplied with the nitrogen required for its growth—the following conditions are requisite :—The presence of the nitrifying organisms in sufficient quantities, a certain degree of temperature, darkness, sufficient moisture for the development of the bacteria, free aeration of the soil to supply the oxygen necessary, and a base to neutralise the acids as they are produced.

The scanty number of nitrifying bacteria in any subsoil below the cultivated layer helps to explain both its sterile nature when brought to the surface, and the difficulty and length of time required to develop a state of fertility, especially when dealing with a clay soil in which percolation and aeration have been deficient.

The effect of a low temperature in checking the formation of nitrates is well seen in the way the growing corn turns yellow through nitrogen starvation whenever a cold and drying north-east wind chills the ground in spring : the bright green colour returns as soon as warmer and moister soil conditions restore the activity of the nitrifying bacteria in the surface layer. King found in the top foot of soil when oats were turning yellow only 0·026 parts of nitric nitrogen per million of dry soil, whereas in soil where the oats were green on the same date there was 0·255 parts of nitric nitrogen per million, itself a small amount. The greater warmth of a light soil also causes it to form nitrates quickly in the spring, and so assists in producing an early growth.

But in obtaining early crops, even when the land is rich, a dressing of ready-formed nitrate is often of the greatest assistance, for the development of very early crops may easily outstrip the rate at which the nitrates

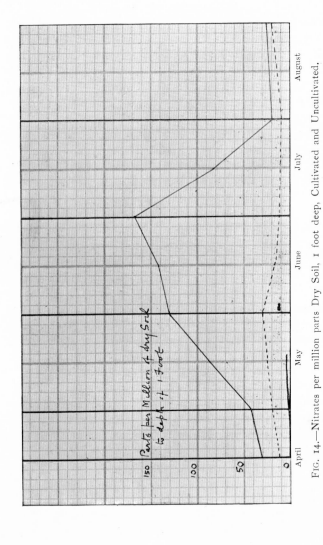

Parts per Million of dry Soil
to depth of 1 foot

Fig. 14.—Nitrates per million parts Dry Soil, 1 foot deep, Cultivated and Uncultivated.

they require can be formed in the still unwarmed soil.
Nitrates are much more freely formed in the summer
than in the winter, and as they are not retained by
the soil, they may easily be washed away when the
crop has been removed, unless weeds or a catch crop
sown to that end are present to take up the nitrates
and store them as organic compounds of nitrogen for
the future enrichment of the land.

The need for aeration in connection with the nitrifying process has already been alluded to when discussing
drainage: all processes of working and cultivating the
soil assist nitrification, both by the thorough aeration
they effect, and by the mere mechanical distribution
of the bacteria into new quarters, where there are fresh
food supplies. In some experiments of Dehérain's he
found that the drainage water from pots of cultivated
soil, which had been sent from a distance, and thus
much knocked about in travelling and filling into the
pot, contained as much as 466 to 664 parts of nitrogen
as nitric acid per million. The drainage water from the
Rothamsted wheat plots contains only from 10 to 20
parts per million; even the cement tanks at Grignon,
2 metres cube, into which the soil had been filled, gave
drainage water containing only 39 parts of nitric
nitrogen per million. In another experiment a quantity
of soil was thrown upon a floor, and worked about
daily for six weeks; on analysis it contained 0·051
per cent. of nitric nitrogen, as against ·002 per cent. of
nitric nitrogen in the same soil left *in situ.* The diagram
(Fig. 14), due to King, shows the dependence of nitrate
production on temperature and the cultivation of the
soil. The lower curve shows the amount of nitrate
in parts per million in dry soil in the top foot of land,
which was not being cultivated because it carried clover
and oats. The upper curve shows the same results

obtained on well-tilled land carrying maize and potatoes. On the cultivated land the proportion of nitrates rises rapidly until the end of June, when the crop begins to draw freely upon them, and reduces them to a minimum throughout August and September.

One of the best examples of the manner in which the thorough working and aeration of a warm soil promotes nitrification is seen in the management of the turnip crop as usually grown in this country. Though shallow-rooted, and taking away large quantities of nitrogen per acre, it is usually grown with but little nitrogenous manure; phosphates with a little dung or with a comparatively small nitrogenous dressing, being sufficient. The rest of the nitrogen is derived from the rapid production of nitrates, due to the very thorough working of the soil in the warm season of the year that is characteristic of the cultivation of the turnip crop. The production of nitrates by cultivation for the benefit of a succeeding crop by bare fallowing, or of an adjoining crop as in the Lois-Weedon system of alternate husbandry, has been already alluded to. At Rothamsted, nearly 60 lbs. per acre of nitric nitrogen were found in October in the top 27 inches of soil that had been fallowed, as against about half that amount in land which had been under crop. The unmanured alternate wheat and fallow plots showed in September 1878 to a depth of 18 inches 33.7 lbs. of nitric nitrogen per acre after fallow, and only 2.6 lbs. after wheat. In land occupied by cereal crops the drainage waters show that there is practically no nitrate left in the soil by May, or, at the latest, June; they reappear again towards the end of July or in August, and after harvest, if rain falls, and especially if the land be ploughed, nitrification becomes very active. It depends upon the rainfall of the autumn and winter whether these nitrates, formed after harvest, are retained for the succeeding crop or are washed out of the soil. To sum up, increased nitrification, together with the conservation of soil moisture and the warming of the surface soil, are among the chief benefits derived from all forms of surface cultivation.

As so much of the fertility of a soil must depend on the number of nitrifying organisms it contains, attempts have been made to compare soils in this respect, by seeding small quantities of them into a standard solution capable of nitrification and determining the amount of nitric acid formed after a given time.   Although considerable differences are seen in the action of different soils, satisfactory quantitative results have not yet been obtained, because of difficulties in the way of drawing strictly comparable samples of the soils, and the uncertainty still attaching to the amount which should be used for inoculation or the best period of incubation.

Denitrification.

The term denitrification is most properly applied to the reduction of nitrates to nitrites, ammonia, or particularly to gaseous nitrogen, which is brought about by bacterial action under certain conditions. Of late, however, the term has been more loosely used to denote any bacterial change which results in the formation of gaseous nitrogen, whether derived from nitrates, ammonia, or organic compounds of nitrogen.

Angus Smith was the first to observe the evolution of gas from a decomposing organic solution containing nitrates, which were destroyed in the process.   Other observers, particularly Dehérain and Maquenne (1882), with regard to soils, confirmed these results and showed that they were due to bacterial action. In a paper published in 1882, Warington described an experiment in which sodium nitrate was applied to a soil saturated with water; after standing for a week, the nitrate was washed out of the soil, part of it had disappeared, and part had become nitrite. The total of both nitric and nitrous nitrogen only amounted to 20·9 per cent. of that which had been originally applied. That the nitrate had been reduced to gaseous nitrogen was seen by the development of transverse cracks filled with gas in the soil, and it was concluded that some of the nitrogen applied in manures and unaccounted for in crop and soil may well be due to the reduction of nitrates to gas, by the combustion of organic matter with the oxygen of the nitrate, especially in ill-drained soils in wet weather. Gayon and Dupetit, in 1886, isolated two organisms from sewage which would reduce nitrates to gas in the presence of organic matter, the action being chiefly carried on when oxygen was absent; it came to a standstill when plenty of air was supplied, so that the organism had no need to attack the nitrate to obtain oxygen. Both in their experiments and in others, the presence of an abundant supply of soluble organic matter was one of the necessary conditions for the destruction of the nitrates. The denitrifying bacteria are widely distributed. Warington found, out of thirty-seven species of bacteria examined, only fifteen failed to reduce nitrate, twenty-two reduced it to nitrite, and one of them liberated gas. P. F. Frankland, again, found that fifteen out of thirty organisms derived from dust or water would reduce nitrate to nitrite. In fact, a large number of bacteria, when deprived of oxygen and in contact with abundant organic matter, will obtain the oxygen, which they normally require for the breaking up of the organic matter, at the expense of the nitrate.

Many experiments, in which farmyard and other organic manures have been employed in conjunction with nitrate of soda and similar active compounds of nitrogen, have shown a smaller crop for the manures used together than when either was employed singly. These results were particularly apparent when large quantities of material like fresh horse-dung or chopped straw were used in pot experiments. With well-rotted dung, the effect of organic material in depressing the yield which should be given by the nitrate was not so great.

The nature of the results obtained may be seen from the following table, which gives the percentage recovered in the crop of the nitrogen supplied in the manure, when used alone, or in conjunction with fresh horse-dung :—

PERCENTAGE OF NITROGEN RECOVERED (WAGNER).

	Per cent. recovered when used alone.	When used with Horse-dung.
Nitrate of Soda	77	52
Sulphate of Ammonia . . .	69	50
Urine	69	40
Grass	43	20

Numbers of similar experiments in pots have been recorded. In some cases the use of fresh dung has even resulted in a smaller crop than was obtained without any manure at all; but it should be noted that very large amounts of the organic manures were used,

equivalent to 100 tons or more per acre. Similar results
have, however, been recorded in field trials, as in some
experiments of Krüger and Schneidewind's, where fresh
cow-dung was applied at the rate of 23 tons per acre,
horse-dung, 21 tons per acre, and wheat straw at 5·8
tons per acre, on 10th July. These three plots were
in part cross-dressed with urine or with nitrate of soda,
each supplying 43 lbs. of nitrogen per acre. Two successive crops of mustard were immediately grown, and
the amount of nitrogen removed by the crop was
ascertained. Compared with the wholly unmanured
plot, the cow-dung alone slightly depressed the crop,
about 1½ lbs. per acre less nitrogen being recovered;
the horse-dung produced a depression of nearly double
this amount; the wheat straw produced the greatest
depression, its crop containing about 18 lbs. per acre
less nitrogen than that given by the unmanured plot.
Where straw was used with nitrate of soda the two
gave a crop containing 23 lbs. less nitrogen per acre
than the nitrate alone; where urine was used alone,
the produce contained 25 lbs. more nitrogen per acre
than when it was used in conjunction with cow-dung
and straw.

In fine, all the results pointed to the same conclusion—that large amounts of fresh organic manure
not only do not themselves help the crops, but
diminish the effect of other rapidly acting nitrogenous
manures like nitrate of soda, sulphate of ammonia, or
urine.

The action cannot, in the two latter cases at least,
be put down to denitrification proper, unless it is
supposed that nitrification and subsequent denitrification can proceed practically simultaneously in the
same soil. It must either be attributed to the fact
that nitrification is very much checked by the

presence of large amounts of organic matter; or tc the conversion of readily available nitrogen into a comparatively insoluble albuminoid form in the actual material of the enormous numbers of bacteria that are developed by the free food supply; or, lastly, to those fermentation changes of organic nitrogen com- pounds which result in the liberation of free nitrogen. Several of these changes may take place together; the essential point is, that nitrification does not go forward in the presence of much organic matter, which instead favours all the bacterial processes resulting in the development of free nitrogen.

The conditions indeed which prevail in these experi- ments are scarcely comparable with the ordinary practices of agriculture.   Enormous quantities of fresh organic manure are employed immediately before the crop is sown, the temperature of the pots, or of the ground in the field experiment quoted, is very high, so that it is easy to see that an abnormal condition, both as regards nitrification and the supply of oxygen and water, must be developed.

There are not lacking both long-continued experi- ments and ordinary farming experience to show that nitrates and other artificial manures can be used in conjunction with dung with the best effects.

For example, the mangold crop at Rothamsted shows the following average results for the recovery of nitrogen from various nitrogenous manures used first with mineral manures alone and then with annual dressings of 14 tons per acre of farmyard manure, a quantity that never would be employed so frequently in practice:—

[TABLE.

Nitrogenous Dressing.	Yield. Tons per acre.	Nitrogen.		
		In Manure.	Recovered in Crop.	Percentage recovered per 100 in Cross-dressing.
PLOTS MANURED WITH PHOSPHATES AND ALKALINE SALTS.				
Nitrate of Soda . .	17·95	86	67·2	78·1
Ammonium Salts . .	15·12	86	49·3	57·3
Rape Cake . . .	20·95	98	69·4	70·9
Ammonium Salts and Rape Cake . .	24·91	184	103·0	56·0
PLOTS MANURED WITH DUNG.				
Nothing . . .	17·44	200	63·3	31·6*
Nitrate of Soda . .	24·74	286	115·8	61·0
Ammonium Salts . .	21·73	286	105·6	49·2
Rape Cake . . .	23·96	298	111·1	48·8
Ammonium Salts and Rape Cake . .	24·05	384	129·8	36·2

* Percentage of Nitrogen in dung recovered.

It will be seen that all the nitrogenous cross dressings produce an increase of crop when added to the farm-yard manure. When the cross dressings are used on plots receiving only non-nitrogenous manures, the nitrogen recovered varies between 56 and 78 per cent. of that supplied in the manure; when they are used in conjunction with dung, the recovery of nitrogen in the increased yield above that produced by dung alone varies between 36 and 61 per cent. That the recovery is smaller in the latter cases is due to the fact that with such excessive amounts the yield ceases to be proportional to the supply of nitrogen, being limited by other factors.

Denitrification is only likely to cause rapid loss of nitrogen when large quantities of nitrate are applied to undrained or sour land, or when they are used with excessive amounts of fresh dung, which has not been rotted and so deprived of much of its soluble organic matter. Of course, a steady loss of nitrogen due to such causes as have been enumerated above must also be expected wherever large quantities of organic nitrogenous manures are accumulating in the land. If, for example, we compare 2 and 3 of the Broadbalk wheat plots at Rothamsted, the latter of which is unmanured and the former receives dung containing 200 lbs. of nitrogen per acre every year, we find that at the end of the fifty years, 1844-93, the dunged plot contained in the top 18 inches about 2680 lbs. more nitrogen than the unmanured plot, or a mean annual accumulation of 50 lbs. The extra crop grown on the dunged plot would remove a further 31 lbs., thus leaving 119 lbs. per annum to be accounted for, either as nitrogen washed away in the drainage water or lost as gaseous nitrogen by denitrification processes.

Iron Bacteria.

Another series of bacteria playing an interesting part in certain soils, consists of those which secrete hydrated ferric oxide or bog-iron ore in undrained soils, where the soil water contains ferrous bicarbonate in solution. Winogradsky investigated four of these organisms, to whose vital processes he considered the presence of soluble ferrous salts was essential. Molisch, however, regards the secretion of ferric hydrate as, in a sense, an accidental accompaniment of their growth, much as the separation of large quantities of silica, so characteristic of the straw of cereals, is unessential to their development. It has already been noted that these iron earths do not form in soils containing calcium carbonate, which seems to prevent the formation of any soluble ferrous compounds.

Fungi of Importance in the Soil.

Allusion has already been made to the fact that a large number of fungi inhabit the soil—*Penicillium, Mucor, Trichoderma, Spicaria,* etc., *Cladosporium, Cladothrix,* and various wild yeasts, *Monilia,* etc. — all of which aid in breaking down the organic matter. Many of these fungi possess the power of attacking ammonium salts applied as manure, withdrawing the ammonia and setting free the acid. To this action is due the acidity produced by the long-continued use of ammonium salts as manure, as seen on the experimental plots at Rothamsted and Woburn. At Woburn the soil is light and sandy, containing but little lime, and the application of ammonium salts containing 50 lbs. ammonia per acre every season for twenty-four years, has rendered the land practically incapable of carrying the crops. A moderate dressing of lime, however, restores the fertility. The following crops were obtained in 1900 on the barley plots :—

	Ammonium Salts only.	Minerals +Ammonium Salts.
With no Lime	5·6	12·3
With 2 tons Lime, applied Nov. 1897	28·9	33·7

The soil had become acid to litmus paper where the lime had not been used : it is interesting to note that though barley would not grow, oats flourished freely on this sour soil. There are, however, two special organisms which merit further consideration—the fungus which clothes the finer rootlets of many classes of plants, forming mycorhiza and the slime fungus, or *Plasmodiophora* which causes the disease known as "finger-and-toe" or "club" in turnips and other cruciferous plants.

The term "mycorhiza" is applied to the symbiotic combination of the filaments of certain fungi, whose complete development is as yet unknown, with the finest rootlets of certain plants. Sometimes the fungus forms a sort of cap on the exterior of the short rootlets, which are generally without root hairs; in other cases it penetrates the cortical tissue of the root itself, which may also be furnished with root hairs. According to the researches of Frank, the fungus of the mycorhiza lives in symbiosis with the higher plant, attacking the humus and also the mineral resources of the soil, and passing on the food thus obtained to the host plant. In some few cases the host plant possesses no green assimilating leaves, and is wholly dependent upon mycorhiza to obtain its necessary carbon from the humus. Such a case is seen in the *Neottia Nidus-avis*, or Birds' Nest Orchis, to be found chiefly amongst beech underwood in this country.

More generally, the host plant is capable of nutrition in the ordinary way when growing in media in which nutrient salts are abundant, but becomes mycotrophic in soils and situations unfavourable to the production of directly absorbable food—as, for example, in heaths and moors, where the soil is almost wholly humus, or beneath the shade of trees, where nitrates are rarely found and where illumination is insufficient for much assimilation. Later researches, particularly those of Stahl, have shown that the symbiosis of mycorhiza, instead of being a phenomenon restricted to a few species, is widely diffused among many classes of plants, and is indeed causally connected with other facts of wide general importance in plant nutrition. It has already been indicated that the cultivated plants give off considerable quantities of water by transpiration; the form and arrangement of their leaves are adapted to expose a large evaporating surface, the root is well developed and provided with root hairs to keep up the supply of water to the plant. There are, however, a number of plants in which transpiration is much less active, and the leaf area is restricted or otherwise arranged to diminish the loss of water, so that the proportion previously stated as existing between the dry matter produced and the water passing through the plants is greatly diminished. A diminished supply of water to the root would, however, necessitate a loss of nutriment to the plant, as both nitrates and other mineral salts enter the plant with the transpiration water. Stahl has shown that, in general, these plants with a small transpiration activity are furnished with mycorhiza, by means of which they obtain food of all kinds from the soil; whereas, on the contrary, the plants, like the cereals, the cruciferous and leguminous plants, Solanaceæ, etc., which give off water freely, are never associated with mycorhiza. Many of the conifers and heaths which grow on dry soils show this correlation of a low evaporation and restricted leaf development with a root-system furnished with mycorhiza.

Another interesting generalisation has also been brought into line with the above facts by the observations of Stahl that the mycotrophic plants with a feeble transpiration do not store starch in their leaves, but contain instead considerable quantities of soluble carbohydrates, chiefly glucose. In normal plants, though sugar is the first tangible result of assimilation, it is rapidly removed from the sphere of action by being converted into starch, such withdrawal of the product of the reaction being necessary if a rapid rate of assimilation is to be maintained. Should, however, sugar accumulate in the cells, the concentration of the cell sap is increased, so that it parts with its water

by transpiration less readily. Though many exceptions can be observed, there seems to be a very
general association of the development of mycorhiza
with a diminished transpiration and the absence of
starch from the leaf, especially among plants like the
orchids, lilies, iris, etc., which often grow in dry or
shady situations, such plants being further distinguish-
able by a shiny, glossy leaf surface. Stahl has again
shown that the average proportion of ash to dry
matter in the leaf is lower for mycotrophic than for
normal plants; the former grow, as a rule, in situations containing but little mineral salts, particularly
in humic soils, where, in addition, the plant is put
into competition for whatever nutriment may be present
with the mycelia of fungi, which everywhere traverse
humus in its natural state. By direct experiment, it
has been shown that normal plants grown in humus
develop better when the humus is previously sterilised
by long exposure to chloroform vapour than when it
is in its fresh condition, full of living mycelia com-
peting successfully for the nutriment. The absence
in the leaf of calcium oxalate and of nitrates is
particularly characteristic of mycotrophic plants.

Stahl concludes that symbiosis between the roots of
plants and the mycelia of fungi is a very general
phenomenon, especially characteristic of plants growing
in soils subject to drought, or poor in mineral salts,
or rich in humus. These mycotrophic plants are
generally of slow growth, possess a feeble transpiration,
and limited root development; their leaves rarely contain starch; they are also characterised by containing a
comparatively small proportion of mineral salts, among
which calcium oxalate and nitrate are notably absent.

To the mycorhiza associated with plants of the
genus Erica the power of fixing atmospheric nitrogen

has been attributed, but the question still requires further investigation.

The existence of mycotrophy has certain interesting applications in practice; there are many plants which can only be cultivated with difficulty in gardens; for example, some of the orchids, ericas, lilies, and others, generally plants which must be grown in leaf-mould, peat, or other material rich in humus. Yet humus alone is not always sufficient for the purpose, the peat or leaf-mould has often to be obtained from a particular place; other materials, though equally rich in humus and possessing similar mechanical properties, prove quite unsuitable. It is easy to surmise that this effect, confined in the main to mycotrophic plants and humic soils, may easily be due to the absence of the proper fungus from the soils found to be unsuitable.

It has also been shown that the difficulty usually experienced in raising seedlings of exotic orchids, which die off in great number just after they have germinated, may, to a large extent, be obviated by mixing with the medium in which the seeds are sown a little of the material in which the parent plants are growing. The young seedling is found to develop mycorhiza at a very early stage, and then only will grow properly.

"*Finger-and-Toe.*"

On many soils, particularly those of a sandy nature, the turnip crop is often almost wholly destroyed by the disease known as "finger-and-toe," "club," or "anbury." Cabbages and other cruciferous crops are equally attacked; so much so, that in gardens which have become infected it is practically impossible to raise crops of this nature. The disease is caused by an organism, *Plasmodiophora brassicæ*, belonging to the slime fungi,

and forming spores which may remain dormant in the
soil for some time, certainly for two or three years. It
has long been known that the best remedy against finger-
and-toe consists in the application of lime; and as far
back as 1859, Voelcker showed that soils on which this
disease is prevalent are deficient in lime; and in many
cases in potash also. Later researches have only served
to emphasise the fact that the disease is associated with
soils of an acid reaction, in which calcium carbonate is
wanting, or present in very small proportions. The
fungus, as is generally the case with fungi, refuses to
grow in a neutral or slightly alkaline medium, and the
only way to get rid of the infection in the land is to
restore its neutrality by repeated dressings of lime. At
the same time, the land should be rested as long as
possible from cruciferous crops; uneaten fragments of
diseased turnips, etc., should not be allowed to go into
the dung, or if they do, the dung should be used on
the grass land. Manures, again, which remove calcium
carbonate from the soil, like sulphate of ammonia, or
acid manures like superphosphate, should not be employed; neutral or basic phosphates, with sulphate of
potash on sandy soils, should be employed instead.

The following figures show the amount of lime dissolved by hydrochloric acid from soils affected with
"finger-and-toe," as compared with spots in the same
field where the disease was not in evidence :—

| | LIME PER CENT. | | | | |
	Voelcker.	Voelcker.	Hall.	Sandy Soil.	Clay Soil.
Soils affected by disease .	·14	·084	·13	·31	·39
Soils free from disease . .	·89	·52	·43	...	...

It must be remembered that in these cases the total lime soluble in acids is given, not merely the lime present in carbonate.

Whenever a turnip crop is seen to be infected with "finger-and-toe" the land should be well dressed with 3 or 4 tons per acre of quicklime immediately the crop has been removed; as long an interval as possible should be given before again taking a cruciferous crop, substituting, for example, mangolds for turnips in the next rotation; every effort should be made to destroy cruciferous weeds like charlock; turnip-fed dung should not be applied, and another dressing of finely divided quicklime should be put on for the crop preceding the sowing of the new turnip crop.

CHAPTER VIII

THE POWER OF THE SOIL TO ABSORB SALTS

Retention of Manures by the Soil—The Absorption of Ammonia
and its Salts ; of Potash ; of Phosphoric Acid—Chemical and
Physical Agencies at Work—The Non-Retention of Nitrates
—The Composition of Drainage Waters—Loss of Nitrates
by the Land—Time of Application of Manures.

MANY of the substances employed as manures are
soluble in water, hence it becomes important to ascertain what is likely to be their fate in the soil, when
their application is followed by sufficient rain to cause
percolation into the subsoil. Of substances containing nitrogen, nitrate of soda, the salts of ammonia,
urea, and kindred bodies, are freely soluble in water;
superphosphate alone of the compounds of phosphoric acid commonly used as manure is soluble; but
sulphate, chloride, and carbonate of potash are easily
soluble.

Not long after the principles underlying the nutrition of plants had been established, Thompson and Way
showed that ordinary soil possesses the power of withdrawing most of the above substances from solution,
and so saving them from washing away into the subsoil
or the drains. Some of the salts, like sulphate of
ammonia, are decomposed, the base alone being re-

tained and the acid draining through. Way found that liquid manure from a dung-heap, which contains both organic and ammoniacal compounds of nitrogen, potash, and a little phosphoric acid, when filtered through a short column of soil, parted with almost the whole of its organic matter and much of its salts to the soil; compounds of calcium were, however, more abundant in the filtered liquid than before. Way's observations were extended by Voelcker, who compared the absorbing powers of different types of soils, and so obtained an idea of the method by which the absorption of each substance was effected; and later researches have only served to confirm the results then obtained. It was found that all the organic compounds of nitrogen, ammonia—either free or in combination—phosphoric acid, and potash were wholly removed from solution by ordinary soil, though some soils were more effective than others; whereas nitrates, sulphates, chlorides, and, among bases, sodium and calcium, were only slightly, if at all, retained. These results are confirmed by the analysis of the water which flows from land drains under normal conditions; this will generally be found to contain nitrates (sometimes in fair quantity), sulphates and chlorides of calcium and sodium, and considerable amounts of calcium bicarbonate, but rarely shows more than a trace of ammonia, phosphoric acid, or potash. The absorptive action of the soil is partly a chemical process, due to interactions with the humus, the zeolitic double silicates, and the calcium carbonate of the soil; and partly physical, dependent upon the extent of surface offered by the soil particles (for the surface of a solid possesses the power of concentrating molecules of any dissolved substance in the layer of solution with which it is immediately in contact). The mechanism of this physical " adsorption " is but imperfectly understood but even pure sand will remove sodium chloride from solution if the filtering column be sufficiently long; it may, again, be illustrated by the phenomenon of "laking," *i.e.*, the power of certain colloid bodies, like the hydrates of iron and alumina, on precipitation, to drag down with themselves many organic substances from solution.

The absorption of the organic compounds of nitrogen by the soil seems to be a physical process of this kind, comparable to the action of charcoal in absorbing ammonia or the strongly smelling products of putrefaction, etc. The deodorising powers of earth for fæcal and decomposing matter are very familiar; this means that fixation in a more or less insoluble and non-volatile state of various organic nitrogen and sulphur compounds is effected, and other inodorous nitrogen compounds are retained in the same way. The absorption is most marked with soils rich in humus or in clay—the soil materials which present the largest surface. The absorptive power of soil for organic compounds of nitrogen is well seen in a sewage farm, the object of which is to so far purify sewage by percolation through a few feet of soil, as to fit it to be turned into a river without danger to health. For example, on the Manchester Sewage Works, in 1900, percolation through 5 feet of soil reduced the organic nitrogen in the liquid from 0·26 to 0·056 parts per million, and the free ammonia from 1·89 to 0·92. It is necessary, also, on a sewage farm to work with soils possessing but a small absorbing power; only sandy and gravelly soils will permit of rapid enough percolation, both to deal with large volumes of sewage and afterwards to aerate themselves and accomplish the destruction by bacterial action of the absorbed material. Stiffer soils would be far more effectual absorbents of the sewage material, but are unsuitable because they do not admit of percolation.

Absorption of Ammonium Salts.

The absorption of free ammonia follows the lines indicated above for the absorption of the organic compounds of nitrogen ; but the salts of ammonia are retained by the soil by purely chemical processes which result in the formation of insoluble salts of ammonia in the nature of double silicates and humates. Way and Voelcker first found, that when either the sulphate, chloride, or nitrate of ammonia in solution is allowed to remain in contact with soil, the base is absorbed, but the acid portion of the salt remains in solution in combination with lime. Voelcker also showed that when soil was shaken up with dilute solutions of ammonium salts, the withdrawal of ammonia from the solution was never complete, but varied both with the nature of the soil and the strength of the solution, a greater proportion being taken from weak than from strong solutions.

The absorption of the ammonium salts by the soil is now known to be due to the combined effects of at least three actions—upon the zeolites, upon the humus, and upon calcium carbonate. With the zeolites a double decomposition takes place, ammonium becomes insoluble, and equivalent amounts of calcium, magnesium, potassium (sodium also on occasion) enter into combination with the acid in the solution, for no acid is absorbed and the whole solution remains neutral.

The reaction is a reversible one, but the clay containing the zeolites is not capable of absorbing more than a certain small amount of ammonium from the strongest solutions of its salts. The following table shows the ammonia absorbed by 100 grams of very pure clay when shaken with 300 c.c. of ammonium chloride solution of varying strengths.

Original Concentration of Solution.	Ammonia Withdrawn.	Ammonia Withdrawn.
	Grams.	Per cent.
N/10	0·126	24·7
N/12	0·115	28·1
N/15	0·104	30·5
N/20	0·090	35·3
N/30	0·068	40·3
N/50	0·049	48·0
N/100	0·031	60·0

Thus from the weaker solutions a smaller total but a larger proportion of the ammonia was removed by the clay, and the removal was never complete. Of course, in the field the amount of soil is so enormously in excess that the absorption of ammonium salts applied as manure is practically complete. Thus at Rothamsted the presence of ammonia in the drainage water is rarely detected, even when heavy rain immediately follows the application of the manures.

With humus, ammonium salts interact in a very similar fashion, calcium coming into solution, and the ammonium forming some insoluble compound with the complex "humic" acids.

With calcium carbonate a double decomposition of the type—

$$(NH_4)_2SO_4 + CaCO_3 \rightleftharpoons (NH_4)_2CO_3 + CaSO_4$$

—takes place, not only with such substances as ammonium sulphate, but also with humic and zeolitic compounds of ammonium, and though the proportion converted into carbonate is small, it is constantly renewed as the ammonium carbonate is nitrified, so that eventually the whole of the ammonium salt applied to the land undergoes this change.

In consequence, the continued use of ammonium salts as a fertiliser results in the depletion of the stores of calcium carbonate in the soil, as may be seen from the following determinations of the rate of disappearance between 1865 and 1904, of calcium carbonate from some of the soils of the Rothamsted wheat field where the calcium carbonate is of artificial origin and is confined to the surface layer of the soil.

Plot.	Manuring.	Rate of Loss of Calcium Carbonate.
	Per acre per annum.	Lbs. per acre per annum.
3	Unmanured	800
5	Mineral Manures only	880
6	„ „ +200 lbs. Ammonium Salts	1170
7	„ „ +400 „ „	1010
8	„ „ +600 „ „	1170
9	„ „ +412 lbs. Sodium Nitrate .	565
10	400 lbs. Ammonium Salts only . . .	1045
2	Farmyard Manure	590

Thus the use of ammonium salts increases the normal loss of calcium carbonate experienced by the soil (due to solution as bicarbonate), and the amount removed increases with the larger applications of ammonium salts. Taking the mean of these and other results obtained at Rothamsted, 200 lbs. of ammonium salts causes a removal of about 120 lbs. calcium carbonate, whereas the amount calculated from the equation given above would be about 160 lbs. That the loss from the plots receiving sodium nitrate and dung is less than from the unmanured plot, is due, in the former case, to the base left in the soil by the growth of plants which derive their nitrogen from sodium nitrate, and in the latter, to calcium carbonate formed by bacterial action from organic calcium salts in the dung.

The Absorption of Potash.

In all respects the absorption of potash follows the same laws as that of ammonia: *i.e.*, caustic potash is absorbed directly, but sulphate, nitrate, and chloride of potash undergo a double decomposition, by which the potash is retained and calcium sulphate, nitrate, or chloride, appear in the water draining through the soil. Voelcker found in laboratory experiments with small quantities of soil that potassium carbonate was more freely absorbed than sulphate, and that clays, marls, and pasture soils were more effective in retaining potash than light loams or sands, which latter had but little absorbing power.

The following table shows some of the results obtained when potash and soda salts were compared :—

Percentage retained.	Potash.	Soda.
Chalky Loam . .	3·6	0·8
Clay	4·0	1·1
Sandy Loam . .	2·6	0·6
Pasture . . .	3·8	1·0
Loam	3·4	1·0
Ironstone Sand . .	1·1	0·6

Both the humus and the zeolitic double silicates take part in the retention of the potash salts, the reactions being exactly similar to those taking place with the ammonium salts. In some of Way's experiments with pure clays the application of potash salts was followed by the appearance of the corresponding sodium salts in the percolating water, though with most soils it is calcium that is turned out of combination. Potash salts applied to the soil also react to a certain extent with the calcium carbonate, giving rise to a little potassium carbonate, the bad effect of which upon the tilth of the soil will be considered later (p. 253). Dyer has examined the soils of the Rothamsted wheat plots which had then been continuously manured in the same way for fifty years, with the view of tracing the fate of the mineral manures applied. The following table shows a comparison of the amounts of potash soluble in strong hydrochloric acid, in lbs. per acre, found in the top 9 inches of soil from four of the plots; one (No. 11) received nitrogen and phosphates, but no potash, every year, the others were variously manured, but all received 200 lbs. per acre of sulphate of potash. Estimates are also given of the total amount of potash applied as manure and removed in the crops over the whole period, so that in the last two columns a comparison can be made between the actual surplus of potash in the manured over the unmanured soils, and the surplus calculated from the differences between the potash added in the manure and removed in the crops :—

Plot and Manuring, per Acre.	POTASH—LBS. PER ACRE.			SURPLUS OVER PLOT 11.	
	In top 9 inches of Soil.	Added in Manure.	Removed in Crop.	Calculated.	Found.
11, receiving no Potash .	5107	15	1190	...	...
7, receiving 200 lbs. Sulphate of Potash .	6793	5037	2550	3662	1686
5, receiving 200 lbs. Sulphate of Potash .	7233	5203	1136	5242	2126
13, receiving 200 lbs. Sulphate of Potash .	7078	5287	2410	4052	1971

On the whole, about one-half of the estimated surplus of potash received by the manured plots still remains in the top 9 inches of soil.

Dyer further estimated the proportions of potash in the same soils which was soluble in a 1 per cent. solu-

tion of citric acid, and found that both the surface and
the subsoil down to a depth of 27 inches contained more
of this readily soluble potash where it had been applied
as manure, than did the companion plot receiving no
potash, as will be seen from the following table :—

Plot.	LBS. PER ACRE OF POTASH, SOLUBLE IN 1 PER CENT. CITRIC ACID.			SURPLUS OVER PLOT 11.	
	First 9 inches.	Second 9 inches.	Third 9 inches.	Calculated.	Found.
11	83	75	101	...	...
7	602	374	179	3662	896
5	799	598	257	5242	1395
13	487	363	235	4052	826

These determinations show that soluble potash salts
applied to the land are retained chiefly by the surface
soil, as much as one-half of the estimated additions of
potash during fifty years' manuring being found there.
Some of the potash, however, sinks further and is
retained in the subsoil; in the top 27 inches a large
proportion—nearly one-quarter of the whole—remains
in such a loose state of combination that it is soluble
in 1 per cent. citric acid, and so may be regarded as
available for the plant.

Absorption of Phosphoric Acid.

The retention of soluble phosphoric acid by the soil
is more easily intelligible, for there are present several
substances capable of forming insoluble compounds
with phosphoric acid—*e.g.*, calcium carbonate, hydrated
ferric oxide, and the hydrated silicates of alumina which
make up so much of clay. Sand and powdered silicates
like felspar have been found to possess little or no
power of removing phosphoric acid from solution, nor

have either soil, clay, or peat which have been previously washed with hydrochloric acid.

The following table shows the percentages of the total phosphoric acid supplied, which were removed from solution by various soils after remaining in contact for the specified times, the ratio between soil and phosphoric acid being about 1000 to 1.

PERCENTAGE OF PHOSPHORIC ACID ABSORBED (VOELCKER).

	After 1 day.	After 8 days.	After 26 days.
Red Loam . . .	60	78	95
Chalky Soil . . .	89	99	100
Stiff Clay . . .	51	62	86
Stiff Subsoil . . .	48	69	74
Light Sandy Soil . .	53	59	73

In an ordinary soil containing a sufficiency of calcium carbonate, the application of soluble phosphoric acid like superphosphate will chiefly result in the precipitation of di-calcium or "reverted" phosphate, wherever the solution meets with a particle of calcium carbonate. This di-calcium phosphate is a compound easily soluble in weak organic acids or in water containing carbonic acid: hence the great value of applications of superphosphate on soils rich in lime, for thus a readily available phosphate is very quickly disseminated throughout the ground in a state of fine division. But on soils poor in calcium carbonate the precipitation will be chiefly effected by the hydrated iron and aluminium compounds, and the resulting phosphates are practically insoluble in water containing carbonic acid, and but little in saline solutions or in weak organic acids. Hence applications of superphosphate to such soils become much less available to the crop, and should be preceded by a thorough liming of the land. Even a subsequent liming on soils containing phosphates of iron or alumina will help to bring them into a more available form, because a double decomposition resulting in calcium phosphate and aluminium or ferric hydrate, will proceed to an extent dependent on the mass of lime present in the medium.

Further evidence of the precipitation of phosphoric acid within the soil is afforded by Dyer's examination of the Rothamsted wheat soils at various depths, after fifty years' continuous manuring with and without superphosphate. By comparing the amount of phosphoric acid contained in the soil of the unmanured plot with that contained in the soils of the plots receiving superphosphate every year, and knowing also the amount removed by the successive crops in each case, it is possible to calculate the surplus that should remain in the manured over the unmanured plots, on the assumption that the soil was uniform at starting. Calculating in this way, Dyer found that no less than 83 per cent. of the phosphoric acid which six of the plots should possess after fifty years' manuring was still present in the top 9 inches of soil, whereas the subsoils from 9 inches to 18 inches, and 18 inches to 27 inches, showed no accumulation of phosphates. Dyer further determined the phosphoric acid which was soluble in a 1 per cent. solution of citric acid, and found that on the manured plots the top 9 inches of soil contained about 39 per cent. of the estimated surplus of phosphoric acid so combined as to be soluble in this medium, whereas in the subsoils the "available" phosphoric acid was, if anything, less for the manured than for the unmanured plots. It has already been pointed out (p. 163) that if the extraction with citric acid be repeated, practically the whole of the phosphoric acid applied as manure and not removed in the crop can be recovered from the top 9 inches of these Rothamsted soils. It is clear, then, that soils well provided with calcium carbonate, as the Rothamsted soil is, will precipitate very near the surface any soluble phosphoric acid applied, and retain it for a long time in a form easily redissolved and obtainable by the plant. It follows, therefore, that superphosphate, the most soluble of the phosphatic manures, can be applied to normal soils in the winter or early spring without any fear of the phosphoric acid being washed out.

The Composition of Drainage Waters.

Further evidence of the fate of the various substances applied as manures, their retention or otherwise by the soil, can be obtained by studying the composition of the water flowing from land drains.

The drainage from the continuously manured wheat plots at Rothamsted, each of which possesses a tile drain running down the centre at a depth of 2 feet to 2 feet 6 inches, has been collected from time to time and completely analysed by Voelcker and Frankland; in addition, systematic determinations of the nitrogen contents have been made for many years. In a general way, the chief constituent of the various drainage waters is lime, either as bicarbonate, sulphate, chloride, or nitrate; soda is the only other base present in any quantity, very small amounts of magnesia, potash, and ammonia pass into the drains. Of the acid radicles, chlorine and sulphuric acid predominate according to the manuring, and the proportion of phosphoric acid is minute; but the amount of nitric acid varies according to the manure applied and the season at which the water is collected.

The following table shows the complete analysis of the drainage water from twelve of the plots :—

COMPOSITION OF DRAINAGE WATERS FROM BROADBALK FIELD, ROTHAMSTED, IN PARTS PER MILLION (VOELCKER).

Plot.	2	3 & 4	5	6	7	9	10	11	12	13	14
Manuring.	Dung.	0	0	Minerals +200 lbs. Ammonium Salts.	Minerals +400 lbs. Ammonium Salts.	+550 lbs. Nitrate of Soda.	0	0	400 Lbs. Ammonium Salts. +Superphosphate. +Sulphate of Soda.	+Sulphate of Potash.	+Sulphate of Magnesia.
Organic Matter	26.1	22.9	19.3	25.7	34.9	26.7	33.6	38.4	29.3	45.3	56.1
Nitrogen as Nitric Acid	16.1	3.90	5.10	8.50	14.0	18.4	13.9	15.3	15.1	17.4	19.2
Nitrogen as Ammonia	0.16	0.12	0.13	0.20	0.07	0.24	0.08	0.17	0.30	0.16	0.09
Lime	147.4	98.1	124.3	143.9	181.4	118.1	154.1	165.6	191.6	201.4	226.7
Magnesia	4.9	5.1	6.4	7.9	8.3	5.9	7.4	7.3	6.6	9.3	11.6
Potash	5.4	1.7	5.4	4.4	2.9	4.1	1.9	1.0	2.7	3.3	1.0
Soda	13.7	6.0	11.7	10.7	10.9	56.1	7.1	6.6	24.6	6.1	5.6
Oxide of Iron	2.6	5.7	4.4	2.7	8.1	5.1	4.0	3.4	3.6	3.7	3.7
Chlorine	20.7	10.7	11.1	20.7	26.1	12.0	32.0	31.6	30.9	36.6	39.4
Sulphuric Acid	106.1	24.7	66.3	73.3	90.1	41.0	44.4	54.3	96.7	86.9	99.7
Phosphoric Acid	...	0.63	0.91	1.54	0.91	...	1.44	1.66	1.26	1.09	1.01
Carbonic Acid	43.3	48.1	44.4	59.0	58.0	73.0	45.4	44.9	64.6	51.1	56.9
Silica	35.7	10.9	15.4	24.7	17.0	10.6	10.9	11.3	17.9	28.3	14.0
Total Solids	476.1	246.4	326.0	407.6	492.4	423.9	406.9	425.9	530.9	544.3	598.6

An examination of these figures shows that the amount of organic matter and ammonia reaching the drains is practically nil; the organic matter supplied as dung, and the ammonia, which is employed up to 400 lbs. of mixed ammonium chloride and sulphate per acre, are wholly retained by the soil. The effect, however, of adding either organic compounds of nitrogen or ammonium salts is to increase the proportion of nitrates in the drainage water. Lime is the chief constituent of the dissolved matter in the drainage waters, the proportion is lowest for the unmanured plot (3), it rises with the application of minerals (5), and rises again with each successive application of ammonium salts (6) and (7). The formation of calcium chloride and sulphate respectively, when the corresponding ammonium salts are applied to land containing calcium carbonate, has already been discussed: it is well seen in the increased richness in lime, sulphuric acid, and chlorine of the drainage water from 6 and 7, which receive 200 and 400 lbs. respectively of ammonium salts, as compared with 5, which receives the same minerals without any nitrogen compounds. Plot 11 receives superphosphate in addition to the ammonium salts which 10 receives: the effect of the gypsum contained in the superphosphate is seen in the increased lime and sulphuric acid content of the drainage water of 11. The increase is not so great, however, as that caused by the addition of sulphates of potash and magnesia to the superphosphate and ammonium salts (plots 13 and 14) whereas sulphate of soda causes little loss of lime (12). The use of nitrate of soda on plot 9 causes no increase in the proportion of lime in the drainage water, but a large quantity is removed, chiefly as sulphate, from plot 2, receiving dung every year. The quantity of lime removed annually in this way will be very great: assuming a mean annual drainage equal to 10 inches of water, the unmanured plot will lose about 220 lbs. per acre per annum of lime : equivalent to about 400 lbs. of carbonate of lime, whereas the analysis of the soil shows (p. 216) an annual loss of about 800 lbs. per acre. The discrepancy between these two figures is due to the fact that the results are calculated from but a small number of analyses of the drainage water, the amount of which is also very uncertain. When 400 lbs. of ammonium salts are used as manure, either alone or with minerals, the increased loss of lime calculated on the same basis amounts to 126 lbs. or 225 lbs. of carbonate of lime per acre per annum, as against about 240 lbs. found from the analysis of the soil.

The amount of magnesia lost is small, 5 to 20 lbs. per acre per annum, nor is the amount reaching the drainage water much increased by its application as manure to plots 5, 6, 7, 9, and 14.

The amount of potash lost is still smaller, from 3 to 12 lbs. per acre per annum, but it is distinctly dependent on the amount supplied as manure, being at a maximum with the dunged plot (2) and the plot receiving minerals only (5), and greater from all the other plots receiving potash than from those without it, *i.e.*, 3, 10, 11, 12, 14. The use of sulphate or nitrate of soda increases the amount of potash in the drainage water, not so, however, the use of sulphate of magnesia. Practically all the soda, chlorine, and nearly all the sulphuric acid, that are applied in the manure pass through into the drainage water.

A comparison of the drainage waters in winter and spring shows that they are more concentrated in the winter, because the manures (excepting the nitrate of soda) have then been recently applied : the chlorides wash out first, then the sulphates, and as the season advances not only is the total amount of

P

lime present much diminished, but it comes away chiefly as carbonate. With the growth of the crop in spring the nitrates disappear from the drainage waters.

The amount of nitrates found in the drainage water varies not only with the time of year, but also according to the interaction of temperature, growth of crop, cultivation, and percolation. Nitrates are only rapidly produced when the temperature of the soil has risen : if the percolation is not excessive the crop may remove the nitrates as fast as they are formed, but a heavy rainfall in the spring before the nitrates have been much drawn upon by the crop, or one just after the land has been broken up in the autumn and is still warm, will result in a considerable washing out of nitrates. At the same time a certain amount of moisture in the soil is necessary for the formation of nitrates, and the crop itself may so dry the soil as to reduce nitrification considerably. The following table (p. 227) shows the estimated loss of nitrates from the same wheat plots at Rothamsted as have previously been dealt with, during two years, each of which has been divided into two periods : firstly, from the date at which the nitrogenous manures were sown up to harvest; and secondly, from harvest round again to the sowing of manures in spring.

The diagram (Fig. 15) shows the same results in a graphic form.

The seasons were rather exceptional, the summer rainfall and drainage in 1879 and the winter rainfall in the following year being both above the average. It will be seen that except on the autumn manured plot 15, the loss was greatest from plot 9 receiving 550 lbs. of nitrate of soda, and this excess of loss was chiefly in the summer drainage water of 1879; the figures are, however, exaggerated by the fact that half the nitrate

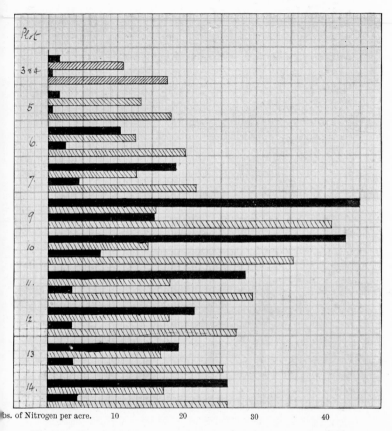

FIG. 15.—Losses of Nitrogen in Drainage from Rothamsted Wheat Plots.

Black = Losses in Summers 1879, 1880.
Shaded = Losses in following Winters.

[To face page 226

plot received no mineral manures, and therefore grew
but a scanty crop. The losses during the winter months
are more nearly the same for all plots, and represent to
a large degree the nitrification of the organic residues in
the soil. The losses from the plots receiving minerals
and varying amounts of ammonium salts (5, 6, and 7)
increase with each application of nitrogen: the losses

NITRIC NITROGEN IN DRAINAGE WATER.—LBS. PER ACRE.

Plot.	Manuring, per Acre.	1879-80.		1880-81.	
		Spring Sowing to Harvest.	Harvest to Spring Sowing.	Spring Sowing to Harvest.	Harvest to Spring Sowing.
3	Unmanured	1·7	10·8	0·6	17·1
5	Minerals only.	1·6	13·3	0·7	17·7
6	Minerals + 200 lbs. Ammonium Salts	10·1	12·6	2·2	19·8
7	„ +400 „ „	18·3	12·6	4·3	21·4
9	„ +550 „ Nitrate of Soda	45·0	15·6	15·0	41·0
10	400 lbs. Ammonium Salts alone .	42·9	14·3	7·4	35·2
11	Do. do. + Superphosphate	28·3	17·7	3·4	29·6
12	Do. do. + Sulph. Soda .	21·2	17·5	3·3	27·2
13	Do. do. + Sulph. Potash .	19·0	16·4	3·7	25·3
14	Do. do. + Sulph. Mag. .	26·0	16·8	4·2	25·9
15	Minerals + 400 lbs. Ammonium Salts in Autumn	9·6	59·9	3·4	74·9
	Estimated Drainage—inches .	11·1	4·7	1·8	18·8

from the plots receiving ammonia and various mineral
manures diminish as the mineral manure becomes a
more complete plant food, because the greater growth of
crop thus secured more completely removes the nitrates
as they are formed, besides hindering nitrification by
drying the surface soil.

The effect on nitrification of crop and surface
cultivation is well seen in the following table of results

obtained by Dehérain, who collected the drainage from
cement tanks 2 m. cube and systematically filled with
soil taken from corresponding depths in the field. The
soils had been several years in the tanks, so that they
had settled down into practically normal conditions,
though the effect of the aeration and disturbance of
the soil in filling the tanks is still visible in a rather
high rate of nitrification. Each tank carried the crop
indicated in the first column.

Cropping.	Drainage.	Nitrogen as Nitric Acid.
	Inches.	Lbs. per acre in Drainage Water.
Fallow, no cultivation . . .	11·2	186·70
Rye Grass	7·8	2·28
Oats	7·3	7·37
Maize	6·9	21·60
Wheat, followed by Vetches . .	6·6	12·90
Wheat	7·5	28·70
Fallow, hoed	11·5	196·56
Fallow, no cultivation . . .	11·2	158·00
Fallow, hoed and rolled . . .	11·2	183·20
Vine	7·5	36·20
Sugar Beet	7·2	0·27

The rainfall of the year in question, March 1896 to
March 1897, amounted to 28·8 inches, most of which
fell in the autumn. The most noteworthy results are
the effect of the various crops in diminishing the loss
of nitrates, which is not wholly to be attributed to the
quantity taken up by the crop, because the sum of the
nitrogen removed in the crop and that carried off in
the drainage water is never equal to the nitrogen
removed from the uncropped plots by the drainage
water alone. During the comparatively dry spring
months the crops leave so little moisture in the soil that
nitrification is checked, and the total production of

nitrates is less where there is a crop than on the moister uncropped plots.

When the wheat was followed by a crop of vetches the loss of nitrates during the comparatively wet autumn was considerably reduced. Lastly, the hoeing of the fallow plots resulted in a considerably increased production of nitrates.

Time of Application of Manures.

The facts set out above as to the retention of most of the soluble constituents of manures by the soil, while the nitrates are liable to wash out, have an important bearing on the season at which artificial manures should be sown. In the first place it is evident that there is no danger of losing phosphates, or even of their washing deep into the soil, when employed in their most soluble form as superphosphate. It is the general custom to sow superphosphate with the drill for roots at the same time as the seed: the large quantity of manure near the seedling in its early critical stages is probably valuable, and as the roots of swedes and turnips do not extend very deeply, the phosphoric acid may be placed in the most likely place to reach them.

But for more deeply rooting crops, hops and fruit or even mangolds, it seems probable that superphosphate is often applied rather too late in the season, and that if used as a winter instead of a spring dressing it would have a better chance of getting well diffused through the soil. Basic slag and other insoluble phosphates should be used in the winter or even the autumn: there is no risk of loss, and as much rain as possible is wanted to get them distributed in the soil. As regards potash salts, Dyer's experiments go to show that they descend further in the soil, and are a little more subject to washing than the soluble phosphates : for this reason, where sulphate of potash is employed, as for potatoes, it will best be sown with the seed. Where kainit is used, it is best employed as a winter or autumn dressing ; there will be little loss of potash, for this will get fixed chiefly in the surface soil. But the chlorides, which are present in kainit and are sometimes not wholly beneficial in their action upon the crop, will be removed and washed out into the drains or the subsoil water by the winter rains : the magnesia salts also will be precipitated within the soil, and to a large extent removed from possible action upon the crop. Turning to the nitrogen compounds, it is necessary to keep in mind that all of them will become transformed into nitrates which are liable to be washed out. All insoluble organic manures should be put on before or during the winter : the decay processes will begin, resulting in the formation of amino-acids, ammonia, etc., which will become fixed in the soil, but the low winter temperatures will not permit of much nitrification. Liquid manure and similar materials containing such readily nitrifiable substances as urea and ammonium carbonate, should be reserved until early spring, so that the crop may be growing whenever nitrification begins. Ammonium salts are very rapidly nitrified, so that they should only be used in spring. At Rothamsted nitrates begin to appear in the drainage water immediately after the application of the ammonium salts to the wheat plots in March if rain falls, and one of the plots which has its ammonium salts applied in autumn shows not only a considerable falling off in crop but also large quantities of nitrates in the winter drainage waters.

The following table shows the amounts of nitrates removed in the drainage water from the two plots which receive 400 lbs. per acre of ammonium salts with mineral manures, only differing in the fact that on plot 7 the ammonium salts are sown in March, and on plot 15 in October; also the average crops of grain and straw for the twenty-three years, 1875-97.

1879-1881.—LBS. OF NITRIC NITROGEN PER ACRE.

Plot.	1879-80.		1880-81.		CROP.	
	Spring Sowing to Harvest.	Harvest to Spring Sowing.	Spring Sowing to Harvest.	Harvest to Spring Sowing.	Grain.	Straw.
					Bushels.	Cwt.
7	18·31	12·63	4·29	21·38	31½	31
15	9·62	59·92	...	74·94	28½	26½
Drainage	11·1″	4·7″	1·8″	18·8″	...	...

That sulphate of ammonia will to some extent persist in the soil, and become available for a succeeding crop, after even a whole year has elapsed, is to be seen from the results of the Woburn experiments upon wheat. Some of the plots at Woburn receive mineral manures every year, but ammonium salts or nitrate of soda only every alternate year: in both cases the crop falls very much in the years of no nitrogen, but the decrease is by no means so marked with ammonium salts as with nitrate of soda, which latter seems to leave no residue whatever.

The soil at Woburn is an open sandy loam; but in the years for which the results are quoted (see Table, p. 232) the rainfall was low.

The difference between the results set out in the above-mentioned table and those obtained upon the corresponding plot at Rothamsted, where the dressing of ammonium salts every other year seems to leave no residue for the following year, may perhaps be set down to the different texture of the two soils. The ammonium salts are converted which are washed down into the subsoil; at Woburn they can rise again by capillarity, as the soil, though sandy, is still fine in texture; at Rothamsted the soil is too close-grained to admit of any considerable movement of the subsoil water back to the surface.

Plot.	1899.	Bushels.	1900.	Bushels.
8B	Minerals only . .	20·3	Minerals + Ammonium Salts . . .	27·3
8A	Minerals + Ammonium Salts . . .	33·1	Minerals only . .	16·2
9B	Minerals only . .	9·8	Minerals + Nitrate of Soda . . .	27·7
9A	Minerals + Nitrate of Soda . . .	41	Minerals only . .	6·8
4	Minerals only, every year . . .	6·9	Minerals only . .	5·9

The experiments recorded above and the results of the examination of drainage waters go to show that nitrate of soda should only be employed when there is a crop in possession of the ground and ready to seize upon the salt as soon as it becomes diffused through the soil. Only on dry soils can it be safely applied as early as the sowing of the seed; in wet climates sulphate of ammonia will often be preferable if the soil is warm enough to induce reasonably quick nitrification, and when large quantities of nitrate are wanted they should be put on by successive applications of not more than 1 cwt. per acre at a time.

CHAPTER IX

CAUSES OF FERTILITY AND STERILITY OF SOILS

Meaning of Fertility and Condition—Causes of Sterility : Drought, Waterlogging, Presence of Injurious Salts—Alkali Soils and Irrigation Water—Effect of Fertilisers upon the Texture of the Soil—The Amelioration of Soils by Liming, Marling, Claying, Paring, and Burning—The Reclamation of Peat Bogs.

IN discussing the question of fertility, a difficulty at the outset crops up in the definition of the term " fertility " : we are dealing with something intangible and dependent upon so many varying factors that it becomes a matter of judgment and experience rather than of scientific measurement. We have to distinguish between the fertility proper, "the inherent capabilities of the soil," to use the language of the old Agricultural Holdings Act, which is the property of the landlord, and for which the tenant pays rent; and the "condition" or "cumulative fertility," the more temporary value which is made or marred by the tenant. Though in the main it is easy to feel the distinction, it is often difficult, if not impossible, to draw a line of demarcation between them. Clearly the farmer in a new country on virgin soil is dependent wholly on the inherent fertility of the land, but with much of the land in this country it is hard to say how far its value is inherent, or due to long-continued cultivation. When a tenant by many years of skilful management makes a good pasture, the improvement is rightly credited to him, as fertility which he has accumulated: the next tenant must regard the same pasture as part of the inherent capacity of the soil. Again, a farmer working on the old four course rotation, selling only corn and meat and purchasing neither feeding stuffs nor manures, is dependent on the fertility of the soil: another farmer, carrying on an agricultural business such as market gardening or hop-growing, and putting more into the land every year as manure than he takes out as crop, is only using the land as he would a building, as a tool in a manufacturing process.

Fertility proper is by no means a wholly chemical question, dependent upon the amount of plant food the soil contains; in many cases the physical conditions which regulate the supply of air and water to the plant, and as a corollary, the bacterial life, are far more potent in producing a fertile soil than the mere amount of nutrient material it contains. Especially is this the case in an old settled country like England, where manure is cheap and abundant; here a fertile soil is often one which is not rich in itself, but one that is responsive to, and makes the most of, the manure applied. Clay soils are not uncommon which show on analysis high proportions of nitrogen compounds and potash, and again no particular deficiency in phosphoric acid, but from their closeness of texture they offer such resistance to the movements of both air and water as to carry very poor crops. Some light soils again, such as those on the chalk, would be regarded on analysis as rich, but they are made so persistently dry by the natural drainage, that only in a wet season do they keep the crop sufficiently supplied with water for a large crop production. On nearly all poor soils it is impossible to effect much improvement by the use of manures; in fact, manuring will not turn bad into good land, the conditions limiting the amount of crop being other than the food supply. Of course, by the continued incorporation of humus into a light soil, its physical texture may be improved at the same time as its richness, until it becomes sufficiently retentive of water for the needs of an ordinary crop, just as a heavy soil may be lightened by similar additions of humus. It has already been mentioned that many subsoils, especially of the heavier loams and clays, are extremely infertile when brought to the surface, even though they may possess a fair proportion of phosphoric acid and potash and be artificially supplied with nitric nitrogen. Some of this effect is due to texture, part to the very scanty bacterial flora they possess, but it is to be noted that in arid climates the subsoils, which are not more fine-grained than the surface soils, do not show the same infertility when brought to the surface.

The soils which show the greatest fertility are, as a rule, soils of transport, uniform and fine-grained in texture, but with particles of a coarser order than clay predominating, so that, while lifting water easily by capillarity, they are freely traversed by air and percolating water. As a rule, they also contain an appreciable amount of organic matter at all depths; in Britain they have been deposited from running water, and represent the silt from which both the coarsest sand and the finest clay particles have been sifted, together with a certain amount of vegetable debris. We have nothing comparable with the typical "black soils" of the North American prairies or the Russian steppes, which contain very large proportions of organic matter to considerable depths in the subsoil: as, for example, a soil from Winnipeg that contained 0·428, 0·327, 0·158, and 0·107 per cent. of nitrogen in the top 4 feet of soil successively. Many of these deep rich soils appear to be wind-borne: in all cases they are of very uniform texture, and represent the accumulated residues of ages of previous vegetation in a form that is capable of decay and nitrification so as to become available for subsequent crops. In a peat bog there is equally an accumulation of organic matter and nitrogen, but the mass is infertile because of the acid character of the humus (which causes the absence of the valuable bacteria, such as those fixing nitrogen and nitrifying ammonia), the deficiency of mineral plant foods, and the bad mechanical condition which affects the supply of air and water. In the main, then, a fertile soil is one rich in the débris of previous vegetation, one which has been so sorted out by running water, wind, the agency of worms, etc., as to possess a very uniform texture, adapted to satisfy the needs of the plant for air and water. Mechanical texture is of fundamental importance: in this country many soils owe their value to this property alone; for example, the Thanet Sand formation in East Kent (a very fine-grained sand or silt), though it contains but little plant food, yet carries some of the best fruit and hop plantations in the kingdom, and farms on it command a high rent.

Condition.

The question of condition has equally its chemical and its mechanical side; it is well known that on any but the lightest soils continued cultivation makes the texture better and renders it easier to obtain a seed bed. On clay soils the effects of bad management are very persistent; any ploughing, rolling, or trampling when the soil is wet will so temper the

clay that the effect is palpable until the land has been
fallowed again or even laid down to grass. Once
protected from the action of frost, stiff soil which has
been worked when at all wet never seems able to
recover its texture, as may be seen by examining the
clods that are to be found on digging up an old post,
the result of the trampling when the post was originally
put in. The dependence of "condition" upon the
maintenance of a good texture is to be seen in the
custom of regarding wheat as an exhausting crop,
whereas few of our farm crops withdraw less plant
food from the soil. The popular opinion really
represents the fact that the wheat crop occupies the
land for nearly a year during which period it receives
little or no cultivation and so falls into a poor state of
tilth.

From the chemical side "condition" means the
accumulation within the soil of compounds that will
by normal decay yield sufficient available plant food
for the requirements of an ordinary crop, *e.g.*, of
organic compounds of nitrogen which readily nitrify,
of phosphoric acid and potash compounds which readily
become "available" for the plant.

The condition of land cannot be restored all at once
by manuring; the residues of manures left in the soil
after the first season are slow-acting, *i.e.*, only a small
proportion of them becomes available year by year,
so that there must be a considerable accumulation of
such residues before the proportion becoming available during the period of growth is sufficient for the
crop. *Per contra*, the condition can be only too easily
destroyed by cropping without manure; the unexhausted
residue left after each year is successively less and less
active, the crop falls off rapidly, till at last a sort of
stationary condition is reached, and the somewhat inert

materials, still left in large quantity, liberate year by year a fairly constant proportion of active plant food. The plots at Rothamsted which have been cropped without manure for more than fifty years show but little less average production during the last twenty years than in the twenty immediately preceding. For example, the unmanured wheat plot shows the following crop in bushels of dressed grain :—

First 23 years, 1852-74.	Second 23 years, 1875-97.	1898.	1899.	1900.
$14\frac{1}{8}$	$11\frac{5}{8}$	$12\frac{1}{8}$	12	$12\frac{1}{4}$

Condition may best be regarded as a state of equilibrium when the land will continue to give a good return in crop for the manure applied; as a rule, the crop recovered by no means contains the whole of the material applied as manure, a certain portion being retained in a comparatively inactive form. With the land in condition the remaining nutrient material required for a good crop is supplied by the dormant residues in the soil which have become active : at the same time, these reserves are protected from depletion by renewal from the inactive portions of the current manuring. On the other hand, if the land is in poor condition the crop gets little or no assistance from the soil, but is grown from the active part only of the manure : the rest of it accumulates and begins to build up condition, which, however, does not tell on the yield for some time. As a practical consequence, it is noticed that only land in good condition gives a paying return year after year for the application of manure : yet if the experiment be made of omitting the manure on a portion of the land for one year, there is little corresponding reduction of yield, as

though the manure went to keep up the "condition,"
and the crop was grown out of that rather than from
the manure applied.

From the point of view of analysis the estimation of
the "condition" of a given piece of land is a difficult
matter on which light is only just beginning to be
thrown by the determination of "available" plant food,
such as the nitrates and the phosphoric acid and potash
soluble in dilute acid solvents. By considering such
factors as these and the amount of humus soluble in
alkali, the ratio of the soil carbon to the nitrogen,
and the proportion of calcium carbonate, the agricultural chemist may form an idea as to the immediate
state of the land. Doubtless, the prevalence and distribution of such necessary bacteria as those causing
nitrification are also important factors in determining
the fertility, but on this point we are without exact
information. It will be seen that "condition" is one
of the most valuable of the properties of the soil to
the cultivator; as it may be destroyed or created by
the tenant during his occupation of the land, it should
be as far as possible a tenant's asset, to be bought by
him on entry and valued to him on leaving. The
difficulty which even an experienced man finds in
putting a value on so intangible an item makes it
almost impossible to assess the condition of a farm,
but it is desirable in every way that the outgoing
tenant should be encouraged to maintain the condition
of his farm by giving him due compensation for the
unexhausted value both of manures and foods used
in the latter years of his tenancy.

Fairy Rings.

The significance of "condition" and its dependence
upon a supply of recently decayed organic matter is

well seen in the development of "fairy rings" in pastures. "Fairy rings" are circles of dark-green grass, common enough in poor pastures, which are found to extend their size every year, leaving the grass within the ring of a lighter colour and of generally poorer aspect than that outside. On examining the soil immediately outside a ring, it is found to be full of the mycelium of one or two common species of fungi, but the mycelium rarely occurs in the soil beneath the ring itself, and never in that within the ring. The ring appears to be dependent on the growth of the fungus, which starts at one point and draws upon the humus reserves contained in the soil. Having consumed whatever humus is available, the mycelium must proceed into the annular area of soil immediately round the first patch, thus from year to year it spreads outward. After the death of the fungus, there is left behind in the soil it has just occupied a quantity of organic matter, which readily decays and becomes available for plant nutrition; thus a ring of luxuriant vegetation immediately follows the death of the fungus. In other words, the humus of the soil, slow to decay and nitrify in the usual way, is changed into material undergoing rapid change by its preliminary conversion into the tissue of the fungus. At the same time, as the supply of rapidly acting plant food has been solely derived from the soil, the ultimate result is the impoverishment of the soil within the ring by the development of the fungi and the subsequent luxuriant growth of grass.

The following figures relate to the composition of the soil (mean of five examples) within, on, and outside fairy rings :—

	Carbon per cent.	Nitrogen per cent.	Nitrates per million.
Outside the ring . .	3·30	0·281	2·44
On the ring . . .	2·99	0·266	11·46
Inside the ring . . .	2·78	0·247	1·03

It will be seen that the unchanged soil outside contains the most carbon and nitrogen; the ring itself contains an intermediate amount, and the least is contained within the ring after the luxuriant vegetation has passed away. The soil on the ring is in high condition, because the organic residues it contains are recently formed and will change rapidly; after they have been cropped out, the land is less able to support a crop, even though there is still much plant food left in the soil. The last column in the table (the analysis of a single example only) shows the difference in available nitrogen; and though in a pasture there are never many nitrates to be detected, so rapidly are they seized upon by the crop, still the organic nitrogen compounds in the soil must be in a more nitrifiable condition on the ring to yield the results there shown. Doubtless an investigation of the nature and distribution of the bacteria and micro-fungi in and about a fairy ring would throw further light on the varying fertility of such closely neighbouring areas of soil, but no data are at present available.

Sterility of Soils.

Few soils occurring in this country can be described as absolutely barren, yet from time to time land is met with which yields such poor crops that it may fairly be designated as sterile. The causes of sterility are various; amongst them may be enumerated both the want and the excess of water due to texture and situation, deficient aeration, the absence of calcium carbonate, and the toxic action of certain compounds, such as the salts of magnesia, iron pyrites or ferrous salts generally, and common salt itself. An acid reaction of the soil, which is highly prejudicial to vegetation, is generally brought about by one or other of the causes enumerated above.

The sterility brought about by a deficiency of water is only seen in this country when the soil is so entirely composed of coarse sand that it possesses no retentive power for the rainfall; even then the absolutely bare condition does not persist long, and may be attributed as much to the lack of nutriment as to the want of water. Little by little vegetation is found to creep over recent deposits of coarse sea-sand and shingle, until a turf is established. As a rule, such deposits have permanent water at a comparatively short distance below and by this the vegetation is maintained; but where a coarse, open-textured sand occupies the uplands, as on the Bagshot and Lower Greensand formations of the south of England, or the Bunter beds of the Midlands, the soil is kept so poor that it has largely remained common heath land, never having been worth the expense of enclosing. Allusion has already been made, under the head of drainage, to the evils which ensue in a waterlogged soil: from time to time clays are met with of so close a texture that the vegetation suffers in an analogous manner through deficient aeration. On certain areas of the Oxford Clay and London Clay, and the Boulder clays derived therefrom, pastures degenerate after a few years into a mass of creeping rooted plants like bent grass, and the land must be broken up afresh in order to aerate it before any crop can be grown.

Sterility due to chemical causes is perhaps most

generally caused in this country by the absence of calcium carbonate from the soil. When this happens on light sandy land it will become evident by the tendency of black mild humus to accumulate, by the paucity of leguminous plants in the herbage, and by the prevalence of fungoid diseases like "finger-and-toe." On strong lands, and when accompanied by water-logging, black acid peat accumulates: the soil shows an acid reaction, oxide of iron forms below the surface, and the soil water contains soluble iron salts, as is seen by the iridescent scum which spreads over any water standing in the ditches.

Another source of sterility is the presence of un-oxidised iron salts in the soil : many clay subsoils are coloured dark blue or green by double ferrous silicates like glauconite, or by finely disseminated iron pyrites. Until these materials become oxidised to ferric hydrate, the soil remains sterile : particularly is this the case with iron pyrites, which in the form of marcasite easily oxidises to yield both ferrous sulphate and sulphuric acid. Voelcker has recorded three instances of soil sterile through these causes : one was land reclaimed from the bed of the Haarlem Lake, which contained 0·71 per cent. of iron pyrites and 0·74 per cent. of ferrous sulphate, as well as some insoluble basic sulphate of iron. Another example of land reclaimed from the sea contained 0·78 per cent. of pyrites and 1·39 per cent. of ferrous sulphate. Cultivation with a free use of lime and chalk is the best means of ameliorating such soils, which always show an acid reaction.

Kearney and Cameron in America have shown that salts of magnesia possess, even in solutions of great dilution, a toxic action upon plant roots, which is much diminished if calcium salts be present at the same time. Loew at the same time has indicated that a comparative excess of magnesium over calcium in certain soils results in sterility. With this may be correlated the fact that the soils resting upon the serpentine, which is a compound containing magnesia, are notoriously poor, also that certain very impoverished clays on the Wealden formation contain a high proportion of magnesia.

Sterility caused by salt is sometimes to be seen in this country in the marshes near the sea : more often a "salting," even where the sea has regular access, is clothed with vegetation which is able to endure very considerable proportions of salt. Most farm crops will grow in soil containing 0·25 per cent. of salt, and in the reclaiming of the old sea lake of Aboukir in Egypt, it was found that grasses would grow freely when there was still as much as 1 per cent. of salt in the soil, and a scrubby winter crop of barley was grown on soil containing more than 1½ per cent. "With 2 per cent. of salt in the soil, a fair crop of dineba (grass), 2 feet high, can be grown ; with 1 per cent. it attains its full height of 4 feet, and sells as a standing crop at from 20s. to 25s. per acre. For 'berseem,' or clover, the percentage of salt should not exceed ½, and about the same for 'sabaini (quick-growing or seventy-day) rice.'" Much, however, depends upon the relations between water supply and evaporation, as to the amount of salt in a soil which would be tolerable to vegetation. From time to time cases occur in this country of crops being destroyed, and land rendered sterile by the incursion of sea water ; the effect is not always apparent at first, though sea water contains as much as 2·7 per cent. of sodium chloride and 0·5 per cent. of other soluble salts, but the permanent pasture becomes seriously injured, and for two or three years even the arable land yields very indifferent crops. Dymond has attributed this after effect to the injurious action of the sea water on the texture of the soil, due to the attack of the sodium chloride upon the double silicates of the soil, lime in particular being displaced by soda. The result is the deflocculation of the clay, which will not settle down for many weeks when suspended in water. The sodium chloride of the sea water would also interact with any calcium carbonate in the soil, giving rise to sodium carbonate, the deflocculating effect of which upon the clay has already been noticed. Biological effects may also be surmised : it is always seen that the earth worms are killed in the land which has been flooded with sea water, and in view of the known unfavourable effect of chlorides on nitrification, it is possible that the rate of production of nitrates in the inundated soil is seriously lessened.

Alkali Soils.

In arid climates the rainfall is often insufficient to produce percolation through the soil and subsoil into the underground water system ; in consequence, the salts produced by the weathering of the rocks tend to accumulate in the subsoil, and may be brought to the surface by capillary rise so as to cause almost entire sterility. Such bad lands are known in America as "alkali soils," but they are well known in India and in Egypt, and indeed are common to all countries possessing a small rainfall and great evaporation. In its most aggravated form alkali land, particularly at the end of the dry season, shows an actual white efflorescence of salts at the surface ; all vegetation is destroyed, except one or two plants which seem tolerant of large quantities of saline matter, such as "greasewood," *Sarcobatus* sp., or the Australian "saltbushes," *Atriplex semibaccatum,* etc. In some cases the alkali is chiefly located at a slight depth in the soil, and only effloresces on spots a little below the general level, where the subsoil water comes to the surface. A heavy rainfall may be followed by a rise of alkali, because a connection is then established between the saline subsoil water and the evaporating surface, whereupon a continuous capillary use of salts takes place, followed by their crystallisation at the surface. *Per contra*, the establishment of a soil mulch, and shading the ground with a crop, so that evaporation only takes place through the leaves, will aid in keeping the alkali down. The composition of the salts varies; as a rule, sodium chloride predominates, with some sulphates of sodium, magnesium, and calcium, in which case the material is known as "white alkali." Under other conditions the material is really alkaline, containing carbonate and bicarbonate of soda; the saline solution then dissolves some of the humus present in the soil, and also causes the resolution of the clay material into its finest particles, so that the soil forms an intensely hard black pan when dry, which is known as "black alkali." The carbonates are far more injurious to vegetation than the neutral salts; few plants can bear as much as 0·1 per cent. of sodium carbonate, but are tolerant of 0·5 to 1 per cent. of the other salts.

Though the alkali salts are sometimes chiefly sulphates, more commonly sodium chloride is the main constituent, together with the products of its action in mass upon calcium carbonate and sulphate. The diagram (Fig. 16), due to Hilgard, shows the distribution with depth of alkali salts in this type of soil at Tulare, California; the greatest accumulation of salts takes place at a depth of 30 inches, the point to which the annual rainfall penetrates. One of the most difficult features presented by the cultivation of land in arid regions where alkali occurs in the soil, comes from the

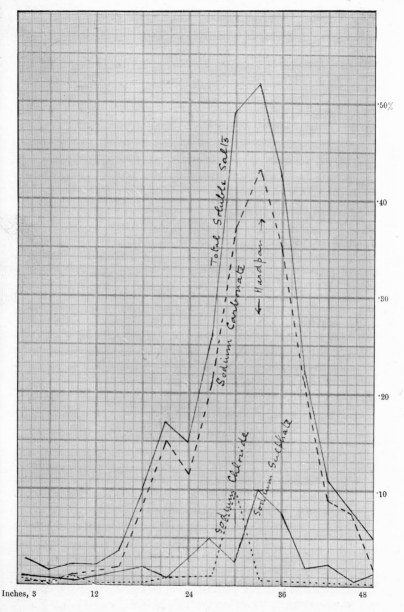

Fig. 16.—Nature and Distribution of Alkali Salts (Hilgard).

[To face page 246

tendency of the sterile spots to spread and the alkali to
be brought to the surface as soon as irrigation water is
employed, for without irrigation agriculture is hardly
possible.   Many districts, which at first carried good
crops and were even laid down in fruit or vines, have been
ruined through the rise of alkali to the surface brought
about by irrigation; in fact, in all these arid regions it
becomes exceedingly dangerous to raise the water table
in the land anywhere near the surface, because capillarity
then causes a rise of the salt changed water, and evaporation concentrates it on the top.   Just as some of the worst
alkali land occurs where rain falling upon the surrounding mountains finds its way by seepage through the
subsoil rich in salts and then rises to the surface in the
dry basin areas below, so the introduction of irrigation
canals pouring large volumes of water upon the land,
may equally establish the capillary connection between
the subsoil salts and the surface.   The following extract
from Bulletin No. 14, U.S. Dept. of Agric., Div. of Soils,
dealing with alkali soils in the Yellowstone Valley,
shows the evil effects of incautious irrigation :—

"Irrigation has been practised for twelve or fifteen
years.   The water for the main ditch supplying the
valley is taken out of the river nearly 40 miles above
the town of Billings.   When the country was first settled,
and indeed above the ditch at the present time, the
depth to standing water in the wells was from 20 to 50
feet, and there was no signs of alkali on the surface of
the ground.   Under the common practice of irrigation,
however, an excessive amount of water has been applied
to the land, and seepage waters have accumulated to
such a degree that water is now secured in wells at a
depth of from 3 to 10 feet in the irrigated district, while
many once fertile tracts on the lower levels are already
flooded, and alkali has accumulated on them to such an

extent that they are mere bogs and swamps and alkali flats, and the once fertile lands are thrown out as ruined and abandoned tracts."

Nor is it necessary that the subsoil be charged with salts for irrigation to produce alkali land; the mere continual evaporation of ordinary river or spring water may cause such an accumulation of saline matter at the surface as is harmful to vegetation. This is well seen in Egypt, where perennial irrigation is practised with the Nile water, and the following quotation from Willcock's *Egyptian Irrigation* will explain the action that takes place :—

"The introduction of perennial irrigation into any tract in Egypt means a total change in crops, irrigation, and indeed everything which affects the soil. Owing to the absence of rain, the land is not washed as it is in other tropical countries, unless it is put under basin irrigation.

"An acre of land may receive as many as twenty waterings of about 9 cm. in depth each, *i.e.*, a depth of water of 1·80 metre per annum, which is allowed to stand over the soil, sink about half a metre into the soil, and then be evaporated. Since the Nile water, especially in summer, has salts in excess, these salts accumulate at the surface, and if not eaten down by suitable crops, soon appear as a white efflorescence. While the spring level is low, capillary attraction cannot bring up to the surface the spring water, which generally contains a fair proportion of salts, but where the spring level is high the salt-carrying water comes to the surface, is there evaporated, and tends to further destroy the soil. In old times the greater part of the cultivation land was under basin irrigation, and was thoroughly washed for some fifty days per annum; while the rest, consisting of the light sandy soils near the

Nile banks, was protected by insignificant dykes, which dykes were burst every very high flood, and thus allowed to be swept over by the Nile and washed once every seven or eight years. All this is at an end now in the tracts under perennial cultivation, and other remedies have to be found."

The only remedy for the evils attending irrigation is the introduction of drainage channels at a lower level than the canals bearing the irrigation water; in this way the percolation through the soil, which in humid climates naturally removes the salts not taken up by the crops, is effected artificially; there is some apparent loss of water, but this is absolutely necessary to maintain the land free from injurious salts. As an example, the following passage may be quoted from one of Major Hanbury Brown's reports on Egyptian Irrigation:—

"It has been ascertained that the blessing of improved water supply which has resulted from the barrage having been made to do its duty, has been attended in some localities with the evils due to infiltration and want of drains. The remedy, as pointed out in last year's Report, is to remove the want of drains by digging them, and to provide the means of washing out the salt brought to the surface, by infiltration in the shape of a liberal supply of water, by which the salt would be carried away in solution along the drains, or be forced down below the surface of the soil to a depth at which it would be harmless. The liberal water supply is not to be obtained except by the construction of a storage reservoir at Aswan or elsewhere."

It was the neglect of drainage, when irrigation canals were introduced, that led to so widespread a deterioration of land in Egypt. To quote from Lord Milner's *England in Egypt* :—

"But perhaps the worst feature of all was the neglect of drainage, which was steadily ruining large tracts of country. Even where drains existed, they were frequently used also as irrigation channels, than which it is impossible to conceive a worse sin against a sound principle of agriculture. In some cases these channels would be flowing brimful for purposes of irrigation, just when they should have been empty to receive the drainage water. Elsewhere the salt-impregnated drainage water was actually pumped back upon the land.

"It was the want of drainage which completed the ruin of the Birriya, that broad belt of land which occupies the northern and lowest portion of the Delta, adjoining the great lakes. There are upwards of 1,000,000 acres of this region, now swamp, or salt marsh, or otherwise uncultivable, which in ancient times were the garden of Egypt."

It has been the business of the English irrigation officers since the occupation to restore and improve the drainage system, and to begin the reclamation of the salted areas by cutting drainage canals and passing enough of the abundant winter flood water through the soil to wash out the salts into these drains.

Hilgard in California has also indicated that it is impossible to wash the salts from the soil, even by leaving the water to stand upon the surface for some time, unless provision is made to remove the salted water by underdrainage. In the case of black alkali, however, the soil has become too impervious to allow water to percolate at all; the first remedial measure is to incorporate considerable quantities of gypsum with the soil; this will interact with the sodium carbonate, producing sodium sulphate and calcium carbonate, at the same time precipitating the humus in a flocculent form. If now underdrainage be brought into practice the soluble salts can be washed through, and a very fertile soil results, owing to the presence of the finely divided humus and calcium carbonate. Where underdrainage is hardly practicable because of the expense, irrigation water should be used in as limited amounts as possible, and every care should be taken to keep the surface tilled and under crop, so as to minimise evaporation from the bare ground. In humid countries like our own, damage due to the accumulation of salts are rare; the author has, however, seen one case where the vegetation of a lawn was destroyed during a hot dry spell of weather by continuously applying water in quantities which never washed down into the subsoil, but evaporated every day. An efflorescence practically identical with white alkali is sometimes seen on greenhouse borders, which are constantly watered, but never in sufficient quantities to cause percolation; and gardeners again are familiar with the check of growth which sometimes occurs in the case of plants long in one pot and constantly watered with hard water. The remedy is to water from time to time so heavily as to cause abundant percolation and thus wash all the salts out.

Closely related to some of the phenomena presented by alkali soils are certain secondary effects upon the texture of the soil which are produced by the action of some of the salts used as artificial manures. A good friable texture in a heavy soil depends upon the clay particles being generally flocculated and gathered together into little aggregates, which give the soil a coarser grain until they are resolved into their ultimate particles by incautious working when the clay is in a wet state. It has already been shown that acids and most soluble salts, particularly those of calcium, possess a strong flocculating power, whereas the soluble alkalis—the carbonates and hydrates of sodium, potassium, and ammonium—are active deflocculators, causing the clay particles to separate into their most fine-grained condition.

It has long been recognised that large or frequent dressings of nitrate of soda had an injurious action upon the tilth of the soil, causing it to remain very wet, and then to dry into hard, unkind clods. Since nitrate of soda is very hygroscopic, the wetness induced in the land was attributed to the absorption of moisture from the atmosphere by the nitrate of soda, but when it is considered what a very small proportion the water absorbed by as much as 5 cwt. of nitrate of soda would bear to the hundred tons which is the approximate weight of an acre of soil an inch thick, it is obvious that the difference in water content so induced would not be sensible.

Clay soils, in fact, which have been treated with nitrate of soda, do not show any excess of water; but they are very much deflocculated, as may be ascertained by comparing the appearance after standing of a jar of distilled water rendered turbid by shaking up in it a gram of the soil, with a second jar in which the water has been shaken with a gram of the same soil in its normal condition. But nitrate of soda itself possesses flocculating powers even when concentrated, hence the observed deflocculation can not be due to the direct action of the fertiliser upon the clay. However it has been found that when plants feed upon a nutrient solution containing nitrate of soda, an excess of the nitric acid is withdrawn by the plant, and part of the soda is left in the medium combined with the carbon dioxide secreted by the plant. The existence of this soluble alkali after the growth of the plant can be verified by

experiments with water cultures, it can also be extracted
from the soil of the Rothamsted plots which have for
many years been manured with nitrate of soda. Small
as the amount may seem to be, it is quite sufficient to
account for the deflocculation of the clay and the
defective tilth observed on heavy land after nitrate of
soda has been used.

The bad repute of nitrate of soda as exhausting or
scourging the land, is less due to any sensible diminution
in the stock of plant food in the soil that follows its use,
than to the deflocculation it sometimes induces, and the
consequent deterioration of the texture of the soil.
As a remedy lime is not effective, since it is an alkali
itself; instead the nitrate of soda should be used in
conjunction with acid flocculating manures like superphosphate, or a mixture of nitrate of soda and sulphate
of ammonia should be used as a nitrogenous manure,
because the two manures will act upon the soil in
opposite ways, the nitrate of soda as an alkali and the
sulphate of ammonia as an acid. Dressings of soot are
also effective; not only does it assist the soil mechanically,
but also the small percentage of sulphate of ammonia it
contains possesses some power of flocculating the clay.

Other fertilisers which give rise to an alkaline
reaction in the soil are sulphate of potash, common
salt, and other soluble salts of sodium and potassium,
which as has already been noticed (p. 217) interact
with calcium carbonate in the soil, and give rise to a
little soluble alkaline carbonate. The injurious effects
of sulphate of potash upon the tilth of the heavy soil
at Rothamsted is very evident on the mangold field,
where the plots receiving this fertiliser every year
become excessively sticky and clinging in wet weather,
and dry, with a hard caked surface. It has often been
noticed that applications of potash salts and common

salt have depressed instead of increasing the yield ; this may probably be set down to the deterioration of tilth that ensues when the soil is heavy and also contains calcium carbonate. Some fertilisers, on the contrary, aid in the flocculation of clay soils, the most effective being superphosphate, which is acid and contains gypsum, an effective flocculating agent. The ammonium salts, which give rise to free acids, in consequence of the withdrawal of ammonia by the moulds, etc., living in the soil, act as very potent flocculators, and at Rothamsted, for example, give rise to an open and friable soil, as compared with the neighbouring plots receiving nitrate of soda. Lime, which is the chief flocculating agent employed in practice, is only effective when it has become dissolved as bi-carbonate in the soil water.

Amendments of the Soil.

Many soils, without being absolutely sterile, carry very poor crops until their physical character has been altered by the admixture of some considerable quantity of one or other of the constituents of a normal soil that may happen to be originally wanting. These amendments of the soil by the mixture of other soils date from the time that enclosures first began to be made ; they were perhaps at their height during the early years of the nineteenth century, after the middle of which they rapidly diminished as it began to be less and less remunerative to "make" land, until at the present time the fall in the prices of produce and the rise in the cost of labour have put an end to all such operations. Among other causes of this neglect may perhaps be set down the increased use of artificial manures ; men began to take too exclusively a chemical view of the functions of the soil, and shirked expenditure which did not seem to add directly any food for the plant. However, it is probable that with modern facilities for moving earth on a large scale by steam power, the improvement of much poor land might even now be profitably undertaken.

The operations which may be grouped under the head of "amendments of the soil," comprise—drainage, which has been dealt with elsewhere; the marling and claying of light sands; the reclamation of peat bogs; the improvement of clay soils by liming and chalking, or by paring and burning; and lastly, the creation of new alluvial soils by warping.

Warping.

The operation of "warping," or "colmetage," is only possible in the vicinity of tidal estuaries, where lands exist below the level of high water, and is in this country practically confined to the estuaries of the Humber and Ouse. Warping is carried out by the construction of a wide drain protected by sluices from the tidal river to the low land, which is first divided by embankments into compartments of various sizes up to 150 acres. When the embankments have become consolidated, the flood tide, heavily charged with suspended matter which is really fine earth brought down by the river, is admitted into the compartment, where it deposits most of its silt and is allowed to run off when the level of the water in the river has fallen during the ebb. The operation is repeated until a layer of silt has formed 1 to 3 feet thick over the land, which is then dried and brought under crop. As the chief deposit is always near the mouth of the drain, where the velocity of the silt-bearing current is first checked, the position of the inlet must be shifted about to secure a uniform deposit all over the land and to distribute the valuable fine silt which settles furthest from the inlet. In some cases the sluice gates are automatic, and water is admitted and drawn off at every tide, but in others only every other tide is admitted, thus giving time for the deposit of the finer particles, and greatly improving the character of the resulting land. As a rule, only the spring tides are utilised, because the suspended matter is then at its maximum, and the process is confined to the summer months, to avoid danger from flooding when there is much land water about. In exceptional cases land may be warped 2 or 3 feet deep in one year—from January to June—in other cases, where the water is less charged with sediment, or the land is at a higher level, an efficient warping, which should not be less than 18 inches deep, requires three or four years. When finished, the land is allowed to dry and consolidate, drainage grips are then thrown out, and a light crop of oats, in which are sown clover and ryegrass, is taken; after the seeds have been down two years the land is generally ready to carry wheat. Warp soils are, as a rule, fertile, and noted for growing seed corn of high quality; they are to all intents and purposes artificial alluvial soils, composed entirely of the finer sands and silts without much clay material, and are comparatively rich in organic débris and other plant food, except perhaps potash. The fertilising of the Egyptian land by the red Nile flood water, the formation and improvement of river meadows by winter flooding, are both analogous to the process of "warping."

Marling and Claying.

Many light and blowing sands, almost too pure to

permit of any vegetation, have in their immediate
neighbourhood a bed of marl or clay which can be
easily incorporated, practically creating a soil where
there was none before. Among the New Red Sandstones of Cheshire and the Midland Counties beds of
true marl occur and were at one time enormously
worked, so that every farm and almost every field shows
its old marl pit; the sandy Lower Greensand soils in
the Woburn district have been extensively marled from
the adjoining Oxford clay, and many of the Norfolk
soils have been made out of blowing sands, by bringing
up the clay which immediately underlies them. The
earlier volumes of the *Journal of the Royal Agricultural
Society* contain numerous accounts, showing how much
land was brought into cultivation by these means in
the first half of the nineteenth century.

> " He that marls sand may buy the land,
> He that marls moss shall suffer no loss,
> But he that marls clay flings all away."

The usual practice in Norfolk was to open pits down
to the marl or clay, dig and spread it at the rate of
50 to 150 loads to the acre on a clover ley or turnip
fallow. In some cases trenches were opened all along
the field, and the clay thrown out on either side. By
the action of the weather, drying and wetting, followed
by frost, the clay comes into a condition to be harrowed
down, after which it can be ploughed into the ground.

The effect of marling or claying is more evident after
a year or two than at once, because the fine particles
become each year more thoroughly incorporated with
the soil. The effects are to be seen in increased crops, the
production of better leys and pastures, greater resistance
to drought, and particularly an increased stiffness in the
straw where manures are used to grow the crop.

R

Marl containing carbonate of lime is always far more valuable than clay; pure clay is so little friable, and so sterile itself, that it effects an improvement only slowly; marl not only ameliorates the texture but adds at once a supply of carbonate of lime, potash compounds, and in some cases phosphoric acid also. Clay and marl both have a tendency to sink, and eventually require renewing, but if well done will last for thirty to fifty years, because the accumulation of humus and fibrous root-remains, due to the increased crops, itself binds the soil together.

At the present day the need of marling or claying on a small scale is often seen in old gardens, particularly in old town gardens which are situated upon gravel soils, initially very short of the finer soil particles. The constant breaking of the surface by cultivation, and the use of large quantities of stable manure, which decays and leaves the soil open, result in a continual washing down of the finest particles, until the remaining soil loses all power of cohesion and of resisting drought, falling into a dusty powder immediately on drying. A coating of clay in the early autumn, or, better still, of good marl, is the only method of giving consistency to such a soil and soon remedies its worst defects, such as susceptibility to drought and rapid fluctuations of temperature, and tendency to produce soft vegetation, very liable to disease.

Reclamation of Peat Land.

One of the earliest methods of bringing peat land in the Fens and similar districts into cultivation was, to dry the land by means of open drains and break up the surface with the breast plough; the clods were then gathered together, and burnt when dry, afterwards the ashes were spread and a crop of rape taken.

The fire was never allowed to burn too fiercely, the object being to obtain charred residues rather than white ashes. The effect of burning the peat was to provide a certain amount of ash rich in saline matters and particularly in alkaline carbonates, thus correcting the two great faults of the remaining peat, its deficiency in mineral matters, and its sour reaction. At the same time the weeds and other coarse vegetation occupying the surface were destroyed, and a clean seed-bed prepared for the crop. However, the process of burning is a very wasteful one, involving the loss of the combined nitrogen contained in the accumulated organic matter, and after a few repetitions the land was found to be seriously depleted of its reserves of humus. Burning became replaced in the Fens by a marling process, especially where the peat was of a sandy nature ; trenches were opened to the bed of marl or clay always found beneath the peat, and the clay thrown out and spread at the rate of 100 loads or so per acre, the burning process being reserved for the first reclamation, when a mass of surface vegetation had to be got rid of. In other districts, where marl is less available, peat has to be brought into cultivation by draining the land with open cuts, allowing some considerable time to elapse during which the peat dries, shrinks, and consolidates, and then correcting the acidity with lime. It is desirable to use large dressings of mineral manures like basic slag and kainit to compensate for the deficiency in mineral matter, especially where the peat is initially of an acid character. In the Fens the peat is sometimes found to be mild humus containing lime ; this does not respond to liming, and gives better crops with superphosphate than with basic slag.

Paring and Burning.

When the poorer clay soils were first taken into cultivation, a beginning was generally made by " paring " the surface with the breast plough, and "burning" the clods as soon as they were sufficiently dry. The clods were made up into heaps a yard or so in diameter with the brushings of the hedges and all the rough surface vegetation, together with as much clay as was judged prudent. Each heap was then allowed to burn slowly and char the clay, without permitting the heat to rise sufficiently to vitrify the clay or dissipate such valuable material as the alkalis of the ash. The resulting ashes effected a great improvement in the soil : the clay was partially dehydrated, or at least coagulated, thus providing a certain amount of coarse material to ameliorate the texture ; in the charred clay also, some of the potash was rendered more available, while the plant residues provided mineral salts and alkalis to promote nitrification. The drawback to the process is the inevitable loss of nitrogen to the soil ; but any one who has noticed how freely crops grow on the patches of arable land where couch heaps have been burnt the season before, will see that, for the time being, the fertility of the soil is increased by the process. Other advantages of burning lie in the destruction of weeds and insect life of all kinds, and although it has been almost wholly discontinued at the present day, the older writers on agriculture are unanimous as to its beneficial effects in bringing poor clay land into cultivation. Recent investigations also show that heating the soil to low temperatures, such as that of boiling water, bring about a great increase in its productivity, probably owing to a rearrangement of the bacterial flora of the soil, for complete sterilisation is only effected at higher temperatures. The subject is still obscure, but these effects of heating the soil may well be a factor in the value of such processes.

A variation on the old process of "clod burning" consists in "border burning," in which clay is dug from one corner of the field and burnt by means of the couch and other weeds cleaned off the land, the hedge trimmings, etc.; the burnt clay is then spread over the surface to improve the texture of the soil. Without doubt the latter process might still be profitably adopted where heavy clay land is under the plough; if every year some clay were added to the fires made from the weeds and hedge trimmings, valuable material for lightening the soil would be obtained without wasting too much soil nitrogen.

Of course the incorporation of any large-grained material will improve the texture of clay soils; in some cases sand has been dug and spread with advantage; road scrapings, town refuse, and even coal ashes help to lighten the soil, though, in the case of gardens, coal ashes should be avoided.

Liming and Chalking.

Of all the methods of improving the soil, other than actual manuring or cultivation, none is more important than the incorporation of lime or chalk. It has already been indicated that many soils exist, chiefly clays and sands, containing less than 1 per cent. of carbonate of lime; on all such land liming produces very pronounced effects, both on the physical texture of the soil and on the character of the resulting vegetation.

It is on the clays and other strong soils that lime produces the greatest alteration in texture; its effect in coagulating and causing the finer particles to form into aggregates, which remain loosely cemented by the carbonate of lime, has already been discussed. The soil becomes much less retentive of water, percolation is increased so that the limed land is drier and warmer, admits of cultivation at an earlier date in the spring, and is far more friable when dry. In fact, the liming gives a coarser texture to the clay soil, and all the effects pertaining to the coarser texture, such as diminished capacity for retaining water and consequent greater warmth, less shrinkage and tendency to cake on drying, are all manifest after the application of lime. It does not, however, follow that the crop will mature more readily though the season is made earlier through liming; in many cases in dry seasons crops upon clay ripen prematurely, because the drying up and shrinkage of the impervious clay cut the roots off from all access of moisture. The liming, by opening up the soil to the motion of water by surface tension, keeps the plant growing for a longer period; at the same time, the increased amount of plant food rendered available also tends to prolong the duration of growth. On very light soils the addition of lime acts to a certain extent as a binding material, and increases the cohesion and water-retaining power of the soil, but it is not so effective in this respect as humus. Besides its physical effect upon the texture of stiff soils, lime has a very powerful chemical effect, liberating freely the reserves of plant food of all kinds in the soil and rendering them available to the plant; so that on soils naturally deficient in carbonate of lime, manures of all kinds can only find their proper value if lime be also used from time to time. On soils that have been under intensive cultivation for a long time immense reserves of plant food have been accumulated, which only require the addition of lime to bring them into action. As an example may be quoted the result of applying lime to an old hop garden at Farnham, Surrey, where the soil consisted of an alluvial loam, very deficient in carbonate of lime, and heavily dressed with organic manures for many years previously. The plots chosen for comparison received a complete artificial manure with or without 1 ton of lime per acre; the figures for the crops in the following table have been reduced to percentages to eliminate the great fluctuations due to season.

Year.	ARTIFICIAL MANURES.	
	With Lime.	Without Lime.
1895	100	70
1896	100	84
1897	100	80
1900	100	81
1901	100	90

Of course, as lime itself supplies no food to the plant, but only sets in action the dormant residues already present in the soil, the forcing of crops by the aid of lime alone soon results in the exhaustion of the land. Hence the old saw:—

> "Lime, and lime without manure,
> Will make both land and farmer poor."

The exact effect of lime in promoting fertility depends upon the plant food in question. We have already seen that all the decay processes which result in the oxidation of the humus are promoted by the presence of a base to combine with the organic acids produced by the decay, and, in particular, that the presence of an easily attacked base is necessary for nitrification. As a nett result, the oxidation of the humus and the formation of nitrates is much increased by a dressing of lime, which, indeed, is the first indispensable step towards rendering available the rich organic residues accumulated in a sour soil. As regards the mineral constituents, lime has a very marked power of bringing potash into a soluble state; the double hydrated silicates of potash and alumina, etc., which result from the partial breaking down of felspars and are the sources of the potash of our soils, are decomposed, lime being substituted for the potash going into solution. It is a case of mass action, where the addition of one soluble constituent to the soil will increase the amount that goes into solution of all the other constituents which are capable of being replaced by the base added; the extent of the action is therefore dependent upon the amount of lime used. The fact that more potash has been rendered available in limed soils is clearly seen in the character of the vegetation, *e.g.*, in an increased proportion of clovers in the herbage of pasture or hay land. The action of lime as a liberator of potash is illustrated by the effect of a dressing of chalk applied in 1881 to part of the permanent grass plots at Rothamsted; by 1884 differences began to be manifest, the chalk caused a change in the herbage of those plots which had been receiving potash each year for twenty-five years previously, increasing the production as a whole, and particularly increasing the proportion of leguminous plants in the herbage. On the plots, however, which had been receiving no potash, and therefore contained no recently accumulated reserves of this material, the chalk had practically no effect, either in the weight or character of the crop.

To some extent lime seems able to act as a liberator of phosphoric acid in the soil. As pointed out by Thénard, lime is able to act upon the very insoluble

phosphates of aluminium or iron which are present in
many soils, and, by converting them into phosphate of
lime, renders the phosphoric acid more available for
the plant.

Besides its specific actions in thus rendering more
soluble the soil constituents which nourish the plant,
lime exerts a very beneficial action by maintaining
the neutral reaction of the soil; it neutralises the acids
produced by the decay and nitrification (see p. 174) of
the organic matter in the soil, or those due to the
oxidation of materials like iron pyrites in other soils
(see p. 243). Again, as has been shown already, it
is necessary as a base to satisfy the requirements of
artificial manures like sulphate of ammonia, superphosphate, and kainit (see p. 216), or to prevent the soil
being invaded by such organisms as the destructive
fungus causing "finger-and-toe" (see p. 209). It must,
however, be clearly realised that lime is wanted as a
base, not as a compound of calcium, necessary though
calcium itself may be to the economy of the plant; and
that only carbonate of lime (chalk, limestone, etc.) or
quicklime and slaked lime, which promptly become
carbonate of lime when incorporated with the soil, are
capable of acting as the required base. Other calcium
compounds, as superphosphate of lime or sulphate of
lime (gypsum), or phosphate of lime in bones, etc., are
either acid or neutral, and do not supply the base
required to effect the beneficial actions set out above;
they cannot replace lime or chalk—in fact, they do not
contain any "lime" in the farmer's sense. Unfortunately,
it has been too often supposed that the use of artificial
manures, such as superphosphate of lime, removed the
necessity of a periodical liming of the soil, and some
of the neglect into which this all-important operation
has fallen may be set down to the unfortunate confusion

hanging round the word lime. However, as will have been gathered from a consideration of the effects of sulphate of ammonia in depleting the Woburn soil of carbonate of lime, the use of artificial manures generally demands an increased rather than a lessened attention to the periodical liming of the land.

The method of liming which was formerly in vogue consisted in applying very large quantities of quicklime at comparatively long intervals, 100 to 150 bushels per acre (=2 to 4 tons) every eight or ten years, or an initial dressing of 100 bushels, with a further dressing of 50 bushels per acre every third year. The reason for this interval lies in the fact that the best effects of lime are to be seen after the lapse of a year or two; the material becomes carbonate, which, being insoluble, is incorporated with the soil and passes into solution as bicarbonate but slowly. The immediate effect of lime may even be a diminution of the crop if it be used on very rich land, or in actual contact with fresh dung; under these conditions there appears to be some loss of ammonia by volatilisation. Of course the effect of lime is not very persistent, and the dressing must be repeated; as the farmers say, the "lime sinks in the land," *i.e.*, carbonate of lime is removed from the surface soil by solution as bicarbonate.

In carrying out the operation of "liming," the aim should be to ensure as fine a division as possible, so as to incorporate the material intimately with the soil. In some cases the lime is thrown out in heaps on the stubbles in autumn, and slaked by pouring on water, the hot slaked powder into which the quicklime falls being immediately spread over the land. This method only answers with "fat" limes, which slake and fall readily to a dry powder; a better method is to lay up the quicklime in heaps and cover the heaps with soil, in which case the lime slakes gradually to a fine powder that can be spread before the plough. It is not wise to spread the quicklime over the land, as much of it, after slaking and becoming carbonated, remains in lumps which cannot be reduced to a powder.

The expense of liming in this fashion is considerable, and as the action is not immediate, owing to the difficulty of getting the material mixed with the soil, it is desirable to replace it, if possible, by a cheaper process. This has been attained by the use of ground lime, which is at the present time prepared by most lime works for the use of builders; 5 cwt. of ground lime per acre, distributed by a manure barrow or by one of the artificial manure distributors now manufactured, will be found more effective for one or two seasons than ten or twelve times as much applied in the old-fashioned method. Of course such a small dressing of ground lime requires renewing more frequently; but, as the expense is comparatively trifling, both for labour and material, as compared with the older process, it may be hoped that on many soils this all-important operation will assume its old prominence in the routine of farming.

Considerable differences are to be seen in the character of lime made from the various calcium carbonate rocks burnt for lime in the British Islands; in the main a distinction may be drawn between the white "fat" limes made from the White Chalk, the Mountain Limestone and other comparatively pure deposits of calcium carbonate, and the "thin" grey or stone limes made from less pure and more argillaceous limestones. The "fat" limes are the purer, slake readily and swell considerably in the act, forming afterwards a bulky white powder; the "poor" or "thin" limes slake with comparative difficulty and do not increase much in bulk. The "thin" limes partake somewhat of the nature of a cement, setting after mixture with water, and are more esteemed by builders than the "fat" limes, which harden with extreme slowness and are chiefly employed for plastering and kindred work. Naturally the "fat" limes are preferable from an agricultural point of view, both for their purity and the finer condition into which they fall; unfortunately few of the lime works grind the white lime in the ordinary course of trade, as they do the builders' lime.

The lime made by burning the Magnesian Limestone which occurs in Durham, Yorkshire, Derbyshire, and Notts, is disliked by farmers and regarded as injurious rather than beneficial to the land. It contains 50 to 80 per cent. of lime and 4 to 40 per cent. of magnesia, which latter constituent may be the cause of the ill effects.

The following analyses show the mean composition of several samples of "fat" and "poor" lime, being "white" and "grey" lime respectively, made from the Upper and Lower Chalk of the North Downs:—

	White Lime.	Grey Lime.
Caustic Lime	90.20	74.00
Carbonate of Lime . . .	2.40	2.66
Magnesia	0.35	0.38
Oxide of Iron	0.52	1.00
Alumina	1.70	7.60
Silica as Soluble Silicates . .	2.60	8.60
Insoluble Residue . . .	.25	.94
Water, Alkalis, etc. . . .	1.98	4.82
	100.00	100.00

In place of lime, chalk may often be used with advantage when it is readily accessible; for example, on one side of the Chalk formation the Gault and the upper beds of the Lower Greensand, and on the other side the London Clay and the Bagshot Sands, are generally in need of lime, and are never very remote from the outcrop of the chalk. The superficial clays and sands lying on the Chalk itself are often deficient in lime, and may be readily chalked by sinking shallow pits. It must be remembered that much larger quantities of chalk than of lime are needed to produce a given effect; not only is the chalk equivalent chemically to about half its weight of lime, but in practice it can never be reduced to so fine a state of division as lime obtains by careful slaking. In chalking, it is desirable to obtain the soft upper white chalk from a pit, so that it is saturated with quarry water; if then spread over the land in autumn it gets frozen while still full of water, and becomes reduced to a comparatively fine powder which can be ploughed in if on arable soil or spread with a harrow on the pastures. Very large quantities of chalk are used, up to 100 loads to the acre; naturally the effect of such treatment is more permanent than the usual liming.

The custom of "chalking" was very extensively practised during the seventeenth and eighteenth centuries in Hertfordshire on the high plateau land on which the Rothamsted estate is situated. There the "clay with flints" and the "boulder clay," though not, as a rule, more than 10 to 12 feet thick, and resting on the chalk rock from which they have largely been derived, have been completely decalcified by the solvent action of the rain water, and no longer contain more than a trace of carbonate of lime. It was customary to sink bell pits through the clay until the chalk was reached; this was then dug out, hauled to the surface in baskets, and dragged out on to the fields in sledges. Sixty to a hundred or even a hundred and fifty loads per acre were spread, and from time to time the process was repeated. The amount of chalk thus spread upon the surface was considerable ; the surface soil of the arable fields on the Rothamsted estate now contains from 3 to 5 per cent. of carbonate of lime, which is equivalent to 30 to 50 tons per acre ; and since none has been spread for the last seventy years at least, and solution in the rain water has constantly been going on, there must have been nearer 100 tons per acre at the beginning of the nineteenth century.

The result has been practically the creation of a soil fit for arable farming, for some of the Rothamsted fields which had never undergone the operation have had to be laid down to grass, so difficult did their cultivation prove in wet seasons.

Chalk is perhaps more suited than lime to very light sandy soils like the Lower Greensand or the Bagshot beds, for on such dry hot soils the application of quicklime is apt to result in too rapid a decay of the organic reserves of the land ; on clay soils, however, quicklime is preferable, as it is a much more effective agent in coagulating and improving the texture of the clay

CHAPTER X

SOIL TYPES

Classification of Soils according to their Physical or Chemical
Nature—Geological Origin the Basis of Classification—Vegetation Characteristic of Various Soil Types : Physical Structure,
Chemical Composition, Natural Flora and Weeds characteristic of Sands, Loams, Calcareous Soils, Clays, Peat, Marsh,
and Salt Soils—Soil Surveys, their Execution and Application.

PERHAPS the question of the greatest practical importance in connection with the scientific study of soils
is their classification into certain types defined by
their physical or chemical properties, and the alloca-
tion of these types to their appropriate areas, so as to
obtain a soil map of any given district. Despite
disturbing factors, to which allusion will be made later,
certain types of soil persist over wide stretches of
country, and are characterised not only by a general
resemblance in chemical or physical constitution, but
by a corresponding similarity in the natural flora they
bear, and their appropriateness to certain crops. The
constancy of the soil types is the result of a common
origin from the same kind of rock, and the difficulty
lies less in recognising the types than in drawing
boundary lines, so imperceptibly does one class shade
off into another. The only classification that can be
at all general, is one based upon the physical structure

and texture of the soil, viz., into sands, loams, and clays, with subdivisions dependent on the presence or absence of calcium carbonate, and upon the situation, as causing the accumulation or otherwise of humus.

In attempting to review the vegetation appropriate to different types of soil it will be found that two distinct factors must be taken into account — the relations of the soil to water, and its chemical constitution—which factors often interact in a complex fashion, different causes producing the same effect. A plant, for example, may be found upon sand because of its dryness, or, because of the absence of calcium carbonate usually associated with sand; another plant, having adapted its structure to use very small quantities of water, may equally well be found on a dry sand, or on a clay which holds so much water as to be injurious to the ordinary plant.

Plants have adapted themselves to conditions of dryness in very diverse ways; in some cases, as in gorse or broom, the leaf surface is much restricted; in others, the thickness of the cuticle has been increased, or the surface of the leaf is thickly clad with hairs; in other cases the leaves possess special tissues for storing water. Such plants are known as "xerophytes," and are found on soils which appear to differ very much from one another, for a soil may contain plenty of water and yet be physiologically dry, because of the presence of some other constituent hindering the absorption of water by the plant.

The areas on which xerophytic plants are found include not only the true desert areas, where great heat and intense illumination occur during the larger part of the year, but also the pervious sandy soils retaining very little moisture—sand dunes, shingle flats, and the like. Again, the plants of alkali soils and of salt marshes invaded by the sea, develop a xerophytic structure, because they would be injured if they absorbed large amounts of saline soil water. Peaty areas also act in the same way, for it is found that the humic acids in such soils withhold the water from the plant very obstinately. Exposed elevated regions with a low temperature, by reducing the power of the roots to absorb moisture, render it necessary that the plant should lose little by transpiration; hence we see certain conifers flourish both on dry sandy soils and wet elevated moors.

As regards the chemical side of the question, the most important soil constituent affecting vegetation is calcium carbonate; a large number of plants seem absolutely intolerant of lime in the soil, while others are rarely seen off limestone and chalk areas. Even among the humus-loving plants a different flora is found on the acid peaty areas from that prevalent on the mild humus areas where the soil water contains calcium bicarbonate in solution.

But, however characteristic the general aspect of the vegetation may be upon the different types of soil, it is rare to find cases of plants entirely intolerant of a different kind of soil from that which they habitually frequent; many plants show a preference for one soil or other without being exclusively confined to it. For example, the common primrose is undoubtedly a clay lover, yet it will be found widely distributed over all the English soils; the beech and the yew are typical trees of the chalk, good oak and hornbeam of the clay; Spanish chestnut, and many conifers like the Scotch fir, are sand lovers; yet each of these trees will be found commonly enough on other kinds of soils. It will rarely be found that plants will absolutely refuse to grow or even to flourish on soils of which they are naturally

S

intolerant; a lime-hating plant like gorse, for example, will grow freely enough on a calcareous soil in a garden where it is protected from competition. But in nature all plants are subjected to severe competition, and a very small depression of their vitality brought about by the presence or absence of some constituent of the soil, may so turn the scale against them that they are almost invariably crowded off areas of such soil, the exceptions being due to some other favourable factor coming into play locally.

Sands.

The typical sandy soils of this country are either alluvial flats in the lower levels of our rivers, passing into dunes where the sand accumulates near the sea, or are directly derived from some of the many coarse-grained sandy formations developed in England. The Bagshot beds and the Lower Greensand form wide areas in the south-east; the sandy beds of the Oolite produce similar soils in Northamptonshire and the East Midlands; further west and northward the Bunter beds give rise to other very coarse-textured soils, as does the Millstone Grit in more elevated areas in the North.

As these coarse-grained sands have been laid down in rough water, they consist in the main of silica, which alone is able to resist the degree of weathering and attrition to which the original material has been subjected. In consequence, the rock is initially without much calcium carbonate or other material which will yield soluble salts on further weathering; the open texture of the material also results in a very free movement of soil water, and this continues the removal of anything soluble. Occasionally a sandy rock is found which has been largely formed by the disin-

tegration of shells, so that it is rich in calcium
carbonate; but, as a rule, sandy soils are characterised
by poverty in this material. Most soils of this sandy
type seem to possess considerable amounts of oxide
of iron; the actual proportion present may not be so
large as in ordinary soils, but, being spread over the
comparatively small surface offered by the large grains,
it is more in evidence. The phosphoric acid, which
is rarely present in any quantity, generally about 0·1
per cent., is chiefly combined with the oxides of iron.
Because of the general lack of finer particles—in the
main clay derived from the weathering of felspar—
soils of this type are notably deficient in potash.

Despite their warmth and free aeration, sandy
soils often accumulate considerable amounts of humus,
an effect probably due to the absence of calcium
carbonate. Where depressions occur in the general
level of the ground, a layer of impervious ferric
hydrate or "pan" forms below the surface and holds
up the drainage water, which waterlogged condition
is at once followed by an accumulation of peat.

On these sandy areas cultivation is a very artificial
affair, and the soil has practically to be created. The
first necessity is a supply of lime and mineral salts,
to remedy the lack of nutriment; then as much humus
as possible must be obtained, by turning in or folding green crops, or even from their roots and stubble
only. The humus binds the soil together, creates a
reserve of manurial material, and much increases the
retentive power of the soil both for water and mineral
salts.

Being so dry, the specific heat of sandy soils is
exceptionally low; in consequence these soils are
early, and as they also recover quickly from rain, so
that cultivation is not forced to wait much on the

season but can be proceeded with very readily, they are especially suited to market gardening, wherever situated sufficiently near to a large town to enable large quantities of manure to be obtained cheaply. Where the water table is close to the surface, sandy soils can become very fertile, roots range freely in them, and applications of manure have their full effect. Like all light soils, they are apt to become very weedy. Of the crops suitable to soils of this type, spring wheat is often better than the autumn-sown variety; the quality of wheat is, however, generally inferior on sandy soils; barley is better than oats, and maize is worthy of attention as a fodder crop. Swedes, cabbages, and the cruciferous crops generally, are subject to "finger-and-toe," in consequence of the poverty of the soil in lime and soluble mineral constituents.

With certain exceptions, leguminous plants do not grow well on sandy soils, and require considerable supplies of lime and mineral manures; there are, however, some leguminous plants which are characteristically *calcifuges* — *i.e.*, intolerant of lime in the soil — lupins, serradella, and gorse belong to this class. Allusion has already been made to the reclamation of sandy land in Prussia by means of lupins, and probably more use might be made of the crop in this country on similar soils. Experiments made with gorse on the coarse sandy soil of the Royal Agricultural Society's farm at Woburn, indicate that it may become a profitable fodder crop on such soils.

Potatoes are perhaps the best crop on the sandy soils, but require considerable expenditure of manure, including large dressings of potash, to do well. Carrots are another crop particularly appropriate to sandy soils, as they need a deep, fine tilth.

The manuring of sandy soils must be based upon a

liberal use of lime, frequently renewed because of the ease with which water percolates and removes the calcium carbonate. Marling and chalking, wherever such materials are available, are better for the land than the use of quicklime, which is apt to induce too rapid an oxidation of the organic matter. Nitrogen is best supplied in its organic forms, as in well-rotted dung, the guanos, fish or meat manure, rape cake, etc.; nitrate of soda is apt to induce too rapid a growth, and also to be washed away. Sulphate of ammonia is unsuitable, owing to the lack of lime in the soil. Of phosphatic manures, superphosphate is unsuitable owing to its acid nature. Basic slag is also unsuitable as a rule, owing to the small quantities of water retained by the soil, but it answers well on sands where the water table is near the surface; on the whole, neutral easily available phosphates like phosphatic guano and steamed bone flour give the best results on these soils. Potash manures are much needed, and either kainit or sulphate of potash may be used. Gypsum is often used with good effect on such soils in the Wealden area, acting as a liberator of what little potash may be in the soil.

The natural flora of the sandy soils is of a double character—in part *xerophytic*, and associated with the prevailing dryness of the soils; in part *calcifuge*, and dependent on the absence of calcium carbonate. Plants with mycorhiza are abundant, owing, as already explained, to the comparative poverty of these soils in both water and soluble salts.

The characteristic sand trees are the Spanish chestnut, birch, holly, and many conifers; of these the Spanish chestnut and some of the firs, like *Pinus pinaster*, are particularly intolerant of calcium carbonate.

Many of the Ericaceæ, such as common heather and the heaths, cultivated species like the rhododendrons and azaleas of our gardens, are similarly intolerant of lime and associated with sandy soils; at higher levels various species of *Vaccinium* and kindred plants are common. Gorse (*Ulex europæus* and *U. nanus*), broom (*Cytisus scoparius*), *Genista anglica*, *Ornithopus*, and several vetches like *Vicia cracca*, are characteristic leguminous plants of sandy soils. The foxglove (*Digitalis purpurea*), sorrel (*Rumex acetosella*), and in undrained situations the sundews (*Drosera* sp.) are intolerant of lime and are common plants on sandy soils, as also are the common bracken (*Pteris aquilina*), and wavy hair grass (*Aira flexuosa*).

Characteristic weeds of sandy soils are, spurrey (*Spergula arvensis*), and sandwort-spurrey (*Spergularia rubra*), corn marigold (*Chrysanthemum segetum*), and knawel (*Scleranthus annuus* and *perennis*); *Papaver dubium* and *Centaurea cyanus* are also common on such soils. The bulbous buttercup (*Ranunculus bulbosus*) is very frequent on dry pastures, whether sandy or chalky, as is the small bindweed (*Convolvulus arvensis*) of similar soils under cultivation; the silverweed (*Potentilla anserina*), though generally indicative of winter flooding, is to be found on all kinds of poor, light land.

The Loams.

The sandy soils pass by imperceptible stages into the loams—free-working soils containing enough sand to be friable and to admit of percolation, yet retaining sufficient water near the surface to withstand short spells of dry weather. If the sandy fractions of the loam are mainly fine grained, the soil is apt to run and become very sticky in wet weather, afterwards

drying to hard clods; an admixture of coarser sand
results in a better texture.   The loams are typical
soils of arable cultivation and are suitable to all crops;
their manurial requirements vary with the origin of
each soil, and are largely conditioned by its poverty
or richness in calcium carbonate.   While no special
flora can be associated with the loams, there are several
weeds generally taken as indicative of good fertile soils
of this class; such are chickweed (*Stellaria media*),
groundsel (*Senecio vulgaris*), fat hen (*Chenopodium
album*), stinking mayweed (*Anthemis Cotula*), and
the Sow thistle (*Sonchus oleraceus*).   Other weeds
of cultivated land, which only occur when the soil
is capable of carrying fair crops, are goose grass
(*Galium aparine*), the speedwells (*Veronica agrestis*,
etc.), pimpernel (*Anagallis arvensis*), henbit (*Lamium
amplexicaule*), wild poppy (*Papaver rhaeas*), and the
small spurges like *Euphorbia Peplus*.   The alluvial
soils which border the rivers and pass into considerable marshes at their mouths, must, by their
texture, be classed among the loams, and present no
specific features, except where they are waterlogged
and marshy, or near the sea where the subsoil water
becomes so rich in salt as to alter the character of
the vegetation.   The marshy patches accumulate, as
a rule, what has already been described as "mild
humus," owing to the presence of bicarbonate of lime
in the soil water; it is generally accompanied by
deposits of pulverulent ferric hydrate.   The presence
of rushes, of sedges like the carnation grass, or orchids
like *O. maculata* and *O. latifolia*, are characteristic of
these spots requiring drainage.   Lousewort (*Pedicularis
palustris*) is said only to occur in marshes where the
water contains lime.

The salt marshes possess a characteristic vegeta-

tion of what are termed halophytes, plants capable
of resisting a considerable quantity of salt in the
medium in which they grow. Among cultivated
plants, mangolds, asparagus, and crucifers like cabbage,
are most tolerant of salt, and the two former are true
halophytes.

Many halophytes live by acting as xerophytes, and
taking very little water up; they are also able to
store away in their tissues quantities of saline matter
which would be toxic to the majority of plants. The
ash of *Armeria maritima* shows 12 to 15 per cent. of
chlorine in the ash; in *Aster tripolium* the proportion
rises to over 40 per cent. in the ash of the leaves, and
to 50 per cent. in that of the stem; yet although the
plants habitually contain these large amounts of salt,
they will grow perfectly well in ordinary soil where
they can get but little.

The Australian salt-bush (*Atriplex semibaccatum*),
which has already been mentioned as tolerant of a
large amount of alkali in the soil, also removes much
soluble matter—the dry plant containing as much as
20 per cent. of ash, so that the salt content of
the soil may be materially reduced by cropping with
this plant. The halophytes seen in the salt marshes
of this country consist of various species of *Atriplex*,
Beta (the source of the cultivated beets and mangolds), and other Chenopodiaceæ, *Statice armeria*,
Aster tripolium, *Frankenia*, and a number of cruciferous plants like *Crambe*, and *Cakile*, with umbellifers
like *Crithmum*. Some plants show a great dislike to
salt, even in small proportion, *e.g.*, the Rosaceæ,
Orchidaceæ, and the Ericaceæ.

Calcareous Soils.

It is difficult to draw an exact line of demarcation between the loams and calcareous soils, so variable is the proportion of carbonate of lime, owing to its continual removal by the percolation of water containing carbonic acid. Even on the chalk and limestone, where the thickness of the soil layer is to be measured in inches, the surface soil may have its calcium carbonate almost wholly removed, and, again, where the deeper soils of calcareous origin accumulate in the valleys, there is nothing to distinguish them from ordinary loams. However, the general aspect of the calcareous soils containing from 5 to 60 per cent. of calcium carbonate is characteristic, and the natural flora always indicates the presence of much lime. The texture of the calcareous soils may vary within any limits, according to the formation from which they have originated. On the one hand, extremely fine-textured heavy marls exist; for example, the soils derived from the strata at the base of the Chalk and upper beds of the Gault in the south and east of England; on the contrary, fairly coarse sand may form a considerable proportion of the soil, rendering it light in texture, as is the case with many of the soils resting on the chalk of the North Downs. In all cases these calcareous soils are typically sticky when wet, and easily cake on the surface when dried. Such soils, again, lose their organic matter very rapidly by decay; in farming them it is desirable to use every means to increase the proportion of humus by adding farmyard manure, by folding roots on the land, or by ploughing in green crops. Slowly acting nitrogenous manures, like rape dust or shoddy, are valuable; again, there is always enough calcium carbonate present naturally to render to sulphate of ammonia its full value as a source of nitrogen. The lighter calcareous soils require a free use of nitrogenous manures to get good crops. Calcareous soils are generally well provided with phosphoric acid, owing to the organic origin of the calcium carbonate; the rule is, however, by no means universal, the upper Chalk, for example, yields soils with less than 0·1 per cent. of this constituent. Superphosphate is undoubtedly the best source of phosphoric acid for such soils, basic slag is almost without action. The proportion of potash present in these soils is generally reflected in their texture; if light and near the unaltered rock, they are as a rule very deficient in this constituent, and require its addition for the growth of any of the root crops. Salt is generally beneficial as an addition to manures on the calcareous soils.

The calcareous soils are generally warm, dry, and healthy for stock; when deep and sheltered they are extremely fertile; the thinner soils are rather subject to certain insect pests, like the turnip flea. The abundance of worms in chalky pasture is worthy of note. The lighter calcareous soils are notoriously weedy. In addition to the usual weeds of light land, Fumitory (*Fumaria officinalis*), *Geranium molle*, and kindred species, are almost confined to soils with a considerable proportion of calcium carbonate. Two crops are very characteristic of calcareous soils wherever the climate will admit of their growth, viz., sainfoin and lucerne, which flourish excellently, and provide abundant and valuable fodder even on the driest chalk soils.

The natural flora of these calcareous soils includes the beech, yew, and wild cherry, among trees; the juniper, box, mealy guelder rose (*Viburnum lantana*), beam tree (*Pyrus aria*), dogwood (*Cornus sanguinea*), and *Clematis vitalba*, among shrubs.

The vegetation is characteristically rich in flowering plants: amongst the Leguminosæ, the horse-shoe vetch (*Hippocrepis comosa*), bird's-foot trefoil (*Lotus corniculatus*), kidney vetch (*Anthyllis Vulneraria*), are everywhere abundant; milkwort (*Polygala*), bladder campion (*Silene inflata*), *Spiræa filipendula*, burnet (*Poterium sanguisorba*), wild parsnip (*Pastinaca sativa*), sheep's scabious (*Scabiosa columbaria*), chicory (*Cichorium intybus*), and certain of the Gentianaceæ, as *G. amarella* and *Chlora perfoliata*, the viper's bugloss (*Echium vulgare*), and a number of labiates like *Origanum*, are characteristic of the pastures and waste places on chalk and limestone. Amongst grasses, *Avena pubescens*, *A. flavescens*, *Bromus erectus*, and *Brachypodium pinnatum*, are common.

While it has been indicated that many plants are intolerant of lime, others show the effect of any excess in the soils by a stunted development of the plant, often accompanied by a reduced size of the leaf, and a sickly yellow or even white colour. This unhealthy condition of "chlorosis" is particularly noticeable on the stiff marls, which are but little aerated but contain much calcium carbonate; on the Continent it often affects vines, particularly when grafted on American stocks.

Clay Soils.

It has already been indicated that clay soils are those in which the finer fractions of sand, silt, and clay predominate; the presence of any considerable proportion of coarse sand causes the soil to become friable, and would class it with the loams. The texture of clay soils naturally varies very much; the heaviest clays occur in dry climates, where the percolation has not been sufficiently great to wash away many of the finer particles; in the east and south-east of England the Oxford and the London Clay, with the Boulder clays derived therefrom, give rise to the most stubborn and intractable clays. On these soils the old practice of an occasional bare fallow is still carried out, and is almost necessary to maintain the soil in good cultivation. As a rule, the strong clay soils have of late years been laid down to permanent pasture; the cost and the difficulty of arable culti- vation (for much wet weather in autumn or spring may render it impossible to put horses on the land for long periods), and the great fall in prices of both wheat and beans, the staple crops of such land, have rendered it necessary to resort to a cheaper method of farming.

Most clays carry good permanent pasture, because the soil retains enough water to keep the grass growing through any but the longer periods of drought; in very dry years, however, clay suffers severely from the drought; the surface cracks and the subsoil dries through the cracks; the resistance also offered by the close texture of the soil to the capillary rise of soil water renders the winter rainfall less available to the crop than on soils of lighter texture. The benefits accruing from drainage, in making the soil dry more quickly after rain and resist drought better, have already been discussed. Certain clay soils may be found too close textured to carry good pasture; the soil sets so firmly that aeration becomes very defective, and the vegetation degenerates into surface rooting, stoloniferous grasses like *Agrostis alba*.

Owing to their fine division, their origin from the

compound silicates of primitive rocks, and the reduced
percolation which they permit, all clays are comparatively rich in soluble mineral salts.   Many of them show
crystals of selenite ($CaSO_4 2H_2O$) in the subsoil comparatively near to the surface; magnesium sulphate is
often abundant, and strongly impregnates the water
obtained from the wells or the occasional springs to be
found in the clays.   In the Weald of Kent the shallow
wells in the clay yield water that is almost undrinkable,
containing, as it does, from 150 to 450 parts of dissolved
matters per 100,000, consisting chiefly of the sulphates
(with some chlorides) of magnesium and calcium.   The
sulphates often originate from the oxidation of finely
divided iron pyrites.   The presence of ferrous salts
and other unoxidised iron compounds has already
been alluded to as a source of sterility in clay soils
particularly where the subsoil has been incautiously
brought to the surface.   In the cultivation of all land
it is important to keep the surface soil on the top, and
to attempt to deepen the staple with care; but this is
particularly the case with clays, where the land may
easily be injured for years by over-deep ploughing.   No
soils show more marked change than the clays do in
passing from soil to subsoil, both in chemical composition and physical texture.

Many clay soils, especially when undrained, possess
a great tendency to accumulate hydrated ferric oxide
some few inches below the surface, at about the level
to which the soil is ordinarily aerated.   This deposit
sometimes forms a continuous layer or "pan"; in drier
 climates it becomes a kind of "crowstone" gravel, made
up of little nodules of hydrated oxide of iron, containing also manganese.   This material frequently forms
a serious obstacle to cultivation, and requires to be
broken up with a crowbar or a subsoil plough before

any deep-rooting crop can be properly grown. Its origin is perhaps not entirely explained as yet; the respective shares of the iron bacteria of Winogradsky, or the purely chemical actions of solution and reduction by the organic matter and carbonic acid, followed by redeposit on evaporation, is a matter requiring further investigation. The formation of the material is only noticed in clays very poor in calcium carbonate and liable to waterlogging through insufficient percolation.

Owing to their coolness, their retention of moisture, and comparative impermeability to air, humus tends to accumulate in the clay soils; both arable and pasture soils show a higher proportion of organic matter and of humus than is found, as a rule, on the lighter lands; the effect of manures like farmyard manure is also more lasting. The use of more slowly acting nitrogenous manures is therefore not so desirable on the clay soils; on the other hand, sulphate of ammonia is often unsuitable because of the want of calcium carbonate, and nitrate of soda, which often gives the best returns, is apt to affect the texture injuriously.

The clays are very generally deficient in calcium carbonate, often to an extreme degree, much to the detriment of the texture of the soil. The use of lime is of the utmost value to all clay soils, improving the texture, making them drier and therefore warmer and earlier, and rendering available the supplies of nitrogen and potash with which they are often liberally endowed. The excess of magnesia and unoxidised iron compounds which also characterise many clays is corrected by the use of lime.

Many clay soils also show a considerable deficiency of phosphoric acid, and respond freely to dressings

with manures containing this substance. Superphosphate may be used with advantage wherever there is
enough calcium carbonate in the soil, but basic slag
is the typical phosphatic manure for the strong soils
which retain sufficient water to render the phosphates
active. While supplying phosphoric acid, it also
contains free lime in a fine state of subdivision, and
so liberates in a soluble state the reserves of nitrogen
and potash in the soils. It should, however, not be
forgotten that as the basic slag only supplies one
element of plant food, the phosphoric acid, the soil
may easily be exhausted by continual cropping and
manuring with basic slag alone.

Potash is always present in large amounts in clay
soils, 0·5 per cent. soluble in strong hydrochloric acid
is often to be found, while the proportion which can
be extracted after completely breaking up the soil
with hydrofluoric acid may rise to 2 per cent. Clay
soils are late, and their crops grow slowly and ripen
tardily except in specially dry seasons, when the clay
shrinks so much as to cut off all access of moisture
from the subsoil, and prematurely ends the period of
growth; on the other hand, the quality of crops grown
on the clay is often high. The typical crops of strong
land are wheat, beans, and mangolds; owing to the
closeness of the texture of the soils, weeds are much
less in evidence on the clays than elsewhere, though
some few are exceedingly troublesome.

On the poorer pastures, the spiny form of
rest harrow (*Ononis arvensis*), the wild teazel
(*Dipsacus sylvestris*), *Ranunculus arvensis*, and *Genista
tinctoria*, are characteristic and often troublesome
weeds; on cultivated land the "black-bent" grass
(*Alopecurus agrestis*), and field mint (*Mentha arvensis*)
are difficult to deal with. Other plants characteristic

of strong soils are the primrose (*Primula vulgaris*), and the wild carrot (*Daucus carota*).

Peaty Soils.

The accumulation of humus to form peaty soils has already been discussed, and is associated with water-logging, which cuts off the access of air and so sets up an anaerobic fermentation of the residues of the vegetation growing upon the surface. There is always a deposit of ferric hydrate accompanying the accumulation of peat, as explained before. As the reclamation of peaty soils has already been dealt with, it will be sufficient here to indicate that their great characteristic is a deficiency in soluble mineral constituents, notably salts of lime and potash. It has also been mentioned that, as a consequence of the acid nature of the medium, the bacteria of nitrification are absent or few in number. All attempts at the cultivation of peaty soils begin with drainage, and must then proceed on the basis of neutralising the organic acids with lime and providing a sufficiency of mineral food for the plant, thus also inducing nitrification to render available the large quantities of nitrogen which have accumulated. Of the common crop plants, oats and potatoes are perhaps the most tolerant of extreme amounts of acid humus. The normal vegetation of peaty soils is a mixture of xerophytic and calcifuge forms; the Conifers, the Ericaceæ, *Drosera*, *Rumex Acetosella*, *Pedicularis sylvatica*, Sphagnum moss, and many sedges and rushes, are characteristic of sour, peaty soils. Other characteristic plants are more properly Northern or Arctic species, and, occurring only in the uncultivated uplands, need not be considered here.

Soil Surveys.

To render the scientific study of soils properly available for the service of the agriculturalist, more is required than the examination of single samples of soil, representing, at the best, only the land dealt with by one person. Over any wide district, not only would such work become expensive and practically endless, liable also to many sources of error through local and accidental variations of the soil on the spot from which the sample was drawn, but each analysis would lose the greater part of its value if it could not be co-ordinated and brought into line with others drawn from soils of the same type. A general soil survey of a district, so as to be able to lay down a plan of the distribution of the various soil types, accompanied by a discussion of the broad characteristics of each, should be the basis upon which the interpretation of the analysis of the soil of any particular field is to be founded. Only by comparison with the type can the analysis of any particular soil be properly inter-preted—*e.g.*, the fact that a soil from a given arable field contains 0.15 per cent. of phosphoric acid takes a very different aspect when it is known that the soils of the same type contain as a rule 0.18 to 0.20 per cent. of phosphoric acid, particularly if, also, the response of that kind of land to phosphatic manures is known by field trials, or from the accumulated experience of farmers. The first question which requires settle-ment is how far a soil survey is possible; to what extent can the boundaries of soil types be traced; are the various types sufficiently constant over a wide area to render this mapping feasible? In many cases there seems to be little but confusion, even in the soils on a single farm; field differs from field, and great variations may be manifest even within the confines of a single field. But, in the main, each soil type has a well-defined area, within which it presents a reasonably constant composition and texture, and though the boundaries cannot be laid down with the precision of the outcrop of a stratum, the zone of transition from one type to the other may be indicated with approximate accuracy.

The basis upon which any soil survey must be constructed is the origin of the soils; each geological formation, for example, will give rise to a distinct type of soil if it has been formed *in situ;* should the weathered material have further undergone transport by water, two or more types may have been constructed by the sorting action of the water. It is also well known that a geological formation may change very considerably in lithological character in passing from the lower to the upper portions of the bed. For example, stiff as the London Clay is, the upper beds become increasingly sandy in character, so that it is not easy to draw a line of demarcation between the soil arising from these beds and those due to the Bagshot Sands above. The lower beds of the Gault Clay are also very pure, and give rise to a stiff clay deficient in calcium carbonate; the upper beds become marly, and form soils indistinguishable from those due to the contiguous Chalk Marl. Similarly, a geological formation may show a progressive change of character in passing into a different area, which change will be reflected in the soils derived from them. For example, the Great Oolite limestones of the Cotswolds shade off into sandstones in Northamptonshire, and the Hythe beds of calcareous sandstone in East Kent become pure coarse-grained sandstones in West Surrey. However, in the main, geological origin may be taken as the basis of a soil survey, to which must be added the further subdivisions due to the causes enumerated above, or to the local movements of rain-wash or ill-defined drift, that may alter the character of the soil without being of any particular geological importance.

A soil map will consist of a " drift " map, with some further details showing the superficial formations occupying the surface of the ground, and notes regarding the local variations in the type of soil derived from each particular stratum. The aim of a soil survey is to carry further the work of the geological survey as regards the superficial formations ; the only classification which can be adapted will be one based upon the physical texture of the soil, and indicated by such conventional terms as clays, clay loams, sandy loams, marls, etc. At the same time, the map must indicate the various origin of the different loams which may be found in the area under survey, and, by reference to the accompanying text, should give those details of physical structure and chemical constitution which characterise the soil, but which cannot be set out except by an over-elaborate classification.

The field portion of the work of a soil survey consists in the exploration of the subsoil by means of an auger, aided by any natural sections which may be displayed. The boundary between two soil types may generally thus be laid down by the aspect of the soil and subsoil ; from time to time, however, samples must be retained for more detailed examination in the laboratory, whenever the look and touch of the material are not sufficient for a decision *in situ.* An immediate examination with the microscope, the behaviour of the soil with acid, or a rough sifting in a stream of water, will, as a rule, be sufficient to refer a given example of subsoil to one type or another. Complicated cases arise from time to time, especially in

the river valleys, where alluvium of varied epochs and
rain-wash of not very different origin may be hope-
lessly intermingled.   In many cases, however, where
the outcrop of the originating formations is broad, and
where the gradients of the country are slight, the soil
may be extremely constant in composition over a wide
area, so that the survey has only to notice such minor
variations as the grading from a lighter to heavier type
as one descends a slope, or the occasional influx of
drift material by creeping from a neighbouring area.
The further work of a field survey will be the selection
of typical samples of soil and subsoil for detailed
examination and analysis in the laboratory, the col-
lection of such data as the distance to, and nature of
ground water, and any particulars which may be
available locally, as to special features in the working
of each type of soil, or in the growth of its crops;
the nature and character of such deposits as "brick
earth" in each district can also be reported.   The
samples for detailed analysis should be taken where a
general survey of the district indicates the soil as most
likely to be typical of the formation, and free from
admixture with drift and other accidental intrusions.
At the same time, since the soil in the main will by no
means be so pure as the typical samples, a much larger
number of samples should be taken and subjected to
a less detailed examination, by way of ascertaining
within what limits the normal variation of the soil is
confined.

The number of type samples to be taken must be
entirely decided by an examination of the circum-
stances; in continental areas, where deposition has
been very uniform over wide districts, one or two
samples may be sufficient to characterise an extensive
soil type; in other cases the local variations may be so

much in evidence that the "typical soil" can only be constructed by putting together the results of many separate determinations.

But the practice of constructing a typical soil for analysis by mixing together equal fractions of many samples drawn in the area in question, is not to be recommended. Not only may an entirely foreign or accidentally impure sample be introduced without detection, but, further, the limits of variation normally to be expected in individual soils of the same type is just as important as the composition of the type itself. Again, the existence of unsuspected systematic variations is entirely obscured by any process of mixing samples. The character of the information which should accompany the soil maps must largely depend on the purpose of the survey, whether it is concerned with the agriculture of an old and settled country, or whether it partakes of the nature of an exploration, and aims at showing the capacities of the land for new crops and industries. In the United States, for example, the latter form of soil survey is exemplified; in many parts of the country agriculture is so recent that there is no accumulation of experience as to the crops most suited to each kind of land; hence the survey, by comparisons of the texture of the soil, the climatic conditions, and the depth to ground water, with the conditions prevailing in better known areas, can directly tell the settler with what crops he is most likely to succeed. The cultivation of special crops like tobacco and sugar beet, to take two examples of special interest at the present time in the United States, can be extended into new districts possessing suitable soils, with a minimum of the risk which must always attend the introduction of a novel form of culture. The suitability of other classes of land for irrigation, the nature and extent of already existing alkali patches, and the most promising methods of reclamation, are also prominent features in the work of the United States soil survey. As the crops in a new country of this kind are in the main grown by the aid of the natural fertility of the soil alone, and fertilisers are little used, the chemical examination of the soil becomes of less importance than the mechanical.

In a settled country like our own, the character of the information to be derived from a soil survey is of a different order; the land has been under cultivation so long that a great mass of local information, based upon experience, exists as to the character even of individual fields.

Hints as to the cultivation, based upon the texture of the soil as determined by analysis, would be too general to be of any service; indeed, it is rather to be hoped that by collating many mechanical analyses with the information derived from men possessing long experience of the soil, further light can be shed upon the connection between physical structure and the finer points of tillage. The suitability of the different types of soil to new crops—as, for example, the extension of the area under fruit—can be ascertained, and many expensive mistakes due to planting on unsuitable land could be saved to the farmer. Suggestions can also be made as to the amelioration of the soil by drainage, or by the incorporation of materials like clay, chalk, or marl, occurring in the vicinity. Fifty years ago, no department of British agriculture was more carefully attended to than the improvement of the texture of the soil, and great tracts of what is now fertile land were practically created; lower values to-day have caused this important matter to be almost entirely neglected.

But the chief application of a soil survey in this country lies in the information that can be afforded as to the use of manures ; enormous economies might be effected in the bills of almost every farmer using artificial manures, if the latter were properly adapted to his soils and crops. Farmers are often recommended to carry out manurial trials upon their own farms until they have ascertained the peculiarities and specific requirements of the soil, but advice of this kind treats altogether too lightly the somewhat delicate business of conducting field experiments. Putting aside the mechanical difficulties attending a trial of this kind, and the overpowering effect of minor inequalities of the ground and other accidental conditions which so often nullify the experimental treatment, it is rarely that the farmer will be found able to arrange a scheme of experiment likely to give information of permanent value. If one may judge from the published accounts of many field experiments carried out in this country by public bodies, which so often show a misapprehension of the points really at issue, there is every probability that the individual farmer will be as often misled as guided by the results of his own experiments. The design and conduct of field experiments must be left to the expert, who surveys the subject from a wider standpoint, who can compare various trials, and is in a position to continue them for a period of years, rejecting at any early stage a considerable proportion which are inevitably vitiated by some concealed local peculiarity. A body of experts conducting a soil survey and field experiments simultaneously in the same area and co-ordinating their results, can give advice of the most definite character as to the scheme of manuring to be adopted for each soil type. The fundamental factor requiring consideration in this matter, and brought out in the soil survey, is the proportion of lime normal to each soil type; knowing this factor, and the retentivity of the soil for moisture under ordinary conditions of rainfall, one can decide upon the character of the manures for most loamy soils. Soils of more specific character, like the sands or clays, present more character- istic deficiencies of some of the manurial constituents, so that for many crops the use of manures like phosphates and potash is wholly determined by the soil and not the crop.

It is not too much to say that the information as to the manuring which is being accumulated at many experimental centres throughout the country can only be rendered properly available by the execution of a soil survey in the district under consideration. In many countries a soil survey has been made part of the national service for the agriculturist; the mag- nificent publications of the Division of Soils of the United States Department of Agriculture form a case in point. In Prussia, the maps and reports of the Laboratorium für Bodenkunde at Berlin may be con- sulted as models of the thoroughness and refinement to which work of this kind can be pushed; the Gembloux Station in Belgium is executing a system- atic chemical survey of the Belgian soils. In France, the work rests with the local authorities of each Department, but in parts is being carried out, as witness the beautiful maps due to the single- handed work of M. Gaillon, Director of the Station Agronomique de l'Aisne at Laon. In Britain the great initial want is the publication of drift maps of the geological survey on the 6-inch scale; the 1-inch to the mile survey, which alone has been published, or even executed in most districts, is too small to admit of necessary detail. It is also very often laid down on an early cadastral survey, which makes the identification of the modern boundaries a matter of difficulty. If the country were in possession of a series of "drift" maps on the scale of 6 inches to the mile, the work could be rapidly supplemented by soil surveys and analyses executed by the local agricultural colleges and research institutions, until every farmer could be put in possession of that exact knowledge of the soil which is fundamental to all farming operations.

APPENDICES

NUMBER . . .	1	2	3	4	5	6
DISTRICT . . . {	WISLEY, SURREY.		WOODNESBOROUGH, KENT.		TEYNHAM, KENT.	
FORMATION . . .	Bagshot Sand.		Oldhaven Beds.		Thanet Sand.	
NATURE . . . {	Very poor, light land, much of it in waste.		Very Light Sand, valuable for Market Gardening, but not for General Farming.		Light loam of great repute for fertility.	
TILTH	Arable.		Arable.		Arable.	
	Soil.	Subsoil.	Soil.	Subsoil.	Soil.	Subsoil.
Moisture	0·79	1·01	1·05	2·04	1·62	1·71
Loss on Ignition . .	3·32	2·18	3·33	1·93	3·46	2·49
Nitrogen	0·10	0·07	0·12	0·08	0·16	0·04
Potash	0·31	0·17	0·33	0·38	0·35	0·47
Potash, soluble in 1 per cent. Citric Acid . . }	0·02	...	0·018	...	0·019	...
Lime	0·10	...	0·31	...	0·58	...
Magnesia . . .	0·12	...	0·23	...	0·26	...
Alumina	0·92	...	1·74	...	2·34	...
Ferric Oxide . . .	0·57	...	1·38	...	2·10	...
Oxide of Manganese .	0·04	...	0·05	...	0·14	...
Calcium Carbonate . .	0·01	0·04	0·02	0·01	0·33	0·05
Phosphoric Acid . .	0·05	0·03	0·06	0·05	0·10	0·07
Phosphoric Acid, soluble in 1 per cent. Citric Acid . . }	0·012	...	0·017	...	0·044	...
Sulphuric Acid . .	0·03	...	0·05	...	0·01	...

DIX I.

OF TYPICAL SOILS.

Fine Earth—Air-dried.

7	8	9	10	11	12	13	14	15	16
SUTTON BY DOVER, KENT.		BENTLEY, HANTS.		MARDEN, KENT.		WANBOROUGH, SURREY.		WOODCHURCH, KENT.	
Chalk.		Upper Greensand.		Alluvial.		London Clay.		Weald Clay.	
Light loam, "sheep and barley land."		Good loam, noted for fertility.		Heavy loam, rather poor.		Heavy loam, of fair repute.		Very heavy clay, of little value.	
Arable.		Arable.		Arable.		Arable.		Arable.	
Soil.	Subsoil.	Soil.	Subsoil.	Soil.	Subsoil.	Soil.	Subsoil.	Soil.	Subsoil.
6·76	4·18	3·23	4·22	2·40	3·16	3·91	2·94	4·07	3·62
9·28	7·37	4·60	4·03	6·11	3·78	4·38	3·88	8·73	5·37
0·25	0·13	0·19	0·12	0·18	...	0·19	0·06	0·26	0·12
0·43	0·60	0·60	0·63	0·90	...	0·33	0·67	1·03	1·11
0·018	...	0·025	0·031	0·006	...	0·017	...	0·012	...
...	...	2·61	2·61	0·99	...	...	...	0·70	...
0·69	...	0·38	0·48	0·37	...	0·35	...	0·31	...
6·45	...	9·87	...	8·44	...	4·14	...	6·45	...
4·27	...	2·25	2·06	3·92	...	2·47	...	8·81	...
0·16	...	0·12	0·16	0·03	...	0·71	...	0·08	...
18·1	11·4	0·47	3·48	0·64	0·18	0·06	0·08	0·08	0·03
0·19	0·17	0·27	0·15	0·12	0·06	0·06	0·03	0·11	0·05
0·001	...	0·16	0·08	0·009	...	0·014	...	0·004	...
0·09	...	0·06	0·12	0·06	...	0·04	...	0·08	...

APPENDIX II

BIBLIOGRAPHY

The following short list of references will take the student to some of the more important original sources of information on each of the subjects treated of in this book. They have been selected from among the great mass of papers that exist, not because they are necessarily the most important, but as suggestive in themselves, and likely to lead the student to make further acquaintance with the methods as well as with the results of research. Several of the papers also contain a series of references to other workers in the same field.

THE ORIGIN OF SOILS.

1. RISLER, E.—*Géologie Agricole*, 4 vols., Paris, 1884-97.
2. MERRILL, G. P.—*Rocks, Rock Weathering, and Soils*, New York, 1897.

ANALYSIS AND COMPOSITION OF SOILS.

3. LAUNFER AND WAHNSCHAFFE.—*Mit. a. d. Laboratorium für Bodenkunde*, B. III., h. 2, Berlin.
4. PETERMANN.—*Recherches de Chimie le*, III., Brussels, 1898.
5. HILGARD, U.S. Dep. of Agric., Div. of Chem., Bull. 38, 1893.
6. HILGARD, U.S. Dep. of Agric., Div. of Soils, Bull. 4, 1896.
7. HILGARD.—*Soils*, The Macmillan Company, New York, 1906.
8. MITSCHERLICH, E. A.—*Bodenkunde für Land u. Forstwirte*, 1905.
9. LAWES AND GILBERT.—*Rothamsted Memoirs*, V., No. 19.
10. DYER.—*J. Chem. Soc.*, 1894, 65, 115.
11. DYER.—*Phil. Trans.*, 194, B. (1901), 235.
12. DYER.—U.S. Dep. of Agric., Bull. 106, 1902.
13. HALL, PLYMEN, AND AMOS.—*Trans. Chem. Soc.*, 1902, 81, 117 ; 1906, 89, 207.
14. HALL.—"Analysis of Soil by the Plant," *J. Agric. Sci.*, 1905, 1, 65.

APPENDIX II

303

Soil Physics.

15. WARINGTON.—*Physical Properties of Soils*, Oxford, 1900.
16. KING.—*Physics of Agriculture*, Madison, Wis., 1901.
17. HILGARD.—U.S. Dep. of Agric., Weather Bureau, Bull. 3, 1892.
18. WHITNEY.—U.S. Dep. of Agric., Weather Bureau, Bull. 4, 1892.
19. HELLRIEGEL.—*B. z. d. nat. Grundlagen des Ackerbaues*, Braunschweig, 1883.
20. LAWES AND GILBERT.—*Rothamsted Memoirs*, Vol. III., No. 11 ; Vol. V., No. 5.
21. BRIGGS.—U.S. Dep. of Agric. Year-Book, 1900, 397.
See also Hilgard, No. 7 ; Wollny, No. 20.

Soil Organisms.

22. WOLLNY.—*Zersetzung der Organischen Stoffe*, Heidelberg, 1897.
23. OMELIANSKY.—*Compt. Rend.*, 121 (1895), 653 ; 125 (1897), 970.
24. WINOGRADSKY.—*Compt. Rend.*, 121 (1895), 742.
25. LAFAR.—*Technische Mycologie*, 2nd ed., Fischer, Jena, 1904.

Fixation of Nitrogen.

26. LAWES AND GILBERT.—*Phil. Trans.*, II., 431, 1861 ; B. I., 1889.
27. LAWES AND GILBERT.—*J. R. Ag. Soc.*, E., 3rd s., II., 657, 1891.
28. HELLRIEGEL AND WILFARTH.—*D. Land. Vers. Stat.*, 460, 1887.
29. NOBBE AND HILTNER.—*D. Land. Vers. Stat.*, 1899.
30. WINOGRADSKY.—*Compt. Rend.*, 118 (1894).
31. MAZÉ.—*Ann. de l'Inst. Pasteur*, 11 (1897).
32. JACOBITZ.—*Cent. für Bakt.*, II., 1901, 7, 783.
33. BEIJERINCK.—*Cent. für Bakt.*, II., 1902, 9, 3.

Nitrification.

34. SCHLOESING AND MÜNTZ.—*Compt. Rend.*, 80 (1877), 1250.
35. WARINGTON.—*J. C. S.*, 1878, 1879, 1884, 1891.
36. LAWES, GILBERT, AND WARINGTON.—*J. R. Ag. Soc.*, E., 2nd s., 19 (1883).

37. WINOGRADSKY.—*Compt. Rend.*, 113 (1893), 116.
38. DEHÉRAIN.—*Ann. Agron.*, 19, 409.
39. KING.—Wisconsin Ag. Exp. Station Annual Reports, 17 (1900), 18 (1901).
40. BOULLANGER AND MASSOL.—*Ann. Pasteur*, 1903, 17, 492.

DENITRIFICATION.

41. GAYON AND DUPETIT.—*Compt. Rend.*, 95 (1882), 644.
42. WAGNER.—*D. Landw. Presse*, 1895, 123.
43. WARINGTON.—*J. R. Ag. Soc., E.*, 3rd s., 8.
44. STOKLASA.—*Cent. f. Bakt.*, 7 (1901), 260.

MYCORHIZA.

45. STAHL.—*Jahrb. f. wiss. Botanik.*, 34.

ABSORPTION OF SALTS BY SOIL.

46. WAY.—*J. R. Ag. Soc., E.*, 1st s., 11, 323 ; 13, 123.
47. VOELCKER.—*J. R. Ag. Soc., E.*, 1st s., 21 (1860), 93 ; 25 (1864), 333.
48. VOELCKER.—*J. R. Ag. Soc., E.*, 2nd s., 10 (1874), 132.
49. LAWES, GILBERT, AND WARINGTON.—*J. R. Ag. Soc., E.*, 2nd s., XVII. (1881), 241 ; XVIII. (1882), 1.
50. HALL AND GIMINGHAM, *Trans. Chem. Soc.*, 91 (1907), 677.

ALKALI SOILS.

51. HILGARD.—U.S. Dep. of Agric. Year-Book, 1895, 103.
52. HILGARD.—Univ. of California Ag. Exp. Sta. Bull. 128 (1900).
53. WILLCOCKS.—*Egyptian Irrigation*, 2nd ed.

SOIL SURVEYS, ETC.

54. SCHIMPER, A. F. W.—*Pflanzen Geographie*, Jena, 1898.
55. U.S. Dep. of Agric., Div. of Soils, "Field Operations," 1901.
56. WHITNEY.—"Tobacco Soils," U.S. Dep. of Agric. Bull. 11, 1898.
57. VEITCH.—"Maryland Soils," Maryland Ag. Exp. Sta. Bull. 70, 1901.
    See also Nos. 3 and 4.

INDEX

PRINTED BY
OLIVER AND BOYD
EDINBURGH

2

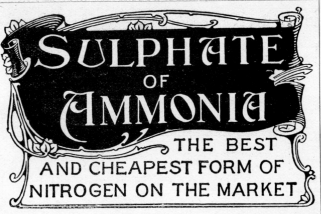

SULPHATE OF AMMONIA

THE BEST AND CHEAPEST FORM OF NITROGEN ON THE MARKET

	Average Crops per Acre, United Kingdom, for 10 years (1899-1908).	Crops per Acre obtained with SULPHATE OF AMMONIA, 1909-1910.	
TURNIPS	13·49 Tons	44 Tons	Heaviest Crop
		35 ,,	Average ,,
SWEDES	13·49 ,,	42 ,,	Heaviest ,,
		33 ,,	Average ,,
MANGELS	19·62 ,,	84 ,,	Heaviest ,,
		46 ,,	Average ,,
POTATOES	5·85 ,,	22 ,,	Heaviest ,,
		16 ,,	Average ,,

Thus showing that the proper use of SULPHATE OF AMMONIA yields Crops

Two or three times as heavy as the 10 years' average (1899-1908) for the United Kingdom.

PAMPHLETS, containing RECIPES FOR ALL CROPS, also information as to sources of supply of Manures,

CAN BE HAD POST FREE OF

SULPHATE OF AMMONIA COMMITTEE,
4 FENCHURCH AVENUE,
LONDON, E.C.

3

5

THE BULB BOOK
OR, BULBOUS AND TUBEROUS PLANTS FOR THE OPEN AIR, STOVE, AND GREENHOUSE

CONTAINING PARTICULARS AS TO DESCRIPTIONS, CULTURE, PROPAGATION, ETC., OF PLANTS FROM ALL PARTS OF THE WORLD HAVING BULBS, CORMS, TUBERS, OR RHIZOMES (ORCHIDS EXCLUDED)

BY JOHN WEATHERS

Author of "A Practical Guide to Garden Plants," "French Market-Gardening," "Beautiful Bulbous Plants," "Beautiful Roses," "Beautiful Trees and Shrubs," "Beautiful Garden Flowers," "School, Cottage, and Allotment Gardening," etc.

With numerous Illustrations. Medium 8vo. 15s. net.

Information regarding this large and important group of garden plants is so scattered and so difficult for the ordinary gardener (whether professional or amateur) to obtain, that this work is intended to fill the gap that has hitherto existed, or has at least been only very imperfectly filled. The Author possesses the great advantage of being not only a well-known and experienced gardener of many years' standing, but also a capable plant artist. He has an intimate acquaintance with his subject, and for more than twenty years past he has been making sketches from actual specimens of the finest bulbous and tuberous plants to be found in cultivation. For the first time many of these original sketches will appear in this volume, the importance and value of which will be recognised by all interested in the subject.

LONDON : JOHN MURRAY, ALBEMARLE STREET, W.

6

7

The Vegetable Garden

ILLUSTRATIONS, DESCRIPTIONS, AND CULTURE OF THE GARDEN
VEGETABLES OF COLD AND TEMPERATE CLIMATES

BY MM. VILMORIN-ANDRIEUX

of Paris

English Edition published under the direction of W. ROBINSON

Numerous Illustrations.   Demy 8vo.   15s. net.

"'The Vegetable Garden' is a complete and authoritative work
upon all that concerns vegetables, and stands unique among works on
the bookshelf of everyone interested in vegetables, for it is not a work
for the grower alone."—*Garden.*

French Market-Gardening

INCLUDING PRACTICAL DETAILS OF "INTENSIVE CULTIVATION" FOR
ENGLISH GROWERS

BY JOHN WEATHERS

Author of "A Practical Guide to Garden Plants," etc.

With a Preface by WILLIAM ROBINSON

With numerous Illustrations.   Large Crown 8vo.   3s. 6d. net.

"The best book we have seen on the intensive system of cultivation,
and it is exhaustive and comprehensive."—*Pall Mall Gazette.*

"This useful and interesting work deals with every phase of that
form of intensive culture known as French Gardening. It is well-
written and is easily understood."—*Fruit, Flower and Vegetable Trades
Journal.*

The Culture of Fruit Trees in Pots

BY JOSH BRACE

With Illustrations.   Large Crown 8vo.   5s. net.

"A valuable contribution to a very interesting phase of fruit-
culture."—*Field.*

"Brief, clear, and well founded in the practical wisdom born of
life-long experience in the kind of gardening it describes, the work
cannot but be serviceable."—*Scotsman.*

The Book of the Rothampstead Experiments

BY A. D. HALL, M.A. (Oxon.)

President of the Rothampstead Experimental Station; First President of the
South-Eastern Agricultural College

Issued with the Authority of the Lawes Agricultural Trust Committee

With Illustrations.   Medium 8vo.   10s. 6d. net.

LONDON: JOHN MURRAY, ALBEMARLE STREET, W.